Agriculture in Western Europe

by Michael Tracy

FREDERICK A. PRAEGER, *Publisher*
NEW YORK

Published in the United States of America in 1964
by Frederick A. Praeger, Inc., Publisher
64 University Place, New York 3, N.Y.

Library of Congress Catalog Card Number: 64-16690

Printed in Great Britain

Acknowledgments

I am grateful to Mr P. Lamartine Yates for valuable advice in the planning of this book. Professor Michel Cépède has kindly assisted me with the chapters on France; Mr Gavin McCrone with those on the United Kingdom. I am indebted to Mr T. W. Fletcher for help on nineteenth-century problems; Mr J. R. Bellerby has also provided useful material. Mr A. Deheeger-Ozanne has assisted with the analysis of recent international developments. Mr A. Simantov has read my typescript and made many valuable comments. It is evident that I alone am responsible for the opinions I express.

I owe a special debt to my wife, who has borne patiently with the disruption of family life which this work has involved and has assisted me in many ways.

Paris   Michael Tracy
December 1963

Contents

Introduction

Much has been heard in recent years about the problems of agriculture – about rising surpluses and falling prices, about the inadequate share of the farming community in rising standards of living, about the cost to the rest of the community of subsidizing agriculture in one way or another. These problems have made themselves felt in almost all the economically advanced countries of Western Europe and North America.

The difficulties of agriculture, moreover, have threatened to impede progress in other sectors as well. Since protection against outside competition is generally an essential element in the support given to farmers, it has proved difficult to remove this protection in the process of general economic integration in Western Europe. The different measures of support in force in different countries cannot easily be combined in a common policy. Agriculture is thus one of the greatest problems facing the European Economic Community, and constitutes the principal economic obstacle to the inclusion in the Community of the United Kingdom. Progress in freeing trade between North America and Western Europe also depends largely on the extent to which the barriers against agricultural imports into Western Europe can be lowered.

The rapid growth of food production, resulting largely from a new technological revolution in agriculture but stimulated also by artificially high prices in importing countries, has caused international trade in the agricultural products of the temperate zone to stagnate, in some cases even to fall. The prices of these products on world markets have risen much less than those of manufactured goods. Countries which depend on agricultural exports have thus found themselves in a difficult situation. Attempts to solve these problems by international agreement have had only moderate success, and the United States alone can afford to relieve the pressure by massive shipments of food to the hungry and less-developed parts of the world.

All these problems have not suddenly made their appearance, but are the outcome of a long series of developments. Already by the early nineteenth century, the agriculture of European countries had been shaped in contrasting ways by differences in its evolution since feudal times and in the influence exerted by economic progress in other sectors. Since that time, European agriculture has been subjected to two great convulsions.

The first of these was the Great Depression which began in the 1880s, when for the first time competition from outside Europe, in particular from North America, made itself felt on a devastating scale. This occurred at a time when most European countries had nearly renounced tariff protection on agricultural as well as on industrial goods. The resulting slump in the prices first of grains, later to some extent of other agricultural products as well, gave rise to different reactions in the various European countries. Britain held determinedly to its policy of free trade and laissez-faire, and allowed much of its agriculture to undergo a long and drastic decline. Denmark too adhered to free trade, but carried out a thorough adaptation of its agriculture to the new conditions, as a result of which Danish agricultural exports became established on the markets of Britain and Germany. Most other countries, including in particular France and Germany, shielded their agriculture behind high tariff walls, and relatively little adaptation took place. These contrasting policies had an important influence on the subsequent development of agriculture in the various countries.

The second great convulsion occurred when European agriculture was drawn into the economic crisis of the 1930s: markets contracted, prices fell and many farmers went bankrupt. This time, laissez-faire was abandoned even in Britain, and all countries attempted to help their farmers – first by raising tariffs against outside competition, then, as these proved inadequate, by more direct restrictions on trade which led to extensive measures of intervention on domestic markets as well. These measures were maintained up to the Second World War, but in most cases they constituted merely a series of expedients. Few countries developed a coherent policy for agriculture; the major exception was Germany under the National Socialist regime.

During and immediately after the Second World War, the major aim was to obtain the greatest possible output of food, and this was sought by assuring farmers of satisfactory prices and adequate outlets for their produce. As food shortages disappeared, price supports were maintained and even reinforced in order to raise farmers' incomes, as these generally failed to increase as rapidly as earnings in other occupations. However, the rapid improvement in farming techniques enabled production to rise faster than the growth in demand, and this trend to over-production indicated a need for lower rather than higher farm prices. This conflict between the need to adapt supply to demand and the desire to give farmers a fair income has become the major problem of European agriculture; governments are finding that it can no longer be solved by traditional measures of price support but that it requires a more radical adaptation of farming structures.

The present study is therefore an attempt to analyse these developments. The year 1880 provides an approximate starting-point, since it was about this time that the agricultural depression began. It has, however, been necessary to give some attention to earlier events, and in particular to describe the movement towards free trade which was marked by the repeal of the Corn Laws in Britain in 1846 and by the Anglo-French Treaty of Commerce in 1860.

The field of study is the area which it is now customary to call 'Western Europe' – more precisely, the North-Western part of Europe, since this book is not concerned with the different problems of the less-developed Southern European countries. However, as it would be impracticable to study in detail all the countries in this region, special attention has been given to Britain, France, Germany and Denmark. The choice of these four is a fairly obvious one: they are the countries of greatest significance in the present European agricultural scene, and their past development – as has been seen above – presents marked contrasts. In dealing with these countries, an attempt has been made to give a reasonably complete explanation of why they adopted the policies they did. This explanation has to be sought not only in developments in agriculture itself but also in the general economic policy of the country, in its attitude to foreign trade, in overall political forces, in the activity of farmers' organizations, sometimes even in personalities.

The final part of this book concerns the problems of agriculture in the present international scene: the attempt to unify different agricultural policies in the European Economic Community, the difficulties caused by agriculture for Britain's attempt to join the EEC, and the repercussions of developments in Western Europe on agricultural exporters overseas.

The problems of agriculture are perhaps too often seen in the limited context of a given country and of the present time. A comparison of the experience of different countries at certain critical periods of their past development may make it easier to understand the present situation and may throw light on the ways in which agriculture must adapt to current economic trends.

Part I

The Great Depression, 1880–1900 —
The First Wave of Protectionism

Chapter 1. General

European agriculture before the Depression

By the middle of the nineteenth century, agriculture in Western Europe had already taken on more or less its present form. The number and size of holdings, the location of farms and farm buildings, the forms of land tenure, were not very different from what they are today. Contrasts between one country and another were already obvious: they were the outcome, firstly, of the various ways in which agriculture had emerged from the typical feudal pattern, whereby most of the land had been arranged in open fields, cultivated by a peasantry owing various rents and services to their lord; secondly, of the extent to which general economic progress had influenced the development of agriculture.

Thus in Britain the enclosure and consolidation of agricultural holdings over a long period led to the creation of comparatively large, unified farms. The landed aristocracy had never been overthrown and indeed played an important role in this process, which they guided to their best advantage: when their feudal power had gone, they still formed an important class of landlords, letting out most of their land to tenant farmers. The process created another class, that of the landless labourers, many of whom were forced off the land and into the growing towns. This move from the land was stimulated by the Industrial Revolution, in which Britain had a long lead over all other countries, and, as a result, the population living from agriculture formed a smaller proportion of the whole in Britain than in any other country. Further, overall economic progress was reflected in agriculture: the structure of agriculture, with large farms and a class of wealthy landowners ready to invest in their estates, made British farming particularly receptive to technological progress, and in the middle of the nineteenth century it was the most advanced in the world.

Denmark also had achieved a favourable agricultural structure, but in a different way. Here the abolition of the feudal system took place to the advantage of the peasants, who were encouraged and aided by the Government to buy the land they farmed. The result was to create farms not so big as in Britain, but big enough for the needs of the time, and conveniently grouped in single units. A remarkably advanced educational system also contributed to forming an independent and progressive farming community.

In other countries of the Continent, the situation was not so good. In many cases the feudal pattern had been violently broken up by revolutionary movements, and the landlords had been expropriated or compelled to sell. Little was done to ensure that the land taken into the possession of the peasants should be arranged in a rational manner so as to give its new owners a decent living. Thus in France (though many large estates survived the Revolution or were re-created afterwards) the majority of the holdings were so small as to be barely viable: nearly 40 per cent of the agricultural area was in farms of less than 20 hectares (in Britain the corresponding figure was under 20 per cent). The practice of dividing land up between the heirs, on the death of the owner, aggravated the problem, both by reducing the average size of farm and by perpetuating the 'fragmentation' of holdings between several separate plots, often at a considerable distance one from another. Similar patterns of land ownership were found in other parts of Western Europe (partly as a result of French occupation during the Napoleonic Wars). In Belgium and parts of West Germany, in particular, there were many small and fragmented farms; in West Germany over half the agricultural area was in holdings of less than 20 hectares. In several other regions of Western Europe – including Switzerland, the Tyrol and parts of South Germany – the feudal system had been overthrown already in the peasant wars of the thirteenth and fourteenth centuries, and a peasant agriculture was firmly established.

In Eastern Europe the situation was totally different. Even

where a degree of emancipation had taken place, it had failed to create a strong peasantry. In the Austro-Hungarian Empire and in Russia, the traditional landed classes remained in power. The new German Empire had in its eastern regions a near-feudal pattern which contrasted sharply with the mainly peasant agriculture of its other regions: the land was still predominantly in the hands of a powerful aristocracy (the 'Junkers'), owning large estates worked by hired labour.

In most of the countries of the Continent, by the middle of the century, the Industrial Revolution had hardly begun to influence agriculture. Farming remained the most important occupation; dissatisfied peasants had not much opportunity to move into expanding industries. There was as yet hardly any stimulus for agriculture to improve its methods: transport and communications were deficient, and there was little flow of new ideas into the country-side. Rural education was often rudimentary, and agriculture remained backward.

The pattern of agricultural trade at this time was very different from what it was to be a few decades later. Generally trade remained unimportant in relation to production. Britain, as a result of its expanding industrial population, had already become a large importer of food; but these imports, in spite of the repeal of the Corn Laws in 1846, hardly constituted a serious danger for British agriculture. France imported some grains, especially wheat, and exported others. Germany imported grain for the consuming and livestock-producing areas of the west, and exported wheat and rye from the great estates of the east. Denmark at this time also exported grain: her export trade in livestock products had scarcely begun. The largest exporter of grain in the world was Russia.

Agricultural trade was thus very largely an intra-European affair. The advance of technology had not yet reached the stage when the agricultural produce of the New World could be transported quickly and cheaply by land and by sea. European agriculture, on the whole, was still untroubled by outside competition.

The growth in competition

The main cause of the subsequent transformation of the agricultural scene was the immense increase in imports of cheap grain coming from North America and also to some extent from Russia. This was the result of the opening up of virgin lands and of revolutionary improvements in methods of transport. In North America especially the availability of vast land resources enabled extremely cheap production, and from the middle of the century steadily increasing use was made of farm machinery – reapers, binders and, later, efficient combine harvesters. Russia's advantage lay in having plenty of land and cheap labour.

In the 1850s American railways began to tap the Great Plains, and by 1884 the Rockies could be reached by seven different railway routes in the United States or Canada. In Russia too, new railways brought grain to ports of the Baltic and the Black Sea. At the same time there was rapid progress in shipping: in the second half of the century ships began to be built not with wood but with iron, later with steel, and this made possible a great increase in their size and carrying capacity. In addition, sail gave way to steam, and the compound engine, which greatly reduced fuel costs, came into use from the 1860s. The extent of the fall in transport costs is indicated in Table 1: during the 1870s and 1880s, the cost of transporting wheat both by rail from Chicago

Table 1

FREIGHT RATES AND PRICES FOR WHEAT

(annual averages, pence per quarter)

	Freight rates		Price of U.S. wheat from Atlantic ports, c.i.f. Liverpool
	Chicago to New York, by rail	New York to Liverpool by steamer	
1870–4	113	66	625[a]
1875–9	72	60	568[a]
1880–4	63	35	531
1885–9	61	25	402
1890–4	53	20	379
1895–9	47	23	356

[a] Including wheat from Pacific ports from 1871 through 1875.

Source: Board of Trade (U.K.), *British and Foreign Trade and Industry* (Cd.1761, 1903).

to New York and by steamer from New York to Liverpool was cut by about half. The price of American wheat arriving in Liverpool fell by even more than the amount of the reduction in transport costs.

The effect of these technical developments might have been felt even sooner but for the Crimean War of 1853–6, which closed the Baltic and the Black Sea to Russian exports, and the American Civil War of 1861–4, which curbed U.S. exports to Europe. The peace which prevailed in America and Europe for forty years after the Franco-German War of 1870–1 provided the conditions necessary for a great expansion of trade.

From 1877 North America had the benefit of four consecutive seasons in which harvests were excellent. In Western Europe, on the other hand, these were bad years: the harvest of 1879 was disastrous. Previously, small crops had been accompanied by higher prices which helped to maintain returns to farmers. Now,

Table 2

EXPORTS OF WHEAT

(annual averages, million bushels)

	U.S.A.	Canada	Russia	India	Australasia
1851–60	5	..	41	..	..
1861–70	22	..	75	..	..
1870–4	59	1	55	1	..
1875–9	107	3	71	6	..
1880–4	136	4	65	29	..
1885–9	110	3	95	36	..
1890–4[a]	170	9	104	30	8
1895–9[a]	184	16	107	15	3

[a] Data include wheat flour (in wheat equivalent) – the amounts involved, however, are relatively small.
.. Not available, but probably nil or negligible.

Sources: S. B. Clough and C. W. Cole, *Economic History of Europe* (Boston: Heath, 1952); R. F. Crawford, 'An Inquiry into Wheat Prices and Wheat Supply', *Journal of the Royal Statistical Society*, March 1895; Helen Farnsworth, 'The Decline and Recovery of Wheat Prices in the 'Nineties', *Wheat Studies* (Food Research Institute, Stanford University), June–July 1934.

however, exports from the United States rose sharply, doubling within a few years (Table 2): prices in Europe fell instead of rising, and farmers suffered severe losses. From then on grain prices fell steadily. The whole period from about 1873 to 1896 was one of general economic depression and falling prices, which aggravated the problems of agriculture.

In the late 1880s, American grain exports for a time ceased to rise, and there was a slight recovery in prices. But the 1890s brought a renewed crisis. In 1891 the United States had a record crop and exports once again rose substantially. At about the same time, Russia was increasing its exports, Canada was beginning to make an impact on the world market, and the Suez Canal was facilitating trade from India and Australia. Grain prices fell once more in 1892, and in 1895 they reached their lowest point: the world price of wheat was then little more than half the pre-depression level.

Reduced wheat crops in 1895 and 1896, partly due to some contraction in the wheat area in response to the lower prices, helped to relieve the pressure. At the same time, rising production costs in the United States made themselves felt: by about 1890 all the productive land had been occupied and the price of land began to rise. Also, domestic consumption in the United States was rising. Grain prices thus recovered gradually from about 1896 onwards, helped by a general improvement in the economic situation. By the turn of the century the agricultural depression had spent its force, and the years leading up to the First World War were favourable to farmers in both North America and Europe.

In its early stages, the crisis affected mainly the grain market. Later on, techniques of refrigeration began to be applied on a commercial scale: the United States started to ship frozen meat in 1875, Australia in 1877, and shipments grew enormously from then on. However, production of livestock products was rising much less rapidly than that of grains, while with the gradual improvement in the standard of living the demand for livestock products was increasing comparatively fast. The result was that the decline in the prices of meat and other livestock products was never as large as that which occurred for grains. The experience of Britain is a useful guide, since the British market remained free: the prices of livestock products began to fall only in 1885, some

five years later than the beginning of the crisis for grains, and at
the worst of the depression, in 1896, livestock prices were about
three-quarters of their pre-depression level when crop prices were
little more than a half.

This difference in the trend of prices as between crop and livestock products is of considerable significance. It means in the first
place that the effects of the depression were not felt equally by
arable farmers and by livestock producers. The former suffered
directly from the reduced value of their produce. The latter also
suffered a fall in value, but it came later and was not so serious;
moreover, they *benefited* from the much greater fall in the price of
feed grains.

It follows that the best policy for European countries during the
Great Depression was to carry out a shift from crop production to
livestock. Countries which were able and far-sighted enough to do
this stood a much better chance of overcoming the crisis than those
which, in the face of the new trends, persevered with former
habits.

The difference in price trends also leads to a distinction between
large and small farms in a given country. Returns per unit of land
tend to be smaller with crops, so that profitable crop production
requires a fairly large area: grain farming is therefore carried
out mainly on the larger holdings. The smaller farms – peasant
holdings in particular – generally depend for their livelihood on
dairy cows, pigs and poultry; they may produce some grain and
other fodder for the use of their own livestock, but they often need
to purchase additional supplies. It was therefore the larger farms
which were most affected by the crisis.

In some cases the distinction is also geographical. This was
particularly so in Germany, with many large grain-producing
estates in East Prussia. In England, arable farms were found
mainly in East Anglia and parts of the south, while in the north
and west livestock farming predominated. In France, the plains
of the Paris basin were the principal grain-producing region.

These differences are important for an understanding of the
Great Depression. At this time the farmers best able to make their
views known and to exert an influence on official policy were the
larger farmers, particularly when they belonged to a ruling
aristocracy; the peasants were generally unorganized and unrepresented. This suggests that the traditional view of the Great

Depression may exaggerate its severity. Too much emphasis is usually laid on the fall in grain prices and on the unfavourable consequences for arable farmers; not enough attention has been paid to the much less difficult situation of livestock producers.

It also follows that when various European countries introduced measures of protection, they did so largely at the instigation of the bigger farmers and for their benefit, and that for the peasantry the advantages of protection were much less evident.

The free trade interlude

For a short period before the Great Depression, trade between European countries became more nearly free from tariffs and other restrictions than at any other time in history. The impetus came from Britain, where the Free Trade movement had gathered strength throughout the early nineteenth century and achieved its most spectacular success in the repeal of the Corn Laws in 1846. This movement drew its inspiration from the teaching of Adam Smith and his disciples, but it corresponded also to the commercial interests of Britain at the time: with undisputed leadership in industry and commerce, Britain had everything to gain and nothing to lose from the greatest possible freedom of trade.

Having committed herself to free trade, Britain therefore sought to induce other countries to follow along the same path. The liberal doctrines of the Manchester School were not unknown in Continental countries, but the inferiority of their industry as compared with that of Britain made protection seem essential. Somewhat unexpectedly, Britain found an ally in France: Napoleon III, who in 1852 had established himself as emperor, with extensive powers, was favourably disposed towards free trade. He was moreover anxious, for political reasons, to establish close relations with Britain. In 1860, against the opposition of his Parliament, he signed the Anglo-French Treaty of Commerce.

This treaty was of significance not only for the reductions it brought about in French duties (and the comparatively minor concessions by Britain), but also for its consequences as the cornerstone of a series of subsequent treaties between France and practically all other European countries. Each of these was based on the 'most favoured nation' principle, so that the concessions granted to one country were automatically extended to the others.

Thus, throughout most of Europe, trade was freed or subjected only to mild duties.

Trade in agricultural products became even more free than that in manufactures. By 1860 Britain had abolished duties not only on grain but on almost all other agricultural imports, leaving only a few revenue duties. France practically removed agricultural protection in the 1860 treaty, and in 1861 abolished her sliding scale of grain duties. Farmers in Germany were still interested mainly in exporting grain and therefore wanted free trade: the Zollverein's duties on grain had been abolished in 1853. In Italy the moderate Piedmontese duties formed the basis of the tariff for the unified kingdom, and after treaties with France and other countries, agriculture was protected only by low duties on grains. Belgium in 1871 decreed free entry for the main foodstuffs. The Netherlands dropped its grain duties in 1862. In most other countries agricultural trade was free or nearly so.

The protectionist revival

The subsequent return to protection took place gradually and had a number of causes. One of these was the Franco-German War of 1870, and the nationalist sentiment to which it gave rise in both countries. Another, closely associated with this, was the increasing concern with industrial development throughout the Continent; demands by industrialists for protection became more insistent, demonstrating that they at least had never been converted to free trade. Public opinion became increasingly willing to listen to them. These demands were accentuated as prices began a long downward trend, starting in 1873 and lasting till about 1896, with only a short respite from 1880 to 1882; this depression kept wages and profits low and reduced purchasing power. The protectionist movement, especially in Germany, was able to draw inspiration and justification from Friedrich List's school of nationalist economics, with its stress on economic development through protection. Thus, when European agriculture was awakened to the challenge of overseas competition, there was ample scope for powerful protectionist alliances between industrial and agricultural interests.

In FRANCE the reversal of policy was marked by the tariff of 1881, which introduced moderate protection for industry and made large increases in the duties on livestock and livestock products. In 1885 and 1887, the duties on all major agricultural products were very substantially raised. The Méline Tariff of 1892 gave increased protection to both industry and agriculture. These measures remained substantially unchanged up to the First World War: in 1910 a modernized tariff brought some increase in protection for industry, but no important change in agricultural duties.

GERMANY's reconversion to protection began with the tariff of 1879, which restored duties on various manufactures and also imposed moderate duties on agricultural products. In 1885 and 1887 there were further and substantial increases in the grain duties. This protectionist policy was the work of Bismarck: after his dismissal in 1890, Germany for a while followed the opposite course. Germany's need by then was to obtain expanded markets for her industrial exports, and in a series of commercial treaties Bismarck's successors made limited reductions in the agricultural duties in return for advantages for German exports. But this led to violent opposition from the farming sector and in particular from the powerful Prussian landowners. It also gave rise to violent controversy as to the desirability of Germany becoming an increasingly industrial nation. Satisfaction was finally given to the agricultural interests with the tariff of 1902.

ITALY re-established protection in 1878, mainly with the object of protecting her infant industries, but the duties were moderate because of the desire not to provoke retaliation against Italy's agricultural exports. Various revisions were made in subsequent years. The main change in policy occurred with the tariff of 1887, which raised the duties on both industrial and agricultural products. By then industrialists had become increasingly sensitive to foreign competition, while grain-producing farmers were suffering from the universal fall in prices. The producers of export commodities – wine, olive oil, fruit, vegetables – had little competition to fear and did not want foreign countries to discriminate against their exports, but as in other countries the large grain producers were the most influential. One of the first results of the 1887 tariff was in fact sharp retaliation by France; there followed a tariff war between the two countries lasting till 1892, and normal trade relations were not restored till 1899. This brought great hardship to agricultural exporting interests in Italy. Meanwhile the grain producers succeeded in having the duty on wheat raised by successive stages from 3 lire per 100 kg. in 1887 to 7.50 lire in 1898. The protectionist revival in Italy was accompanied by a tendency for the school of national economics on the German model to prevail over economists of the Manchester School: from 1875 the former made its voice heard in the *Giornale degli Economisti*, while an Adam Smith Society was formed and published the *Economista*, but became less and less effective.

Once BELGIUM became firmly established as an independent nation (its secession from the Netherlands took place in 1830), she realized that, as an industrial nation heavily dependent on foreign trade, her interests lay in the greatest possible freedom of trade. But here too the agricultural crisis caused a revival of protectionist agitation and led in 1887 to the imposition of tariffs on livestock and meat. The protection involved remained moderate. In 1895 the duties on a number of agricultural products were raised, but grains (other than oats) remained free.

Economic policy in SWITZERLAND was originally dominated by the liberalism of the Manchester School, and the Constitution of 1874 did not allow the Confederation to intervene in economic matters. Switzerland's trade policy was to obtain advantages for her exports of manufactured goods by offering an open market in agricultural products. Swiss farmers themselves were for a time inclined to favour free trade, because of their interest in exporting cheese and breeding cattle. But when the crisis broke, they too began to demand protection. Though in 1884 and 1887 some duties were imposed on manufactured products, no immediate satisfaction was given to the farmers, except for an increase in the subsidies granted for various purposes. Protection for agriculture was first introduced with the tariff of 1891. Like the Belgian tariff, this left grains largely unprotected: grains were only a small part of total Swiss agricultural output but they were a large import item, and duties would have weighed heavily on consumers and on users of feed grains. Another feature of the tariff was that the large dairy sector could not be given direct protection, because cheese exports formed an important outlet for this sector and the price of cheese on export markets largely determined the whole price structure for dairy products. The tariff thus concentrated protection on beef cattle and meat, and it was hoped that this would give some indirect help to the dairy sector by diverting part of the milk supplies to feeding more calves. The agricultural duties were raised in the 1902 tariff and modified by treaties in 1905.

From the late 1870s onwards, measures of protection for both agriculture and industry were adopted also by Austria-Hungary, Sweden, Spain and Portugal, while Russia and the United States sheltered their growing industries behind prohibitive tariff walls; in the United States the McKinley Tariff of 1890 extended protection to agriculture, with increased duties on grains and new duties on some other products.

This left a few European countries holding determinedly to free trade principles, the most important of these being Britain.

Agriculture in BRITAIN was no less subject to overseas competition than that of other European countries. In fact a large sector of British agriculture was ruined in the course of the depression; many agricultural workers moved to the towns and much arable land was turned over to grass. 'High farming' gave way to the utmost economy in operations and even to neglect. Yet the British Government refused the slightest degree of protection. Moreover, there was no effective move for protection among the farmers themselves. It was only after the end of the agricultural depression, from about 1903 to 1905, that a vigorous campaign for 'Tariff Reform' was started, but this was based on the desire to secure preferences for Empire trade rather than on the wish to protect British agriculture (indeed, the conflict between the two aims was never satisfactorily reconciled).

DENMARK too held firmly to free trade, but while in Britain the policy was one of pure laissez-faire, Denmark's reaction to overseas competition was to carry out a fundamental transformation of its agriculture. There was a large shift from crops to livestock production, and Danish exports of livestock products became established on the British and German markets.

Developments in the NETHERLANDS were similar to those in Denmark. The importance of foreign trade to the economy had led to a long-standing attachment to free trade principles. When the unprotected Dutch market came to be swamped with foreign goods to which other markets were increasingly closed, and when unemployment began to rise in consequence, a protectionist movement made itself heard. The Government nevertheless withstood these demands. The national Agricultural Council declared that proposals to raise the grain duties would do no good to agriculture, as it would remove the incentive to work and lead to many protective measures which would raise prices of agricultural inputs; it also considered that the situation in the Netherlands under free trade was no worse than in countries which had already adopted protection. This energetic refusal put an end to protectionist claims for agriculture: the farmers thereupon accepted the free-trade policy, set up associations to improve the processing of their products and made use of the training institutes set up by the Government. A justification for this policy could be found in the subsequent increase in exports of livestock products, fruit and vegetables.

It is not easy to give a general idea of the degree of protection for agriculture attained in the course of the Great Depression. Practically all tariff rates were 'specific' (i.e. in terms of weight or quantity), and to express them in *ad valorem* terms involves difficulties in selecting appropriate price data. An attempt was made by Liepmann to compare tariff levels in European countries: the results for foodstuffs in 1913 are shown in Table 3. Both the basic material available and the method adopted leave much to be desired, and the results are not to be regarded as precise. However, it seems reasonable to conclude that in most of the countries which had adopted protection for agriculture, the degree

Table 3

AVERAGE 'POTENTIAL' TARIFF LEVELS FOR FOODSTUFFS, AS A PERCENTAGE OF EXPORT PRICES IN EUROPEAN COUNTRIES, IN 1913

Country	Tariff level
France	29
Germany	22
Italy	22
Belgium	26
Switzerland	15
Austria-Hungary	29
Sweden[a]	24
Finland	49

[a] Fruit and vegetables not included.

Source: H. Liepmann, *Tariff Levels* (London: Allen & Unwin, 1938).

of protection before the First World War lay somewhere between 20 and 30 per cent.[1]

Factors influencing the choice of policies

The preceding pages have shown the wide divergence in the policies followed during the Great Depression. In most countries, including in particular France and Germany, there was a purely defensive reaction, taking the form of greatly increased tariff protection. Britain held to laissez-faire, and an adjustment was forced on agriculture in the form of contraction and decline in the arable sector. In Denmark and the Netherlands, on the other hand, there was a positive response, characterized by the absence of defensive measures and a deliberate adaptation and improvement of agricultural production and marketing.

What was responsible for these differences? It seems that a considerable number of factors played a role. Perhaps the first was the general attitude in each country towards economic policy and in particular to trade. Britain, with its early start in the Industrial Revolution, had a clear advantage in the maximum freedom of trade. Small countries like Denmark, Belgium and the Netherlands, with a shortage of natural resources, were heavily dependent on trade and favoured free trade for that reason. France and Germany, on the other hand, wanted to develop their industries and needed protection to do so; with their extensive domestic resources they could afford to restrict trade (at least up to the point when, in the case of Germany, markets had to be found for industrial exports).

Economic theory played a part, but probably only a small part, in shaping public attitudes. There is no doubt that List was the dominant influence on academic thinking in Germany, as Smith

---

[1] The method used was to select thirty-eight foodstuffs, said to represent a 'fair sample' of goods in European trade; to calculate for each country the incidence of duty on each of these foodstuffs, on the basis of 'normal prices' – i.e. the export prices of the leading European exporting countries in the year in question; and to work out an average of the various duties for each country. The average was unweighted, so it took no account of the varying importance of different items in the imports of each country: indeed each country was not necessarily an importer of all the thirty-eight foodstuffs. This difficulty was recognized by the author, who accordingly called his results 'potential' tariff levels.

and Ricardo were in Britain, and their respective theories provided powerful arguments for the opposing camps of Protectionists and Free Traders. But Kindleberger, in a study of the different responses to the agricultural depression, rightly observes:

> It might be fair to say that the economists of Britain and the national economists of Germany provided the rationale for the action taken rather than its impetus. And the relative unimportance of this function may be indicated by the action of France and Italy, taken in the absence of any distinctive rationale.[1]

The extent of public willingness to support agriculture was another important factor. Prevailing opinions were composed of elements of both reasoning and sentiment. The resort to agricultural protectionism in both France and Germany owed much to a widespread belief in the virtues of rural life and in the disadvantages of a high degree of industrialization. In France this sentiment was expressed in an extreme (but vague) form by Jules Méline, particularly in his book *Le retour à la terre*. In Germany, discussion on this point took the form of an academic debate on the 'Agrar-oder Industriestaat' issue, and the arguments of Professor Adolf Wagner, the main advocate of the 'Agrarstaat', carried great weight: he stressed the social disadvantages of the rise in the urban population and the risks – which were not only strategic – of excessive dependence on food imports.

On the other hand, the main argument working against public willingness to protect agriculture was the effect on food prices. In Britain, the successful campaign against the Corn Laws had left a deeply-engrained hostility to any form of tax on foodstuffs: 'cheap bread' remained a powerful rallying-cry. In other countries, this was an argument frequently used by Free Traders, but with little success.

The strategic argument – the need to ensure self-sufficiency in food supplies in time of war – was part of the general case for an 'Agrarstaat' and was frequently advanced in almost all countries as a justification for protection. This argument certainly played a role, but perhaps less than is sometimes thought: it was an additional reason for statesmen to satisfy pressure from agricultural

[1] C. P. Kindleberger, 'Group behavior and international trade', *Journal of Political Economy*, February 1951, p. 37.

interests, rather than an independent factor influencing policy. Perhaps it manifested itself most clearly in reverse: there is no doubt that a vital factor in Britain's indifference to the fate of her agriculture was her undisputed mastery of the seas and her possession of rich food-producing colonies.

These factors outside agriculture helped to determine the possibilities for forming protective alliances between industrial and agricultural interests. At critical stages in France, Germany and Italy, such alliances were responsible for restoring protection to both industry and agriculture. This union could be maintained only so long as the common interest in obtaining protection was stronger than conflicts of interest in other respects. Some such conflict between the two sectors was always inevitable. Protection for industry was liable to raise the cost of farm tools and equipment, possibly also of farm wages. Protection for agriculture might, by raising food prices, cause increased labour costs for industry; it might also raise the price of raw materials. This last problem was usually not serious, since agricultural raw materials for industry were generally produced overseas and not by European agriculture; but an important exception was wool, and it is significant that, even in the countries where agricultural protection went furthest, wool was generally left entirely free from duty, and the result of competition from Australia, South America and South Africa was a drastic fall in the sheep population of Europe. Conflict was inevitable also when industry was concerned with enlarging its export markets: in Germany this problem became acute in the 1890s, and the fact that it was resolved in favour of agriculture demonstrates the political strength of the farmers.

The influence of the farming community was to a large extent a question of the relative size of the agricultural population: the contrast between Britain and the other countries needs no comment. It was also determined by the extent to which general democratic evolution had deprived the rural aristocracy of its power. In Britain the political reforms starting with the 1832 Reform Act had dethroned the landed classes; moreover, the division of interests and outlook between landlords and tenants, and also between arable and livestock farmers, prevented the formation of any coherent agricultural pressure group. Denmark was a land of small-to-medium farms, with a highly-developed democracy. But in countries where there remained a dominant class of large landowners (often interested primarily in the price of grain), this group was able to present itself as the representative of the whole agricultural interest, regardless of the real needs of other groups in agriculture, and to exert considerable influence over the course of official policy. Thus in Germany the Junkers remained a coherent group with vestiges of feudal power and an entrenched position in the State, in France the campaign for protection was led by the aristocratic Société des Agriculteurs de France, and in Italy by the big grain producers.

Consequences of policies followed

There is no doubt that where protection was adopted it succeeded in restraining the fall in prices, though not in stopping it. Figure 1 shows the trend of wheat prices in the United States, England, France and Germany, using a five-year moving average to eliminate annual fluctuations. It also indicates the rate of duty on wheat in France and Germany. This shows clearly that till the mid-1880s wheat prices in all four countries followed a similar downward course. Then, as greatly increased tariffs were imposed in France and Germany, prices in these two countries parted company from the 'world' price: the French and German prices in fact remained above the U.S. and English prices by roughly the amount of the tariffs, or by nearly a third.

Shielded from the worst of the depression, farmers in countries where protection was adopted probably suffered a smaller loss of income than those in Britain. In the absence of adequate statistics, it is not easy to assess the extent of this difference. The situation in Britain may not have been as bad as is often thought. It has already been pointed out that the fall in prices affected mainly the big arable farmers, while the smaller livestock producers did not do so badly. Conversely, in France and Germany the benefit of protection went mainly to the large grain growers, and gave much less benefit to the livestock-producing peasantry – perhaps it even harmed them by keeping up the price of bread and (in Germany at least) the cost of purchased feeding-stuffs, as well as by maintaining land values. Such estimates as can be made for France and Germany suggest that in both cases only a minority of the total agricultural population stood to gain from protection on grains. It is true that livestock products were also protected, but

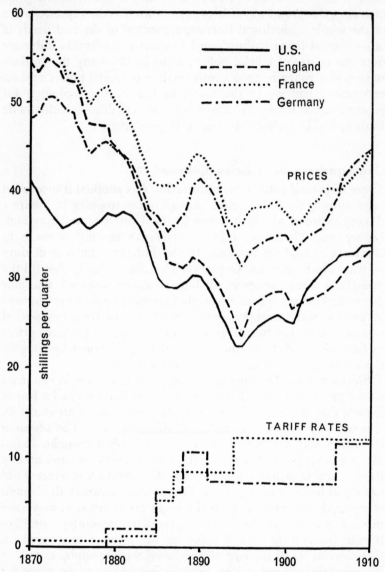

Source: Board of Trade (U.K.), *British and Foreign Trade and Industry* (Cd. 4954, 1909); data for later years completed from national sources.

FIG. I

here overseas competition never exerted such a strong influence, and though precise indications are not easy to obtain it seems unlikely that the effect of protection was so marked.

Denmark and the Netherlands showed the possibility of meeting the crisis by adapting the pattern of agricultural production to the new situation, and thereby laid the basis for a prosperous agriculture making an important contribution to export earnings and to general economic progress. In France and Germany, though the livestock sector did expand, no such adaptation took place: the area under wheat actually expanded during the period, and in Germany the cultivation of rye, under the influence of various protective measures, rose quite out of line with trends in demand at home and abroad.

Equally serious, the preoccupation with tariff policy diverted attention from more constructive measures. In Denmark, the farmers themselves took the initiative in making agriculture more efficient, in particular by building their remarkable co-operative marketing system. In Germany, progress was made in several respects, including the Raiffeisen co-operative banks, but the effects on overall agricultural development remained marginal. In general, farmers in France and Germany came to rely increasingly on tariff protection, and their Governments did little to encourage them to improve their position through higher productivity, better marketing and so forth. The habits of mind thus created proved difficult to shake off.

The movement of manpower off the land seems to have been comparatively slow in France and Germany. In Britain the population occupied in agriculture, even though it was already relatively small by the 1880s, fell substantially between 1881 and 1901 – this at a time when total population was rising fast (Table 4). In France and Germany the population occupied in agriculture appears to have *risen* quite substantially (in Germany most of the rise apparently took place between 1895 and 1907). It is true that the data indicate a fall in the *total* population in agriculture (including non-active persons) in these two countries, but even so the movement does not appear nearly as large as in Britain. (It has to be remembered that statistics of this kind raise difficult problems of definition and are not very reliable.) To some extent these developments were simply a continuation of past trends: in Britain a reduction in the farm population was already well under

Table 4

OCCUPIED POPULATION AND TOTAL POPULATION, IN AGRI-
CULTURE AND IN ALL SECTORS, IN GREAT BRITAIN, FRANCE
AND GERMANY

	Occupied population			Total population		
	Agri-culture	All sectors	Agri-culture as % of total	Agri-culture	All sectors	Agri-culture as % of total
	millions		%	millions		%
GREAT 1881	1·50	12·80	12	..	29·7	..
BRITAIN 1901	1·33	16·31	8	..	37·0	..
% change:						
1881–1901	−12%	+28%	..	..	+25%	..
FRANCE*a* 1881	7·89	16·54	48	18·2	37·7	48
1891	..	..	..	17·4	38·3	45
1906	8·86	20·72	43	..	..	..
% change:						
1881–91	..	..	..	−5%	+2%	..
1881–1906	+12%	+25%	..	..	..	..
GERMANY*b* 1882	8·21	19·0	43	19·2	45·2	43
1895	8·29	20·1	41	18·5	51·8	36
1907	9·88	26·2	38	17·7	55·8	32
% change:						
1882–95	+ 1%	+ 6%	..	−4%	+15%	..
1882–1907	+20%	+38%	..	−8%	+23%	..

a 'Agriculture' includes forestry and fishing.
b 'Agriculture' includes forestry.
.. Not available.

Sources : See corresponding tables in country chapters.

way as a result of the early Industrial Revolution and there were
greater opportunities in non-farm employment than was the case
in the other two countries. Also, in Britain it was mainly the
agricultural labourers who moved to the towns; in countries where
a peasant agriculture predominated the move was much more
difficult, for the farm was a home as well as a place of work for

Table 5

COST OF AN AVERAGE WORKING-MAN'S FOOD BUDGET IN DIFFERENT COUNTRIES, IN 1905[a]
(in pence)

	At English consumption levels, but foreign prices				At foreign consumption levels and foreign prices		
	England and Wales	France	Germany	Belgium	France	Germany	Belgium
Bread	27½	31¾	39¾[b]	26⅛	41¾	35¼[b]	41
Flour	12¾	19¾	18	13¾	..	3½	1
Potatoes	7¼	7¼	6¼	6¾	6¾	9¾	13
Sugar	10¾	15¼	12¾	16	5	4¾	3
Bacon	12	..	14¾	11¾	..	7½	6
Cheese	5¼	..	4¼	6⅜	..	3	4¼
Butter	26½	25	27¾	26	15¾	17¼	29¼
Milk	17½	12½	13¼	11¼	10	17	9
Beef	30½	33¼	37	29¼	22⅛	18¼	17⅞
Mutton	9½	12½	13¼	10½	8⅜	–	1¾
Pork	4	4⅝	5	4¼	7	15¾	8½
Total of above	163½	(161⅞)[c]	192	162	(116¾)[c]	132	134⅝

[a] Data for Belgium refer to 1908.
[b] Consists of an 'equivalent' amount of wheat flour.
[c] Incomplete total.
.. Not available.
– Nil or negligible.
Source: Board of Trade (U.K.), *Cost of living in foreign towns* (Cd. 4032, 1908; Cd. 4512, 1909; and Cd. 5065, 1910).

Table 6

WAGES AND HOURS OF WORK OF WORKERS IN CERTAIN TRADES IN DIFFERENT COUNTRIES, AS A PERCENTAGE OF THE CORRESPONDING FIGURES FOR ENGLAND

	France	Germany	Belgium
Weekly money wages	75	83	63
Hours worked per week	117	111	121
Hourly wage rates	64	75	52

Source: As Table 5.

most of those concerned. Protection therefore was only one among various factors, but it seems likely that if France and Germany had not adopted protection, or if Britain had, the results would have been different.

Whatever the effects of protection on farmers, it was certainly against the interests of consumers in general. Some interesting studies published by the British Board of Trade between 1908 and 1910 indicated that urban workers in France and Germany had to pay considerably higher prices for their food than similarly-placed workers in England and Wales, though their earnings were substantially less in spite of longer hours of work. The main results of these studies are summarized in Table 5. The left-hand side of the table indicates the cost in various countries of the average quantities of food consumed in England and Wales: it thus reflects the differences in prices alone, and shows that all major foodstuffs, except milk and potatoes, were dearer in France and Germany than in England. On the other hand, the moderate degree of protection in Belgium is reflected in prices similar to those of England. The right-hand side of the table indicates the cost of the quantities actually consumed in each country, and thus reflects both price differences and variations in the consumption pattern. It appears that the total cost of the food budget was less in all the three foreign countries than in England, but this was due to lower consumption of most items (bread, potatoes and pork being the main exceptions). Considered in conjunction with the much lower earnings of workers (Table 6), these data suggest that agricultural protection in France and Germany substantially aggravated the gap in the standards of living of their working population as compared with that of England.

The fact that these effects on the cost of living did not cause a bigger outcry than they did was probably because the general price trend was downward, and the effect of protection was to restrain the fall rather than to cause an increase in food prices. The burden was thus not an obvious one, but it was nevertheless real and significant: in effect, consumers in France and Germany were largely deprived of the benefits that could have come from cheap imported food.

Chapter 2. The United Kingdom

Evolution in British agriculture

By the early nineteenth century, British agriculture had completed its transformation from feudal patterns and practices. The manorial system of open fields, cultivated in common by a peasantry tied to their lord by bonds of various kinds, had been undermined by the enclosure movement of the sixteenth century, when many of the open fields had been consolidated into individual holdings, generally remaining in the possession of the lord but let out to tenant farmers. As the landlords sought to substitute a few large tenants for several occupiers, the number of holdings fell and their size increased. The mass of the former peasantry formed a new class of landless labourers. Much of the arable land that was enclosed was converted into grass and used for grazing sheep, and as labour requirements were thus reduced, many agricultural workers were forced to the growing towns.

In the eighteenth century, the process of enclosure was carried further. With rising population and hence rising demand for food, agriculture was a profitable occupation, and there was increasing recognition of the advantages of large consolidated holdings as compared with common tillage or pasture. The movement gained the support of Parliament, and an increasing number of private Enclosure Acts were granted, under which agreements between the parties concerned were made binding and permanent. In 1801 the procedure was simplified by a general Enclosure Act.

British agriculture thus came to be characterized by large unified farms, many of them in the possession of wealthy landlords who were prepared to invest heavily in improvements to their estates. The custom being to hand the farm in its entirety from father to eldest son, there was little of the tendency to divide up holdings which plagued agriculture in other countries. It can be seen from Table 7 that though farms of less than 20 acres were

Table 7

AGRICULTURAL HOLDINGS IN GREAT BRITAIN IN 1870, BY SIZE

Size of holding		Number of holdings	Estimated area covered
acres	hectares (approx.)	thousands	thousand acres
under 5	under 2	136	407
5–20	2–8	150	2,252
20–50	8–20	86	3,010
50–100	20–40	64	4,800
over 100	over 40	93	19,940
Total		529	30,408

Source : Agricultural Returns of Great Britain, 1870.

quite numerous, they accounted for only a small proportion of the agricultural area, two-thirds of which was in farms of more than 100 acres.

The result of this transformation was to create an agriculture able to take full advantage of the technological changes which came in the wake of the Industrial Revolution: improved methods of cultivation, new crops, scientific stock-breeding, all leading to the intensive and productive system known as 'high farming'. By the middle of the century British agriculture was recognized to be the best in the world.

The Industrial Revolution brought other changes which fundamentally affected the situation of agriculture. Growing labour needs in industry promoted the movement off the land, so that already by the nineteenth century only a small proportion of the population earned their living from agriculture. Also, the growth in the demand for food was such that it could not be fully satisfied by British agriculture. Till the middle of the eighteenth century, Britain had normally been a net exporter of grain, but from then on imports began to exceed exports in years of bad harvest, until by the nineteenth century Britain's dependence on grain imports was established. This brought into the foreground the issue of the Corn Laws.

The repeal of the Corn Laws

'Corn Laws' had existed in England from the early Middle Ages. Their original purpose was to maintain fair prices by preventing speculation and monopolistic practices: they regulated internal trade and restricted exports. From 1660 onwards, imports too were regulated by a sliding scale of import duties, in which the duty was 2s. a quarter when home prices were at or under 44s., but only 4d. when home prices were at a higher level. However, so long as Britain was normally a net exporter of grain, the Corn Laws were of minor importance as a measure of import restriction.

By the end of the Napoleonic Wars, conditions were different. The Corn Laws became a protective measure, shutting out imports and raising domestic prices. Under a law of 1815, imports of foreign wheat were admitted free of duty when the price of British wheat was at or above 80s. per quarter; otherwise imports were prohibited. Similar provisions were adopted for other grains. In 1822 the system was modified: the price limit at which imports were prohibited was lowered to 70s. per quarter and above this level a sliding scale of duties was applied. A further change was made in 1828: there was no longer any prohibition, but a more complicated sliding scale was introduced.

The average annual price of wheat, which had been above 80s. during most of the Napoleonic Wars, dropped sharply around 1820 and lay between 40s. and 70s. in subsequent decades. At this price level, imports were either excluded or subjected to near-prohibitive duties for most of the time.

The Corn Laws were notorious chiefly for accentuating fluctuations in supplies and prices. Traders had an interest in holding supplies off the market till the price rose sufficiently for imports to be admitted or for the duty to be reduced: there would then be a flood of imports, depressing prices once again.

Given the miserable conditions of much of the urban working

class at this time, the slightest rise in the price of bread was a great evil, and to have relatively low prices at one period was poor compensation for prohibitively high prices at another. Agitation began after the passage of the new law in 1815: it continued during the 1820s, eased off between 1831 and 1836 when harvests were large and prices low, but intensified as prices rose from 1837 on. In 1838 the Anti-Corn Law League was formed, under the leadership of Richard Cobden and John Bright, and began a vigorous campaign. It issued a regular publication and numerous pamphlets and held public meetings, stressing the need for 'cheap bread' and appealing to the interests of the urban population. In 1842 it took an active part in the elections: Cobden himself obtained a seat in Parliament. In the same year Sir Robert Peel modified the sliding scale and eased the degree of import restriction; this, combined with a good harvest, took the edge off the agitation for a while. But the harvest of 1845 was disastrous, and in Ireland the failure of the potato crop owing to blight caused famine. Peel's efforts at reform had so far been opposed by almost the whole of his Tory Cabinet, and though he was now convinced of the need for total abolition of the Corn Laws he still lacked support. He resigned, but after attempts to form another government had failed, he was called back to office with enhanced authority. In January 1846 he announced that from February 1st, 1849, grain would be admitted subject only to a small registration duty (1s. per quarter on wheat) and that in the meantime the duties would be substantially reduced. After a vigorous Parliamentary debate, the Corn Bill received royal assent in June. The Anti-Corn Law League, having achieved its object, dissolved itself the following month.

The success of the campaign for abolition of the Corn Laws established firmly in Britain the Free Trade ideal, and for nearly a century helped to ensure the failure of any attempt to restore protection for agriculture. The outcome owed much to the efforts of the Anti-Corn Law League and its leaders, Cobden and Bright. Their basic theme of cheap bread was simple and easily understood: it appealed directly to the working classes and to humanitarians concerned at the distress of the urban population. Agricultural labourers too saw their interest in cheaper food, and the League even enlisted the support of tenant farmers (though with doubtful success) on the grounds that their rents were fixed on the basis of high prices, so that they suffered from the fluctuations caused by the Corn Laws.

Cobden and Bright, together with the majority of the League's leadership, belonged to the manufacturing class, which was interested in cheap bread in order to save wages. Essentially the repeal of the Corn Laws represented a victory of the manufacturers over the farmers and a concession by the landowning aristocracy, and reflected the shift in the balance of the population and of political power. Lord Ernle, in his standard work on English farming, commented as follows:

> Down to the middle of the eighteenth century, the great preponderance of the nation had been interested in prices both as consumers and producers of corn. Now the proportions were completely altered, and the majority had permanently shifted. The new manufacturing class was rapidly growing; the mass of open-field farmers had become agricultural labourers, whose real wages rose with the cheapness or fell with the dearness of bread. On the other hand, the interests of producers of corn were now represented by a comparatively small and dwindling class of landowners and farmers, who in recent years had enormously raised their own standard of living. Numerically small, but politically powerful, this class was convinced that the war-prices yielded only reasonable profits. The great majority of the population was convinced to the contrary.[1]

The Reform Act of 1832 by no means broke the power of the landed aristocracy, but through the extension of the franchise and the redistribution of Parliamentary seats it added 217,000 voters, mostly in the towns, to the previous electorate of only 435,000.

The repeal of the Corn Laws was the most controversial of a series of tariff reforms which made Britain a Free Trade nation. The process had begun in 1822, when Canning simplified the tariff and reduced some duties; it was pursued by Peel in 1842, 1845 and 1846 with the removal of many duties on manufactures as well as of those on meat, cattle, potatoes, vegetables and other products; it was carried still further by Gladstone in 1853 with more removals and reductions of duty; and it culminated in the

[1] Lord Ernle, *English Farming* (6th ed., London: Heinemann, 1962), pp. 271–272.

Anglo-French Treaty of Commerce of 1860 (the negotiations for which were conducted on the British side by Cobden). The reductions and abolitions of duty promised to France in this treaty were carried through by Gladstone as an independent tariff reform and extended to all other countries. After this, there remained only a few duties, mostly for revenue purposes: these were on sugar (abolished in 1874), manufactured tobacco, wines, spirits and hops (abolished in 1862), together with the small registration duties on grains and flour which were finally removed in 1869.

The Great Depression

For some thirty years after the repeal of the Corn Laws, British agriculture had little difficulty in surviving in its unprotected state. Though grain prices fell sharply from about 1848 to 1850, they recovered from 1853 onwards. The interruption of exports by the United States during the American Civil War (1861–4) gave a further stimulus to grain prices. British farmers benefited also from a series of good harvests. The cultivated area expanded, land values rose, and 'high farming' reached its peak. Seen in comparison with later years, this period was to appear as a 'Golden Age' for British agriculture.

Trouble began with a general economic depression in the late 1870s. In addition, from 1875 to 1879 a series of wet summers caused bad harvests: the crop of 1879 was one of the poorest ever recorded. Formerly, small harvests had generally been accompanied by higher prices, but now a new factor was introduced. Since 1873 grain imports from the United States had been rising (Table 8): in 1879 they increased to such an extent that prices fell, and British farmers suffered severe losses. At this period there was also a series of livestock epidemics: rinderpest in 1877, liver-rot in sheep in 1879, foot-and-mouth in 1883. This combination of disasters ruined many farmers and compelled landlords to remit or reduce rents.

In the 1880s, though imports continued to rise and prices to fall, farmers got some relief from better seasons. But a second crisis occurred when from 1891 to 1894 a succession of cold summers, drought and other difficulties caused bad harvests, and imports from the United States, after a period of relative stability, began to increase again. By the mid-1890s grain prices were the lowest

Table 8

IMPORTS OF MAJOR AGRICULTURAL PRODUCTS INTO THE UNITED KINGDOM

(annual averages)

	Unit	1865–9	1870–4	1875–9	1880–4	1885–9	1890–4	1895–9	1900–4	1905–9
Wheat and wheat flour[a]	million cwt.	35	47	61	74	77	92	98	109	113
Barley	,,	7	10	12	13	18	20	21	23	19
Oats	,,	8	11	12	13	15	15	16	18	15
Maize	,,	14	19	34	29	31	35	52	48	43
Beef[b]	,,	·2	·3	·6	1·0	1·0	2·0	3·0	4·2	5·6
Mutton[b]	,,	··	··	··	··	·8	1·2	3·1	3·6	4·3
Pork[b]	,,	·2	·3	·4	·4	·4	·4	·7	·9	·7
Butter[c]	,,	1·2	1·3	1·7	2·3	*1·6	2·2	3·1	3·9	4·2
Cheese	,,	·9	1·2	1·7	1·8	1·9	2·1	2·3	2·6	2·4
Eggs	thousand millions	·4	·5	·8	·9	1·1	1·2	1·2	2·4	2·2
Wool[a]	million lb.	147	184	201	221	284	311	383	350	397

[a] Wheat flour in grain equivalent.
[b] Both fresh and refrigerated, and, in the case of pork, salted.
[c] Including margarine till 1885.
[a] Net imports.

.. Not available.
*Series not fully comparable before and after this date.

Source: Statistical Abstract for the United Kingdom.

on record: the price of wheat dropped to less than half the pre-depression level. The effects on arable farmers were all the more severe because the troubles of the previous years had eliminated their financial reserves.

From calculations made by J. R. Bellerby (shown in Table 9)

Table 9

NET FARM INCOME IN THE UNITED KINGDOM, AND ITS DISTRIBUTION

(£ million, annual averages)

	Net farm income	Net rent	Wages	Interest	Farmers' 'incentive income'
1867–78	150	36	54	20	40
1879–83	122	33	49	17	24
1884–91	115	28	46	15	27
1892–6	108	23	43	14	27
1897–1905	115	22	43	14	36
1906–14	135	26	46	16	47
1892–6 as % of 1867–78	72	64	80	70	67

Source: J. R. Bellerby, *Agriculture and Industry* (London: Macmillan, 1956), p. 56.

it appears that at this trough of the depression, in the mid-1890s, net farm income in the United Kingdom was down by some 30 per cent as compared with the pre-depression period. The farm wage bill had fallen relatively little (by about 20 per cent) leaving rents and farmers' profits to bear the brunt of the crisis.

Throughout the depression, however, livestock prices were relatively well maintained. Though imports were increasing steadily, helped by the new techniques of refrigeration, a decline in prices began only in the mid-1880s, some five years after the beginning of the crisis for grains. Subsequently, the fall in livestock prices was never so severe: in 1896 Sauerbeck's index (Table 10) reached its lowest point for both crop and livestock products, but while the former stood at 53 the latter was at 73 (1867–77 = 100). Over the whole period of depression, from 1880 to 1900, crop

Table 10

PRICE INDICES OF FOODSTUFFS ON BRITISH MARKETS
(1867–77 = 100)

	1880–4	1885–9	1890–4	1895–9	1900–4	1905–9
CROP PRODUCTS	82	66	64	59	62	67
of which: Wheat	78	58	54	51	50	58
Barley	82	69	68	62	62	65
Oats	83	70	73	63	69	70
Maize	84	67	67	52	68	76
LIVESTOCK						
PRODUCTS	101	84	82	77	85	88
of which: Beef[a]	99	81	80	79	85	84
Mutton[a]	109	92	87	87	91	111
Pork	99	83	86	77	86	89
Bacon	100	87	87	74	82	88
Butter	98	83	83	77	82	88
All foodstuffs[b]	83	70	69	63	71	75

[a] 'Prime' quality: prices of 'middling' quality suffered a bigger price fall (up to 10–15 per cent more at the worst of the depression).
[b] Including sugar, coffee and tea.

Source: Sauerbeck's Index, *Journal of the Royal Statistical Society*, various dates.

prices averaged 68 per cent of the pre-depression level, livestock prices 86 per cent.[1]

After 1897 the prices of most agricultural commodities ceased to fall; gradually they recovered, and British agriculture emerged from the depression. By 1906–14, farm income was back to 90 per cent of the pre-depression level. There seems actually to have been a slight recovery between 1901 and 1911 in the number of persons occupied in agriculture (though the Census Report of 1911 considered that the statistics exaggerated the extent of this revival).

[1] Several of the series used by Sauerbeck relate to imported commodities. Price developments for home-produced commodities may not have been exactly the same. Also, the weighting of the index for all foodstuffs did not correspond to the pattern of British agricultural output. See article by T. W. Fletcher cited below.

But the depression had transformed British agriculture. Between 1881 and 1901 the population occupied in agriculture in Great Britain was reduced from about 1,500,000 to about 1,325,000 (Table 11), this fall being accounted for almost entirely by the departure of hired workers. With the continuing rise of employment in other sectors, the active population in agriculture had been reduced to a mere 8 per cent of the total. Farmers and

Table 11

POPULATION OCCUPIED IN AGRICULTURE IN GREAT BRITAIN, IN RELATION TO TOTAL OCCUPIED POPULATION AND TO TOTAL POPULATION

(thousands)

	Occupied population*a*			Total population of Great Britain
	Agriculture	All sectors	Agriculture as % of total	
1861	1,913	10,463	18	23,128
1871	1,690	11,646	15	26,072
1881	1,500	12,795	12	29,710
1891	1,402	14,676	10	33,029
1901	1,325	16,312	8	37,000
1911	1,381	18,351	8	40,831

a Including persons temporarily unemployed.

Sources: Population occupied in agriculture from F. D. W. Taylor, 'Numbers in agriculture', *Farm Economist*, vol. VIII, No. 4, 1955. Total occupied population from J. R. Bellerby, 'The distribution of manpower in agriculture and industry', *Farm Economist*, vol. IX, No. 1, 1958. Total population from the *Statistical Abstracts*.

landlords had been impoverished. It had become necessary to abandon 'high farming' and to economize in every possible way: both the fixed capital of the farms and the quality of the soil had suffered from forced neglect. A striking change had occurred in the pattern of agriculture: much arable land had been returned to grass, and the wheat acreage in particular was reduced by a half between 1870 and 1900 (Table 12). On the other hand there

Table 12

CROP AREA AND LIVESTOCK NUMBERS IN GREAT BRITAIN

	1870	1880	1890	1900	1910
AREA (million acres)					
Wheat	3·5	2·9	2·4	1·8	1·8
Barley and oats	5·1	5·3	5·0	5·0	4·8
Green crops and roots	3·6	3·5	3·3	3·2	3·0
Other crops and fallow	1·6	1·6	1·2	0·9	1·0
Temporary grass	4·5	4·4	4·8	4·8	4·2
Total arable land	18·3	17·7	16·8	15·7	14·7
Permanent pasture	12·1	14·4	16·0	16·7	17·5
Total cultivated area	30·4	32·1	32·8	32·4	32·1
LIVESTOCK (millions)					
Cattle	5·4	5·9	6·5	6·8	7·0
Pigs	2·2	2·0	2·7	2·4	2·4
Sheep	28·4	26·6	27·3	26·6	27·1

Source: Statistical Abstract for the United Kingdom.

were more cattle and pigs; the number of sheep remained roughly the same.

Interpretations of the Great Depression

The contrast between arable and livestock farming is significant. In an important study of the Great Depression, T. W. Fletcher points out that discussions of this period have given too much attention to the arable sector, and in particular to wheat.[1] Even before the depression, wheat provided only 13 per cent of gross agricultural output in the United Kingdom, 22 per cent in England; it is therefore an inadequate guide to agriculture as a whole. Fletcher observes that while the arable farmers, mainly in the east and south of England, suffered a steep fall in the price of their products, livestock farmers in the north and west not only

[1] T. W. Fletcher, 'The Great Depression of English Agriculture, 1873–1896', *Economic History Review*, April 1961.

experienced a relatively small decline in prices but benefited from the much greater fall in the cost of animal feeding-stuffs. His calculations of gross agricultural output, reproduced in Table 13, show that while the output of the arable sector fell in value (in current prices) from £104 million in 1867–9 to £62 million in 1894–1903, the output of livestock products *rose* from £127 million to £146 million.

The first of the two Royal Commissions which investigated British agriculture during the Great Depression seems to have

Table 13

GROSS AGRICULTURAL OUTPUT

(£ million)

	Total U.K.			England	
	1867–9	1870–6	1894–1903	1867–71	1894–8
Wheat	35	28	8	28	8
Barley	17	18	9	13	8
Oats	11	9	8	4	4
Potatoes	14	14	11	3	3
Hay, straw, fruit and vegetables	20	19	22	14	17
Other crops	7	8	4	3	2
Total crops	104	95	62	65	41
Beef	35	46	42	15	16
Mutton	26	31	25	15	13
Pigmeat	19	23	19	10	11
Horses	2	2	3	1	2
Milk	34	39	44	15	20
Wool	7	8	3	6	2
Poultry and eggs	5	7	10	4	7
Total livestock	127	155	146	64	71
Total agricultural output	231	250	208	130	112

Source: Fletcher, loc. cit.

fallen victim to this tendency to exaggerate the importance of the arable sector. This Commission was appointed in 1879 as the result of pressure by 'Squire' Chaplin, who was the recognized spokesman for agriculture in the House of Commons; he was a firm believer in the crucial importance of corn. The leading members of the Commission belonged to the landowning aristocracy and gentry; it collected evidence mainly from large farmers and mainly from the arable counties of England. The Commission nevertheless concluded that agricultural distress had prevailed over the whole country. It did note that the northern counties of England had suffered relatively little, but it failed to investigate the causes of this difference. It made little distinction between the trend of crop and livestock prices, and saw no implications in the low prices of animal fodder.

The Commission was equally undiscerning about the factors responsible for the depression. Bad seasons seemed to have been the main cause. It considered that foreign competition was also having serious effects, lowering prices even in years of poor harvests, and thought that this competition was likely to continue. Yet the Commission did not see in this a fundamental change in the pattern of world trade, necessitating a corresponding adaptation in British agriculture. It did not ever consider protection, simply stating that the low prices caused by imports had to be accepted. As a piece of economic analysis, this report was dismally inadequate, and inevitably its recommendations bore little relevance to the basic causes of distress.

The ineptness of the first Royal Commission may be contrasted with the insight of Sir James Caird, whose book *The Landed Interest and the Supply of Food* received its fourth edition in 1880, while the Commission was sitting. In this he stated that 'a great change in the agricultural position is impending' as a result of the competition of rich virgin soils in America and the cheapening of transport. This meant that British agriculture should turn to products which could not stand long transport or storage, such as milk, early wheat, vegetables, potatoes, sugar-beet and hay. Sir James saw, moreover, that the consumption pattern was shifting as the working class raised its living standards: bread was giving way to meat, vegetables and other high-quality produce. He concluded that:

Our agriculture must adapt itself to the change, freely accepting the good it brings, and skilfully using the advantages which greater proximity to the best market must always command.[1]

The second Royal Commission on agriculture, appointed in 1894, had a greater variety of members than the first, and though most of the witnesses it heard were again the larger farmers, there was more representation from the north and west of England. A conflict of opinion appeared in the Commission's second report in 1896 (a first progress report was issued in 1894): though all the members of the Commission recognized that the fall in prices had been the chief cause of depression, the majority – consisting of the landed gentry – confined itself thereafter to a discussion of rates, land tax and State loans to agriculture. However, a minority of three, including the chairman, declared that the depression had been far more serious in the eastern and southern counties of England than elsewhere in Britain, and attributed this difference to four factors:

1. The east and south had suffered from particularly unfavourable seasons, starting in 1892;
2. These regions had also been the most affected because they were the chief wheat-growing areas;
3. They had comparatively few small farms, and small farms had done better because they depended less on hired labour and because of their concentration on dairying;
4. Burdens in the form of tithes, land tax and local rates were as a rule much heavier in the east and south, having been determined in relation to the former prosperity of these regions.

In the Commission's final report, in 1897, the conflict was largely resolved and a more careful analysis was made. The depression was attributed mainly to the fall in prices, and it was realized that this fall had been most severe for grain – particularly wheat – and for wool. It was thus not surprising that the worst trouble had been felt in the arable counties, while areas suitable for dairying, market gardening and poultry-raising had escaped comparatively lightly. The Commission's recommendations were limited to the relief of taxes, tithes, railway rates and so on, but

[1] Sir James Caird, *The Landed Interest and the Supply of Food* (4th ed., London, 1880), p. 175.

it did not pretend that these would be a complete remedy. It recognized that foreign competition would cause a further reduction in the arable area, but did not propose to do anything about it.

> The grave situation we have described, affecting no inconsiderable part of Great Britain, is due to a long-continued fall in prices. This fall is attributed by the great majority of witnesses to foreign competition, and, as previously pointed out, we have not been able to find any promise, in the near future at all events, of a material relaxation of the pressure of this competition upon the British producer.
>
> So far, then, as the maintenance of this competition involves the continued depreciation of agricultural values, we must look forward to a further reduction of the area of British land susceptible of profitable arable cultivation, together with a corresponding contraction of our production and a diminution of our rural population.[1]

A purer expression of laissez-faire it would be hard to find. A supplementary report by ten members of the Commission noted that many farmers would like a return to protection, but that 'several of those who are among the warmest advocates of protection told us they did not regard the adoption of that policy as within the pale of practical politics'.[2]

Free Trade, Fair Trade, Empire and Tariff Reform

Following the report of the first Royal Commission, the Government relieved farmers of part of the burden of local taxation, engaged upon a reform of land tenure and took action against animal diseases. In 1889 the Board of Agriculture was created. But otherwise the various governments in power during the Great Depression, Conservative as well as Liberal, adhered strictly to laissez-faire. The only measure of import restriction was the prohibition, in 1892, of imports of livestock from the Continent; this measure, originally applied for reason of animal health, afterwards became permanent.

Throughout the period of the Great Depression, there was

[1] Royal Commission on Agriculture, *Final Report*, 1897 (C. 8540), p. 159.
[2] Ibid., p. 161.

nevertheless much controversy on the tariff issue in general. A constant barrage of Free Trade propaganda was kept up by the Cobden Club, founded in 1866 to encourage 'the growth and diffusion of those economic and political principles with which Cobden's name is associated'. The Club held great sway in the 1860s and 1870s, and though its extreme Free Trade position gradually lost favour it continued to be influential for many years after. Its ideas were generally close to those of the Liberal party.

A reaction against unilateral Free Trade began with a slackening in economic activity in 1868. It was pointed out that even Adam Smith had thought that it might be good policy to use duties in retaliation against restrictions by other countries. This movement died down temporarily after 1870, as the economic situation improved, but it gained force later in the 1870s as a more serious depression began to be felt. 'Fair Trade' then became the motto for those discontented with current policy. The principle was to place home and foreign producers on an equal footing by eliminating 'artificial' differences (for example, export bounties were to be countered by equivalent import duties), but not to level out 'natural' differences in production. A National Fair Trade League was formed, and its policy included the following points:

1. Commercial treaties to be made subject to revision at one year's notice;
2. No duties on imported raw materials;
3. Adequate duties on manufactured goods from countries refusing to admit British manufactures on an equitable basis;
4. 'Very moderate' duties on foodstuffs, but not on the produce of Empire countries admitting British manufactures in 'reasonably free interchange'.

With the growth of imports of grain from the United States, the Fair Trade League provided a platform for advocates of protection for agriculture. Its influence grew after 1885 when the Liberal Cabinet fell and Lord Salisbury, who had already made speeches on behalf of Fair Trade, became the leader of the new Government. One of his first actions was to appoint a Royal Commission to inquire into the causes of industrial depression. This Commission issued a report in 1886, in which a minority put forward Fair Trade arguments. Further, in 1887 the Congress of

Conservative Associations declared itself in favour of Fair Trade. In the Government, however, the Conservatives had joined forces with the Liberal Unionists, most of whom were convinced Free Traders. Lord Salisbury was therefore compelled to disown the Fair Trade movement, which ceased for a while to be an effective political force.

In the 1890s Fair Trade had a new lease of life, as the United States and various Continental countries reinforced their tariffs and a desire for retaliation was increasingly felt. However, the movement was hampered by the reluctance of any political party to take it up openly: there was no question of the Liberals doing so, and the Conservatives still owed their majority to the alliance with the Liberal Unionists.

Around the turn of the century, a stronger protectionist force arose. One cause of this was a lessening of confidence in Britain's command of the seas and of food supplies: in the Boer War of 1899–1902 Britain found herself without friends on the Continent, and Germany was starting to build a powerful navy. Moreover, industry in both Germany and the United States was making rapid progress under protectionist policies, and one-sided free trade began to seem absurd to many people.

The main motive, however, was the question of the Empire, which brought a new dimension to the tariff issue. The first Colonial Conference had been held in London in 1887, and it marked the beginning of a move to closer union. The idea of a commercial union between the countries of the Empire, with preferential duties, gradually gained ground and was supported by the Fair Trade League. In 1902 the fourth Colonial Conference passed a resolution favouring the principle of Imperial Preference. This made a great impression on Joseph Chamberlain, who had been appointed to the Colonial Office in 1895 and was looking for a way of reinforcing imperial unity. In 1903, in a speech at Birmingham, he proclaimed his secession from Free Trade and his belief in Imperial Preference, as well as in the need for retaliation through tariffs against protection by other countries. Later Chamberlain made a similar statement in the House of Commons, but he received no support from the leaders of the Government. Balfour, who had become Conservative Prime Minister in 1902, tried to avoid a split by putting forward a compromise proposal, to the effect that the Government should be given power to force down foreign tariffs by retaliatory duties, but without setting up a general tariff and without putting duties on foodstuffs. This however satisfied neither of the conflicting groups, and soon afterwards both Chamberlain and the Free Traders in the Cabinet resigned.

Chamberlain now unleashed a large-scale tariff campaign, backed by a newly-formed Tariff Reform League and a Tariff Commission. Though Chamberlain began the campaign primarily for the sake of unifying the Empire, the need to get a broad basis of support by appealing to industrial interests in Britain caused the emphasis to be put increasingly on the protectionist aspect. But so far as agriculture was concerned, the reluctance to propose high duties on foodstuffs and the desire to give preference to Empire produce made it impossible to formulate any effective policy of protection. The so-called Tariff Commission produced a report on agriculture in 1906, which stressed the dangers of Britain's dependence on imported food and tried to prove that the small size of British agriculture restricted the market for home industry. It proposed that there should be import duties on agricultural products, and that the revenue from these duties should be used to assist agriculture in various ways. But as preference was to be given to the Empire, which by then was an important competitor for British agriculture, it seems doubtful whether British agriculture would have benefited much from these proposals.

In any case, the tariff campaign failed entirely. The Liberal Opposition, reunited over this issue, made the most of the popular outcry against taxes on food. Balfour, on his side, managed to unite the Conservatives with another compromise formula more to the satisfaction of Chamberlain. But in the general election of 1906, which was fought almost entirely on the tariff issue, the Liberals gained an overall majority of eighty-four seats. Protectionism in general, and above all tariffs on foodstuffs, remained a political taboo until the 1930s.

Factors in the victory of Free Trade

In the last quarter of the nineteenth century, a large and influential sector of British agriculture had been ruined twice over, and little was done to help it. In other countries during this period, the farmers – particularly the large arable farmers – campaigned vigorously for protection, and in general their Governments were persuaded to give them satisfaction. In Britain, not only did the Government make no important move, but among farmers themselves there was little protectionist agitation.

A vital factor in explaining this is, of course, the balance of power as between the urban and the rural population. With its early start in industrialization, Britain had a particularly small part of its population in agriculture. In addition, the political strength of the landed classes had been undermined by the Reform Act of 1832 and thereafter steadily declined; meanwhile the power of the industrial population, to which 'cheap bread' remained a war-cry, had constantly increased. Public opinion was still very much in the sway of the Free Trade ethic – an ethic based not so much upon economic reasoning as upon the aftermath of feeling resulting from the repeal of the Corn Laws. This point is well expressed by Clapham:

> There were plenty of elderly men of affairs in the 'eighties and 'nineties to whom corn law repeal was a vivid and blessed memory; many younger men for whom it had been canonised. So, just because agricultural depression first presented itself as a problem in wheat and wheaten bread, the political chance of its being handled by way of tariffs was almost infinitely small.[1]

There was moreover no chance of a protectionist alliance between farmers and industrialists: the latter attached far too much importance to cheap food and cheap raw materials. Moreover, there was no strong movement for protection in British industry, which as yet had relatively little fear of competition and, on the other hand, had a very clear interest in maintaining export markets.

The strategic arguments for maintaining a large agriculture, which played a certain role in Continental countries nervous about their food supplies, had little impact in Britain, with its extensive food-producing Empire and its undisputed mastery of the seas. It was only after the Great Depression that the growing power of Germany began to give cause for worry on this score.

There were several reasons why British farmers themselves did

[1] J. H. Clapham, *An Economic History of Modern Britain* (C.U.P., 1932), p. 77.

not present a strong protectionist front. One was that they realized how small would be the prospects of success. Another was that they were remarkably slow to become aware of the real nature of the threat from imports: it has been seen above that the difficulties were at first attributed mainly to bad weather. Also, the landlord-tenant system made possible a sharing of the burden: for thousands of tenant farmers the first shock of falling prices was tempered by abatements in their rent.

The prevalence of the landlord-tenant system also made it more difficult to form a united agricultural front. So did the division of interests between crop and livestock producers, which has already been discussed. While in other countries the large arable farmers were powerful enough to draw smaller producers into their movement, or simply to ignore their existence, in England the small livestock farmers of the north and west seem to have been too independent and too well aware of their real interests to fall into such a trap.

As a result, no effective agricultural pressure group was active during this period. The main agricultural organization was the Central Chamber of Agriculture, an association of numerous local Chambers of Agriculture, Farmers' Clubs and Farmers' Associations; it was founded in 1865 and led mainly by large landowners. It did not take the tariff issue seriously until 1892, when it convened a national Agricultural Conference, at which the split between the arable farmers and the livestock producers was evident. A Farmers' Alliance, started in 1879 to represent the interests of tenant farmers, also split on the question of protection and gradually died out. A National Agricultural Union was formed in 1893 in an attempt to combine landlords, farmers and workers in a single body; but its work overlapped that of the Central Chamber and it exerted little influence. The present National Farmers' Union was not formed until 1908.[1]

---

[1] The Central Chamber of Agriculture continued to exist even after the NFU had taken the lead, and was finally wound up only in 1959.

Chapter 3. France

French agriculture before the Depression

The agricultural situation in France around the middle of the
nineteenth century was very different from that of Britain. There
had been no gradual evolution from feudal patterns of land
ownership, but an abrupt break imposed by the Revolution, when
church lands and the estates of the nobles were put up for sale and
peasants were freed from the obligations they owed to their lords.
Under the Restoration monarchy of 1814–30, many large landowners regained their property, but there remained several
millions of small peasant proprietors.[1]

No systematic enclosure movement took place; indeed the law
requiring equal division of property between heirs tended to keep
the majority of farms small and fragmented. In 1882, 5·7 million
holdings were counted: even excluding from consideration 2·2
million with less than 1 hectare which may not have been genuine
farm businesses, there were 2·6 million holdings with between 1
and 10 hectares (Table 14). Moreover, the 5·7 million holdings
included no less than 125 million separate plots, making an average
of 22 per holding; the average area of each plot was a mere 0·39
hectares. At the other end of the scale, there was a minority of
large holdings of 40 hectares and upwards; because of their large

[1] The changes in land tenure during and after the Revolution were complicated. See J. H. Clapham, *Economic Development of France and Germany 1815–
1914* (4th ed., C.U.P., 1945), chap. I.

Table 14

AGRICULTURAL HOLDINGS IN 1882, BY SIZE

Size (hectares)	Number (thousands)	Area covered (million ha.)	Average area per holding (hectares)
0–1	2,168	1·1	0·5
1–5	1,866	5·6	3·0
5–10	769	5·8	7·5
10–20	431	6·5	15·0
20–30	198	5·0	25·0
30–40	98	3·4	35·0
over 40	142	22·3	156·7
Total	5,672	49·6	8·7

Source: Statistique Agricole de la France – Enquête Décennale de 1882.

average size, this group accounted for nearly half the agricultural area.

On the numerous small holdings, progress was difficult. Structural conditions were not the only obstacle: the peasantry was largely uneducated (indeed all too often illiterate) and lacked the capital resources necessary for improvements. In cases where holdings were let to tenants, leases were often short – rarely for more than ten years – and the tenant had no guarantee of receiving compensation for improvements he made. The backwardness and poverty of the French peasantry at this time are well described in the following passage from Augé-Laribé's outstanding work on French agricultural policy:

At this time [around 1880], newspapers and public speakers often referred to the 'remote rural areas'. It was an expression which conjured up terrae incognitae, forgotten, godforsaken villages where the most basic necessities were lacking and where it was not even certain that the French language would be understood. In fact many country districts were very far from any town and indeed from modern civilization. Though the towns were linked by excellent roads and railways, it was a much more difficult matter to reach the villages and penetrate to all the farms.[1]

[1] M. Augé-Laribé, *La politique agricole de la France de 1880 à 1940* (Paris: P.U.F., 1940), p. 55.

French agriculture was indeed largely untouched by the other major influence which had affected farming in Britain – the Industrial Revolution. France's Industrial Revolution began much later than that of Britain; by 1861 the rural population (persons in villages of less than 2,000 inhabitants) still amounted to 26·6 million out of a total of 37·4 million, and 19·9 million of the rural population depended on agriculture for a living. There was as yet little opportunity for impoverished peasants to better themselves by seeking work in the towns, and those who did leave agriculture were impelled by their poverty rather than attracted by any firm prospect of improvement. Moreover, there was relatively little technological impulse to pass from other sectors to agriculture, even if the state of communications and the educational level of the peasantry had been such as to facilitate this process. In another passage Augé-Laribé commented on the unprogressiveness of French agriculture:

The agricultural population, almost in its entirety and in practically every region, did not want to make progress. Its aim was self-preservation: it wanted to maintain itself and its environment unchanged. It did not realize that not to advance is to retreat, that what remains stagnant and does not adapt, in a world in evolution, risks its own extinction.[1]

But a time was reached when drastic changes forced themselves on French agriculture. Augé-Laribé continued:

But now economic progress was speeding up. Steamships had reduced the cost of ocean transport. Railways were ready to take from the ports the grain which had crossed the seas. All the continents were linked by trade. The railway companies gave preferential rates to foreign goods. Techniques of cultivation, which were not new but had remained unknown or neglected, reached a point where no one could afford not to adopt them. Chemical fertilizers forced themselves on the attention of even the most backward farmers. Highly efficient commercial organizations spanned the world. The development of other sectors and the competition of agriculture in foreign lands compelled the French peasants to join a race to which they were not accustomed. They complained about

[1] Ibid., p. 58.

all this agitation. They were short of breath. It was the crisis. Protectionist doctors, anxious to please the patient, prescribed rest, caution, avoidance of draughts; no healing medicines, but soothing drugs. When finally the farmers tried to recover, to exert the strength they gained through their association, it was far too late. Their competitors had outdistanced them.[1]

Free trade – the 1860 Anglo-French treaty

Throughout most of French history before 1860, protectionist tendencies dominated. A short period after the Revolution characterized by liberal tendencies came to an end with the Napoleonic Wars, when under Napoleon's 'Continental System' British goods were prohibited or subjected to high duties. French industry thus grew accustomed to high protection, and vested interests were formed which impeded subsequent attempts at tariff reform. Under the Restoration monarchy of 1814–30, manufactured goods from any origin were liable to be prohibited. Also, for the first time in France, protection was extended to agriculture. The big landowners made common cause with the manufacturers and demanded high import duties, together with freedom to export; the Bourbon monarchy wanted to restore a rural aristocracy and was ready to satisfy these demands. In 1819 a sliding scale of duties on grain, similar to the British Corn Laws, was introduced.

Under the July monarchy of 1830–48, a Free Trade Association was formed by Frédéric Bastiat and Michel Chevalier, along lines similar to Cobden's Anti-Corn Law League. But this movement gathered little public support. The Parliament of the Second Republic after 1848 was still opposed to tariff reforms; in 1850, by a large majority, it rejected proposals to remove protective duties on food and raw materials. The duties on wheat were maintained in principle, though they were suspended after bad harvests on several occasions.

With the Second Empire in 1852, the Free Trade movement found a new champion in Napoleon III, who was impressed by Peel's reforms in Britain. In 1856 he presented to Parliament a further proposal for freeing trade, but this too was rejected;

[1] Ibid., p. 59.

indeed, the Government had to promise not to revive the tariff issue for another five years at least.

Napoleon III and the Free Traders were thus forced to look for other ways to carry out their purposes. As the Emperor had the right to conclude treaties with other nations without consulting Parliament, the device of a commercial treaty with Britain provided a solution. In addition, Napoleon was anxious to establish closer relations with Britain and to reduce France's political isolation. The Anglo-French Treaty of Commerce of 1860 was therefore negotiated and signed in secret, and presented to Parliament as a fait accompli.

The concessions given by Britain to France in this treaty included reductions in the duties on wines and spirits. Much greater changes were made by France: the tariffs on manufactured goods were reduced to moderate levels, and the duties on nearly all foodstuffs and raw materials were removed. Abolition of the sliding scale of duties on grain followed in 1861.

Between 1861 and 1867, France concluded ten other commercial treaties: with Belgium, the Zollverein, Italy, Switzerland, Sweden and Norway, the Hanseatic League, the Netherlands, Spain, Portugal and Austria. Each of these treaties included the 'most favoured nation' clause, so that the relatively low duties resulting from the treaties were extended to the greater part of European trade.

The protectionist revival and the agricultural depression

This edifice of free trade in France was subjected to its first strains after the Franco-Prussian War of 1870. This war led both to a revival of nationalist sentiment in France and to a heavy burden of debt. The Government of the Third Republic, under Thiers, tried to raise import duties in order to obtain more revenue, but this required the revision of the commercial treaties, to which Britain in particular would not agree. In addition, French industrialists objected to Thiers's intention of imposing duties on raw materials. The failure of his customs policy was one of the reasons for Thiers's resignation in 1873.

The next Government was less protectionist, but as the commercial treaties were due to expire around 1878 a revision of the tariff appeared necessary. When the preparation for this began in

1875, a strong protectionist movement began to make itself felt both inside and outside Parliament. The impulse came from the iron and textile industries rather than from agriculture, which was not yet in any special difficulty. The industrialists however needed to make an ally of agriculture in order to win their battle. In this they succeeded, helped by a bad harvest in 1879 which caused discontent among the farmers. The principal agricultural organization, the Société des Agriculteurs de France, adopted the protectionist cause at its General Assembly of 1879: it demanded equality of treatment with industry, pleading the competitive advantage of agriculture in new countries and the relatively heavy burden of taxation on agriculture.

In 1881 the new tariff was adopted. The rates on manufactures were higher than before but still moderate; in the next few years many of the increases were renounced by the Government in a new series of commercial treaties. For agriculture, there were large increases in the duties on livestock and livestock products, but wheat remained subject to only a nominal duty and other grains were still exempt (Table 15).

The protectionist revival thus began before French agriculture got into serious difficulties, and for reasons largely independent of agriculture. But from 1879 on, the effects of overseas competition in grains made themselves increasingly felt. As in Britain, a succession of poor harvests, of which 1879 was the worst, encouraged the growth in imports. French agriculture no longer benefited from higher prices in these years of short supply; in 1882 and 1883, when domestic production recovered, imports were maintained and prices fell drastically.

French agriculture in its backward state was quite unable to compete with the flood of cheap imports. Further, the importance of peasant proprietorship (it was estimated that 80 per cent of the agricultural area was in the hands of owner-occupiers in 1882) meant that there was little possibility for passing on part of the loss of income to landlords, as in England.

The agricultural crisis thus made protection a vital issue. The Société des Agriculteurs de France was disappointed with the 1881 tariff and intensified its campaign. It continued to receive the support of industrialists, who took the opportunity of demonstrating their supposedly disinterested sympathy with the problems of the farmers. In 1885 agriculture received substantial measures

Table 15

TARIFFS ON MAJOR AGRICULTURAL PRODUCTS, 1881–1906

(francs per 100 kg., except where otherwise indicated)

	1881 May 7th	1885 March 28th and 30th	1887 March 29th and April 5th	1892 Jan. 7th	1894 Feb. 27th	1898 April 5th	1899 Feb. 1st	1903 July 31st	1906 July 18th and Nov. 21st
Wheat	0·60	3	5	...	7	...	...	...	...
Oats	nil	1·50	3	...	...	...	...	...	...
Barley	nil	1·50	...	3	...	...	...	...	...
Flour	1·20	6	8	8–12^a	11–16^a	...	...	...	...
Butter	13	...	...	6–13^b	...	...	...	...	...
Cheese (hard)	8	...	...	15–25^b	...	...	...	...	12–35
Eggs	10	...	...	6–10^b	...	...	...	...	...
Beef (fresh)	3	7	12	25	...	...	...	35–50^b	...
Pork "	3	7	12	...	...	...	...	25–40^b	...
Bullocks	15^c	25^c	38^c	10	...	...	...	20–30^b	...
Cows	8^c	12^c	20^c	10	...	...	...	20–30^b	...
Pigs	3^c	6^c	...	8	...	8–12	...	15–25^b	...
Wine^d	5^e	...	...	7–12^{bf}	...	...	12–25^g	...	12–35

Note: (1) From 1861 to 1881, duties were nil or negligible (wine excepted).
(2) Temporary changes in the duties are not indicated.

^{a} Variations according to gluten content.
^{b} 'Minimum' and 'general' tariffs from this date on.
^{c} Francs per head.
^{d} Francs per hectolitre.
^{e} Duty imposed on July 8th, 1871.
^{f} Under 11° proof.
^{g} Not exceeding 12° proof from this date on.

Source: Sirey, *Recueil général des lois et arrêts.*

of protection: the duty on wheat was raised to 3 francs per 100 kg.,
duties of 1.50 francs were imposed on feed grains and the livestock
duties were increased (Table 15). In 1887 most of the agricultural
duties were further increased, that on wheat rising to 5 francs,
which was about a quarter of the prevailing price.

The reinforcement of protection – the Méline Tariff of 1892

Even after these tariff increases, a vigorous fight for further
protection was pursued by both agriculture and industry. The
liberal element in Parliament had been gradually reduced in
successive elections. In the 1889 election campaign, candidates
were requested to sign a programme in favour of agriculture, and
the names of both those who accepted and those who refused
were made public. This election was fought mainly on the
constitutional issue raised by *Boulangisme*, and many candidates
were reluctant to lose the rural vote over the tariff question. The
election gave a protectionist majority: the successful deputies who
had signed the pledge were immediately reminded of it, and a
unified Agricultural Group was formed in Parliament, consisting
of 301 deputies. The Cabinet was at first headed by the liberal
Tirard, but in March 1890 he was overthrown: a Government
with decidedly protectionist leanings took office in which the
Ministers of Commerce and of Agriculture were both members
of the Agricultural Group.

The tariff question soon came to the boil: the commercial
treaties were due to expire again in 1892 and a new tariff was
necessary. In October 1890 the Government put forward its
tariff proposals, which were submitted to a Tariff Commission.

The subsequent discussions were dominated by the personality
of Jules Méline, a former Minister of Agriculture with a long-
standing commitment to protection. He was president of both the
Agricultural Group and the Tariff Commission. The Commission
itself had a strong protectionist majority, and in its report in
March 1891 it recommended duties generally higher than those
the Government had proposed. There followed a long and
vigorous debate in the Chamber and in the Senate. Méline's
main arguments were that other countries had raised their tariffs,
and that agriculture deserved to have equal treatment with
industry as well as protection against overseas competition. He

claimed to be acting in the interests of consumers, since the development of home production would tend to reduce prices.

The Free Traders in Parliament, led by Léon Say (grandson of the famous economist, and a former Minister of Finance), vigorously opposed the Tariff Bill, which was finally passed only in January 1892. It represented almost a complete success for the protectionists, earning its title of the 'Méline Tariff'. It reinforced the whole structure of agricultural protection, imposing higher duties on barley, livestock, meat, cheese, wine, beer and hops, and putting new duties on certain goods which formerly entered free, including maize, rice, vegetables and potatoes (Table 15). The duties on agricultural products generally had an incidence ranging from 10 to 25 per cent; those on industrial products were mostly over 25 per cent, sometimes as much as 60 per cent. The Méline Tariff was reputed to be the stiffest in the world, with the exception of Russia and the United States. However, most agricultural raw materials – wool, skins, cotton, flax, etc. – continued to enter free: here the interests of manufacturers prevailed over those of the farmers.

One of the innovations of the tariff was the institution of a 'general' rate, intended to be the normal one, and a 'minimum' rate, representing the lowest to which the Government could go in negotiations with other countries. This arrangement was another victory for the protectionists, who opposed the freedom of the Government to reduce duties in commercial treaties. For grains and livestock, a single rate was laid down, which could not be changed by treaty.

In principle, imports from French overseas territories remained free of duty, with exceptions for the sake of revenue (on coffee, tea, sugar, etc.). Since most of the products of the overseas territories did not then compete directly with those of French agriculture, this exemption originally raised no great problem. At a later date, rising imports of wine and wheat from North Africa proved troublesome.

Later in 1892, France (like Britain) prohibited imports of cattle for reasons of animal health. This prohibition was maintained till 1903, when it was replaced by duties which were almost equally prohibitive; the system of general and minimum duties was extended to meat and livestock at this time.

After 1892, French agriculture entered on a second period of acute depression, as a result mainly of a renewed increase in imports. In 1894 the duty on wheat was further raised to 7 francs per 100 kg.; the domestic price at this time averaged around 22 francs.

In 1897 a law was passed which was to play an important role at a later period. Entitled *loi de cadenas*, it enabled the Government to raise the duty on major agricultural products without waiting for the agreement of Parliament, the object being to prevent increased imports in the period pending approval.

The 1892 tariff, with the increased duty on wheat of 1894 and those on livestock of 1903, remained substantially unchanged up to the First World War, in spite of the improvement which took place in the agricultural situation after 1900. A revision of the tariff was carried out in 1910: this however primarily concerned manufactured goods and there was no important change in the agricultural duties. The report presenting the Tariff Bill stated:

> We believe that agriculture has everything to gain from simply maintaining the customs arrangements for wheat, barley, rye and maize. This system has proved itself: it has given excellent results which are confirmed and consolidated every day.[1]

Yet Méline, presenting the Bill for duties on grain as Minister of Agriculture in 1885, had declared:

> I do not hesitate to say that, the day when the price of wheat recovers, in conditions which enable French farmers to withstand competition and to remain in business, you may revise this duty or even abolish it, and French agriculture will then accept the sacrifice.[2]

Economics, politics and personalities

France's main reaction to the depression brought about by overseas competition was thus to restore to agriculture a substantial measure of protection. This policy was carried out much more in response to practical and immediate needs than in accordance with any carefully-conceived doctrine. France had neither a Free

[1] *Rapport général de M. Morel*, Chambre des Députés, 11 juillet 1908.
[2] Chambre des Députés, 10 février 1885.

Trade school like that of England, nor an influential body of scientific protectionists like that of Germany. Such influence as economists exerted, however, was mainly in the protectionist direction.

Paul-Louis Cauwès, Professor and Dean of the Law Faculty in Paris, was an eminent economist who argued that protection should be given to assist a nation's economic development. He thought that agriculture was entitled to protection when it needed it, and approved the resort to protection during the depression. It has been suggested that Cauwès provided a systematic theoretical background for the Méline Tariff. In fact this appears doubtful: Meredith, writing in 1904 on protection in France, seems nearer the truth when he said that the role played by scientific protectionists was much less important in France than in Germany.[1] Meredith considered that the 'mercantile protectionists' were the dominant influence: their arguments were not very different from those of the mercantilists of a former period, for the basis of their belief was that imports diminished the sum of employment at home, and that a country would be more prosperous, the smaller its imports in relation to its exports. This view is corroborated by Haight in his history of French commercial policy:

> In many respects the protectionism of 1880–1913 resembled the mercantilism of the seventeenth century. Both aimed at independence of foreign products, saw an inherent goodness in the output of industry, and sought national greatness in productive capacity rather than in the satisfaction of needs.[2]

The title of 'mercantile protectionists' might reasonably be applied to a succession of French politicians during the second half of the century, including Méline and others responsible for the return to protectionism.

On the other side there was a mixed bag of academic Free Traders and businessmen with an interest in free trade, together with some moderate protectionists whose aim was to restrain the excesses of the mercantilists. Careful academic argument was not much in evidence in this group either. The handful of academic Free Traders was never able to get its theories accepted by any

[1] H. O. Meredith, *Protection in France* (London, 1904).
[2] F. A. Haight, *A History of French Commercial Policies* (New York: Macmillan, 1941), p. 58.

political party. Meredith commented acidly that 'no important party in France … has ever been educated in that part of the theory of international trade which is supported by the weight of economic authority all over the world'.[1] Indeed there was a tendency deliberately to avoid abstract arguments because of the unpopularity of 'economists'. Owing to this lack of basic principles, the Free Traders were unwilling to contest the mercantilists' arguments, and contented themselves in the first instance by trying to show that the situation under near-free trade was not so bad as the protectionists made out; when protection was restored, they emphasized the danger of increased costs, of foodstuffs in particular.

The balance of advantage in this argument was with the protectionists. Meredith's diagnosis seems correct:

> The weakness of the position of the Liberals became particularly plain when the demand for agricultural Protection began. The reformers in the 'sixties had not protected agriculture, first, because they wanted to reduce Protection to a minimum, and second, because the agriculturists at that time were, many of them, in favour of Free Trade. Wheat and meat were imported into France in small quantities only … But when with the cheapening of ocean transport and the opening up of new countries the great fall in the prices of agricultural produce began, the Liberals had no logical reply to make to the demand for Protection. Many of them, indeed, objected to 'food taxes', and voted in accordance with this sentiment. But the formula – 'compensatory duties wherever needed' – certainly did cover the case of agricultural produce just as well as the case of manufactures. We need not be surprised that Liberal agriculturists who had been bred upon this formula went over with a clear conscience to the mercantilists as soon as they saw their business interfered with by foreign competition.[2]

Controversy began again with the revision of the tariff in 1910, when the effects of the Méline Tariff were widely discussed. In 1908 Edmond Théry, the director of *L'Économiste européen*, wrote a defence of protectionism (with a preface by Cauwès): this was

[1] Op. cit., p. 40.　　　　　　　　　　　　　[2] Ibid., p. 42.

a much more solidly-based work than other apologies for protectionism.[1] On the other hand, a vigorous campaign against
protection was carried on by certain economists, particularly in
the *Journal des Économistes*, whose editor, Yves Guyot, wrote
numerous articles with titles such as 'La cherté et le protectionnisme'. A Ligue de Libre Échange was formed in 1911 to fight
against the increased cost of living, 'to obtain a reduction of tariffs
and in the first instance the conclusion of commercial treaties'.
The debate however remained on a pragmatic level, as Golob
points out:

> In general, the debates were similar in character to those of
> 1891. The Liberals disclaimed any doctrinaire notions of free
> trade, the protectionists insisted that they were not systematic
> protectionists ... [The Méline Tariff] was attacked as having
> raised the cost of living of the French masses, and defended
> as having saved French agriculture from the destructive
> competition which threatened it.[2]

The main influence on policy thus was not so much the application of any body of principles as the immediate economic realities,
and the consequent agitation of leaders of both industry and
agriculture for protection. The role of the Société des Agriculteurs de France has already been mentioned and needs further
attention.

This body had been founded in the 1860s, and by 1890 it had
about 10,000 members. It was very definitely not representative
of all French agriculture, but was 'essentially a club of dis-
tinguished landowners, members of the old nobility or conservative
upper bourgeoisie who had acquired estates'.[3] Various other
organizations existed, including a Société Nationale de l'Encouragement à l'Agriculture, founded by Gambetta in 1880 as a
Republican counter to the Agriculteurs de France. But the mass
of the peasantry were practically unrepresented.

A law of 1884 legalized association in the form of syndicates,
and the Agriculteurs de France promoted the growth of agricultural syndicates: their number grew to 648 in 1890, with a

[1] E. Théry, *Les progrès économiques de la France : Bilan du régime douanier de 1892*
(Paris, 1908).
[2] E. O. Golob, *The Méline Tariff* (New York: Columbia U.P., 1944), p. 216.
[3] Ibid., p. 43.

membership of 234,000. A national union of agricultural syndicates was founded in 1886 under the patronage of the Agriculteurs de France. The object of the syndicates was joint purchase of agricultural requisites, together with, in some cases, collective sales of farm produce and other activities. They were not intended to engage in politics. Moreover, they remained for a time subservient to the Agriculteurs de France.

It will be shown in the following chapter that the German equivalent of the Agriculteurs de France, the Bund der Landwirte, was essentially an organization of wealthy Prussian landlords, interested above all in obtaining higher prices for their grain, and that the peasantry of West and South Germany, who depended above all on sales of livestock and who got little benefit, perhaps even suffered some disadvantage, from higher grain prices, had little say in events. In the case of France, there is less concrete evidence that a similar situation existed. Still, there was a concentration of larger farms in the arable land of the Paris basin, and it seems probable that their owners were the most influential group. There is certainly no doubt that the dominating voice in agricultural affairs was that of the Agriculteurs de France, and that this was the voice not of the mass of French agriculture but only of its elite. The agitation by this elite for protection, and the emphasis which they laid on wheat, earned them among Free Traders the sobriquet of 'les marquis du pain cher'.

The personality of Jules Méline has been mentioned several times already, and indeed Méline probably had more influence than any other individual over the course of public policy towards agriculture throughout this period. Méline entered Parliament in 1872, and was Minister of Agriculture from 1883 to 1885, introducing in 1885 the new duties on grain. His role in the formulation of the 1892 tariff has already been described. From 1896 to 1898 he was Prime Minister, and demonstrated his attachment to agriculture by taking the Ministry of Agriculture at the same time. His fall in 1898 was inglorious, being a result of his attitude over the Dreyfus Affair (perhaps his most celebrated remark was 'il n'y a pas d'affaire Dreyfus'). He returned to the Ministry of Agriculture during the First World War.

To a certain section of agricultural opinion in France, Méline has remained their greatest Minister of Agriculture. A testimony written in 1928 declared:

As Minister of Agriculture, he sought to promote by all possible means the production which enables us to live, to maintain on the land the mass of the rural population which constitutes the essential element in the nation's prosperity. For this purpose he took every occasion to defend the interests of agriculture and to reconcile them with those of industry.[1]

Augé-Laribé, however, took a different view, accusing Méline of having lacked any constructive agricultural policy:

In matters of progress he favoured slowness, in reforms timidity and in public order the respect of established rights. ... Decidedly the venerable M. Méline, in the list of physicians of the agricultural crises, is entitled only to appear among the charlatans.[2]

Augé-Laribé did not spare Méline's final effort as Minister of Agriculture during the war:

Because of his optimism and inaction, Méline, Minister for over fourteen months, bears a heavy responsibility. It is pointless to say this to those who have remained his admirers even today ... He was unable either to see the whole of the problem or to look ahead. This loyal gentleman, this patriot, thus did great harm to his country.[3]

Méline's basic philosophy was set out in his own book, of which the sixth edition was published in 1912. The title itself was eloquent: *Le retour à la terre et la surproduction industrielle*. The theme was simple: following the movement of labour from the land, there was a state of overproduction and unemployment in industry, which only a return to the land could cure:

There now remains only one field of action and of expansion capable of absorbing all the forces now unemployed ... this is the land, the land which is the nursemaid of humanity, fertile and everlasting.[4]

History can perhaps be left to judge.

[1] G. Lachapelle, *Le ministère Méline* (Paris, 1928), p. 209.
[2] Op. cit., pp. 69 and 108–9.
[3] Ibid., p. 358.
[4] J. Méline, *Le retour à la terre et la surproduction industrielle* (6th ed.,Paris, 1912), p. 97.

French agriculture under protection

Wheat was the product with which the protectionists were most concerned, and for which the effects of protection appear most clearly. The duties imposed in 1885 and 1887 probably contributed to the recovery in prices which took place in the late 1880s, and though they did not prevent a renewed fall in the early 1890s, they ensured that throughout the period from 1885 on, the French price remained above the free market price by approximately the amount of the duty (see Figure 1 in Chapter 1). The growth of imports, already restrained by the duties of 1885 and 1887, gave way to a decline after the further increase in the duty in 1894; as Table 16 shows, imports were actually less after 1900 than they

Table 16

WHEAT: TRADE, PRODUCTION, ETC.

(annual averages)

	Imports[a]	Exports[a]	Production	Area	Average value
	thousand tons			000 ha.	fr. per 100 kg.
1861–5	354	142	7,594	6,896	26
1866–70	430	141	7,378	6,979	30
1871–5	632	242	7,586	6,801	31
1876–80	1,311	154	7,070	6,900	29
1881–5	1,110	24	8,541	6,991	25
1886–90	1,026	13	8,348	7,000	23
1891–5	1,363	24	8,101	6,762	22
1896–1900	613	37	8,918	6,844	21
1901–5	285	28	8,906	6,575	21
1906–10	318	51	8,920	6,562	23

[a] Including flour in wheat equivalent.

Source: Statistique Agricole Annuelle, 1947 (tableaux rétrospectifs).

had been in the 1860s (in Britain, meanwhile, they had trebled). As a result, wheat cultivation in France was scarcely discouraged: the area under cultivation even tended to rise up to 1890, and though it afterwards fell slightly, rising yields resulted in increased production up to the First World War. The area of rye fell throughout this period; that of oats expanded, while barley fell.[1]

There was an increase in imports of cattle and meat in the late 1870s, but this was checked by the increased duties imposed from 1881 on. As a result prices were well maintained throughout the Depression. From 1892, when imports of cattle were prohibited for health reasons, there was a substantial increase in the number of cattle in France, and after 1900 France became self-sufficient in cattle and beef, with occasional export availabilities. The number of pigs also increased.

Table 17

WINE: TRADE AND PRODUCTION

(annual averages, in millions of hectolitres)

	Imports	Exports	Production
1861–70	0·2	2·6	52·9
1871–80	1·5	3·2	49·2
1881–90	9·7	2·4	29·7
1891–1900	7·7	1·8	39·9
1901–10	5·9	2·2	51·8

Source: As Table 16.

Wine was the most important product of French agriculture after grains. In the late 1860s and again from 1879, the vineyards were devastated by phylloxera. The fall in production led to a large increase in imports. After an increase in the import duty in 1892, imports from foreign countries were reduced, and production revived. However, foreign wines were diverted to other markets where they competed with French exports; also, wine from Algeria became established on the French market. The sale of French wine both at home and abroad became more difficult: exports failed to recover to the level of the 1870s (Table 17). Dijol, in a useful contemporary study of the effects of the 1892 tariff, commented as follows:

[1] There is considerable difficulty in obtaining consistent and reliable series of crop areas and livestock numbers in France during this period. One of the problems is that the regular annual data (where available) do not seem to bear comparison with the results of the censuses carried out in 1862, 1882 and 1892. It therefore seems preferable to avoid detailed tables, which could be misleading unless carefully interpreted.

Though it is true that, thanks to protection, French wine production has been put on its feet again, it is also a fact that under protection there has been an artificial expansion of the vineyards, leading to overproduction and to difficulties in finding markets.[1]

The production of sugar from sugar-beet was encouraged not so much by tariff protection as by export subsidies, which were granted in one form or another from 1884. Various exporting countries began to compete, each being forced to increase the rate of subsidy, until at the Brussels Conference of 1902 they agreed to refrain from subsidies. After this, however, France had difficulty in competing and its exports fell off. Dijol again pointed out:

The sugar industry, artificially developed through direct and indirect bounties, but now left to fend for itself, is suffering from all the drawbacks of protection after having enjoyed all its advantages.[2]

Dijol's general conclusion on the effects of protection is of interest:

[The tariff] has given excellent results when it has promoted the normal development of production, but it has had no effect or even undesirable effects in cases where the productive resources of the country have been directed into a type of activity for which France is less well suited than other countries, or in cases where protection has led to an excessive increase in production.[3]

As examples of favourable effects, Dijol lists wheat and other grains, cattle and dairy products; cases of unfavourable effects include sugar-beet, vines and flax.

The case of sheep is also worth attention. What happened here was in complete contrast to developments for all other products. As has been pointed out above, wool was left free from duty, in deference to the interests of the manufacturers; the result was a big increase in imports from the middle of the century on, and a

[1] M. Dijol, *Situation économique de la France sous le régime protectionniste de 1892* (Paris, 1911), p. 78.
[2] Ibid., p. 89.
[3] Ibid., p. 337.

prolonged fall in prices. The number of sheep in France was reduced from 24 million in 1852 to 17 million in 1910, and the fall would have been even bigger but for increased utilization for meat. In 1882 the report on the agricultural census declared:

> Formerly, wool was the most important product of our sheep. Today, with abundant supplies of wool arriving from overseas countries, it has become in France little more than a by-product. While the value of sheep sold for meat amounts each year to nearly 200 million francs, their wool is worth scarcely 78 million francs.[1]

Yet this decimation of the sheep flocks took place without any public outcry, while the difficulties of the arable farmers were made a national issue.

There is little reliable information on the trend in farm incomes during this period. Table 18 suggests general progress in the

Table 18

THE ECONOMIC SITUATION OF AGRICULTURE

	Unit	1852	1882	1892
Gross product of agriculture	fr. millions	8,061	13,461	..
Net product of agriculture	,,	..	1,198	800
Average value of agricultural land	fr. per ha.	1,266	1,686	..
Average value of first-class arable land	,,	..	3,442	2,866
Average wage of male agricultural workers, not fed on the farm, in summer	fr. per day	2·77	3·11	2·94

.. Not available.

Source: Statistique Agricole de la France: Enquêtes Décennales.

agricultural situation up to 1882 and a worsening – but hardly a catastrophe – between 1882 and 1892. Subsequently there are no more data up to the First World War, but there is no doubt that in the period after 1900 there was a substantial improvement. Table 19 indicates a decline, though not a very drastic one, in

[1] *Enquête Décennale de 1882*, p. 247.

Table 19

ACTIVE AND TOTAL POPULATION IN AGRICULTURE, FORESTRY
AND FISHING, IN RELATION TO POPULATION IN ALL SECTORS

	Active population			Total population		
	Agriculture, etc.	All sectors	Agriculture as % of total	Agriculture, etc.	All sectors	Agriculture as % of total
	thousands		%	millions		%
1861	..	..	..	19·9	37·4	53
1866	8,535	16,643	51	19·6	38·1	51
1872	..	..	..	18·5	36·1	51
1876	..	..	..	19·0	36·9	52
1881	7,890	16,544	48	18·2	37·7	48
1886	..	..	..	17·7	38·2	46
1891	..	..	..	17·4	38·3	45
1896	8,501	18,935	45	..	..	..
1901	8,244	19,735	42	..	..	..
1906	8,855	20,721	43	..	..	..

.. Not available.

Sources: For active population: 'Quelques aspects de l'évolution des populations actives dans les pays d'Europe occidentale', *Études et Conjoncture*, November 1954; for total population: *Statistique Agricole de la France: Enquêtes Décennales.*

the total agricultural population up to 1891, where this series ends; the active population in agriculture seems to have declined from 1866 to 1881, and then to have risen once again. Not much faith can be put in these figures, but it does not seem that French agriculture suffered an exodus comparable to that of the British. It should of course be remembered that in Britain it was mainly the farm labourers who left agriculture: the French peasant, to whom the farm was a home as well as a place of work, could not so easily move to the towns. It seems in fact that the number of *chefs d'exploitation* remained fairly stable from 1882 to 1892, while the number of labourers and other *auxiliaires* fell.

Whatever the benefits of protection for the big farmers, and for grain producers in particular, its advantages for the peasantry are questionable. The small peasant usually sold only a part of his grain crop, and he often had to buy flour for bread-making. It seems likely that a high grain price benefited only the occupiers of holdings of 10 hectares at least: such holdings amounted in 1882 to only about 870,000 out of the total of 5·7 million (or 3·5 million if the dwarf holdings under 1 hectare are excluded).

The most serious objection to protectionism (as it was conceived by Méline in particular) was that it diverted attention away from the need for a constructive long-term policy for French agriculture. Most contemporary thinking, even among protectionists, was aware that aid through protection should be only temporary and that agriculture should adapt itself to the new situation. But agriculture was bound by tradition and inertia, and the various governments did little to bring about an improvement. The development of rural co-operation through the syndicates was one of the few achievements of the period, and even here success was limited.

Augé-Laribé, in his study of French agricultural policy, is particularly bitter about this, and mounts a systematic attack on the lack of a consistent policy at this period. He observes that from 1881, when the Ministry of Agriculture was created, to 1914, there were no less than forty-two different governments with nineteen different Ministers of Agriculture; among the nineteen, lawyers and doctors predominated, and only a few were experts in agriculture. They arrived at their post with no prepared plan of action and did no more than attend to immediate problems. Protection through tariffs was the easiest course to follow, and the Ministers of Agriculture were not alone at fault:

There is no doubt that around 1880 agriculture was in a difficult situation and needed help. Since the Ministers of Finance refused to grant the irrigation ditches, the drainage, the access roads, the research and training stations which were essential to its progress through science and enterprise, the only remaining course was to institute customs protection – a remedy which was less effective, more costly for the nation, but profitable to the Treasury, and therefore more easily accepted by the Ministry of Finance.[1]

[1] Augé-Laribé, op. cit., p. 277.

The structure of French agriculture remained almost unchanged: there was no attempt to deal with the problem of small
and fragmented holdings – indeed, it was scarcely recognized as a
problem. Nor was anything done to reform the system of land
tenure and to give tenants some guarantee that by making
improvements they would not be wasting their money (even in
laissez-faire England some important action was taken in this
respect).

Meredith concludes his excellent study of protection in France
by observing that 'the whole structure of protectionist feeling is
reared upon economic pessimism'.[1] The policy followed was
motivated simply by a defensive reaction, with little or no attempt
to progress and adapt.

Food prices, the balance of trade and self-sufficiency

Méline and other protectionists sometimes tried to argue that
protection did not raise the price of food to the consumer, since
national production would be encouraged in the place of imports.
They also tried, in retrospect, to show that tariffs had not raised
prices by pointing to the fact that prices had continued to fall in
most years; sometimes it was even stated that tariffs had *reduced*
prices.

The truth was, of course, that prices of foodstuffs in France fell
to some extent during the depression, but less than prices in
Britain where there was no protection; the result was that after
1900 food cost substantially more in France than in Britain. This
point has been examined in Chapter 1 and need not be dealt
with again here.

During the period under consideration, the reduction of imports
and the expansion of certain exports had the result that France
became a net exporter instead of a net importer of food. Various
protectionists claimed this as a success for protectionist policy. The
limitations of this mercantilist approach are pointed out by
Clapham:

> France remained self-supporting – at a price. The price was
> paid in many ways. Part of it in rather stagnant exports; for
> the nation that will not buy neither shall it sell. Part in the

[1] Op. cit., p. 188.

failure to develop home industries connected with the handling of imported food, and food export industries which require cheap materials.[1]

The need to promote self-sufficiency in wartime was also frequently advanced by protectionists. Thus Méline asked: 'Is there a greater danger for a nation than to have its food supplies in the hands of foreign countries and at their mercy?' and evoked the case of England as a frightening example.[2] There is no doubt that protection maintained the output of certain items and increased the degree of self-sufficiency: by the outbreak of war France produced at least 90 per cent of its requirements of all major crops except maize, and all its needs of meat and dairy products. But when the war came there was a big decline in production, due not only to the loss of part of the territory but also to falling yields, as a result of the shortage of labour, the lack of a prepared plan and the inflexibility of techniques. Large imports of wheat, sugar and meat were soon required. It seems probable that the situation would at least have been no worse if attention before the war had been concentrated on raising productivity instead of maintaining the level of production.

[1] *Economic Development of France and Germany*, op. cit., p. 183.
[2] Op. cit., p. 247.

Chapter 4. Germany

German agriculture before the Depression

The conditions of agriculture in the east of the German Empire were totally different from those which prevailed in the west and south. The eastern part of Prussia in particular was characterized by large estates in the hands of powerful landlords: in six of the eastern provinces, farms of more than 100 hectares accounted for over 40 per cent of the agricultural area, while in the rest of Germany they accounted for little more than 10 per cent (Table 20).

The Prussian landlords, the 'Junkers', owed their position to the fact that East Germany had been conquered from other races; they thus combined the function of large feudal landowners with the prestige of a ruling military caste. At the abolition of serfdom in Prussia at the beginning of the nineteenth century, many peasants were compelled to buy their freedom by giving up part of their land to the lords, who thus actually increased their economic power while the serfs were turned into landless labourers. During further efforts at reform after 1848, the Junkers succeeded in preserving the manor as an administrative unit, and though the peasant became free, he thus remained under his old master's eye and rule. An undemocratic electoral system enabled the Junkers to rule Prussia with little interference, and as Prussia dominated the Empire their influence was great – Bismarck himself belonged to the Junker class.

Table 20

AGRICULTURAL HOLDINGS IN 1895, BY SIZE

Size (hectares)	Number of holdings (000)		Area covered (000 ha.)	
	Prussia[a]	Rest of Germany	Prussia[a]	Rest of Germany
0–2	831	2,405	437	1,371
2–5	219	797	705	2,581
5–20	263	736	2,637	7,084
20–100	104	178	3,776	6,094
over 100	16	9	5,614	2,218
Total	1,433	4,125	13,169	19,348

[a] Six eastern provinces.

Source: Statistisches Jahrbuch.

The soils of East Germany are largely sandy and are suited above all to the cultivation of grain. The standards of cultivation on the estates were high. Until the 1880s this region exported substantial quantities of wheat, rye and other cereals.

In the rest of Germany, the feudal system had almost disappeared by the middle of the century, helped in some areas by Napoleon, though in certain German States the last blows at the system were not struck until the revolutionary movements of 1848. The farming pattern which resulted varied to some extent according to the methods – and the thoroughness – of the reforms in different States. In general, however, small holdings predominated: Table 20 shows that there were relatively few farms with more than 20 hectares and a very large number of tiny holdings (many of which may not have been genuine farms) with less than 2 hectares. Moreover, the practice of dividing the land between the heirs had led to considerable fragmentation. The majority of the holdings were too small to cultivate grain profitably and practised more intensive farming – cows, pigs, poultry and milk were the main sources of revenue. Often these holdings would have to purchase grain both to make bread and to feed their livestock.

By about the middle of the century, agriculture was still by far the main occupation in Germany, providing a living for about half the population. It was only around 1895 that the number of persons employed in industry began to exceed the number in agriculture. However, economic development had begun to accelerate after the formation of the Zollverein in 1834, and the German Empire stood on the threshold of a period of great industrial progress. In the early stages, a primary concern of industrialists was to obtain protection behind which their activity could develop, shielded from the competition of Britain's established industries. Friedrich List's National System of Political Economy provided strong arguments for the protection of young industries.

Free trade and the return to protection

Prussia, after the Napoleonic Wars, had reduced its tariff rates, and the moderate duties which resulted formed the basis of the Zollverein tariff of 1834. This included import duties on grain, but in 1853 these were abolished. The first major change in the Zollverein tariff was brought about by the treaty with France in 1862, which, together with subsequent treaties between the Zollverein and other countries, substantially reduced the rates of duty on manufactured goods. These treaties were carried through Parliament by Bismarck, who had become Minister-President in 1862. His motives were largely political: to secure French support in Prussia's quarrels with Austria and Denmark. The Franco-German Peace Treaty of 1871 renewed trade relations for an indefinite period, establishing 'most favoured nation' treatment on a reciprocal basis.

At this time agricultural opinion in Germany was strongly in favour of free trade. The years from 1850 to 1870 were prosperous; Germany was a net exporter of grain and its agriculture did not need protection. Moreover, the farmers were opposed to protection for industry, since this might raise the cost of agricultural requisites and also lead to reprisals by Britain against German grain exports. The opposition of farmers was largely responsible for the failure of an attempt by the industrialists to retain duties on iron. The leaders of industry thus became aware of the need for agricultural support: as in France, they took the initiative in converting agriculture to protectionism. The task became easier as agriculture began to feel the effects of foreign competition. On the markets of Britain and France, German grain was beginning to lose ground to American supplies. With its growing population, Germany became an importer of wheat and rye, obtaining supplies from Russia, Austria-Hungary and the United States.

In 1876, both a Central Association of German Industrialists and an Association of Tax and Economic Reformers were founded, the latter being composed mainly of large landowners; in 1878 they joined forces in a campaign for a return to protection for both industry and agriculture. At the same time a strong protectionist group was formed in the Reichstag. Bismarck was looking for means of securing additional revenue for the imperial finances and therefore welcomed the idea of restoring import duties. A new tariff was prepared and became law in July 1879. It included moderate duties on grain and increased duties on livestock products (Table 21).

These duties were too low to prevent the fall in grain prices which occurred from 1879 on. German grain by now had been almost completely forced off its former export markets and was meeting intensified competition on the home market. Further protection was demanded.

In 1885, the Reichstag agreed to raise the duties on wheat and rye from 1 to 3 marks per 100 kg.; the rates for other grain and for livestock were also increased. But prices continued to fall. Bismarck was by now a firm believer in import duties on foodstuffs both as a source of revenue and as a means of assisting agriculture, and in 1887 he proposed to raise the duty on wheat and rye to 6 marks. This was too much for many members of the Reichstag, but a rate of 5 marks was accepted, with increases for other grains as well. The price of wheat on German markets was then around 17 marks.

Commercial treaties, 1891-1894

After 1887, agricultural prices recovered for a while, helped by the increased duties but owing also to a lull in overseas competition. This upward movement was accentuated in 1890 and 1891 by bad harvests in Germany and elsewhere: food supplies ran short and there were public demonstrations against the increase in prices. The grain duties were temporarily suspended.

In 1890, Bismarck was dismissed by the Emperor and replaced

Table 21

TARIFFS ON MAJOR AGRICULTURAL PRODUCTS, 1879–1906

(marks per 100 kg. except where otherwise indicated)

Product	1879 July 15th	1885 May 22nd	1887 Dec. 21st	1891 Dec. 6th[a]	1902 Dec. 25th[b]	1906 March 1st[e]
Wheat	1	3	5	3·50	7·50–5·50	5·50
Rye	1	3	5	3·50	7–5	5
Oats	1	1·50	4	2·80	7–5	5
Barley	0·50	1·50	2·25	2	malting: 7–4 feeding: 7	4 1·30
Maize	0·50	1	2	1·60	5	3
Flour	2	7·50	10·50	7·30	18·75	10·20
Butter	20	......	......	16	30	20
Cheese (hard)	20	......	......	15	30	15
Eggs	3	......	......	2	6	2
Meat	12	20	......	15[e]	45	27
Bullocks	20[d]	30[d]	......	25–50[d]	18	8
Cows	6[d]	9[d]	......	......	18	8
Pigs	2·50[d]	6[d]	......	5[d]	18	9
Wine in barrel	24	......	20[f]	20[f]	24[g]	20[g]

Note: From 1865 to 1879, duties on grains were nil and those on livestock products were relatively low.

[a] Rates in treaties with Austria-Hungary and Italy.
[b] Rates provided for under tariff law, with minimum duties for wheat, rye, oats and malting barley.
[c] Rates actually applied on entry into force of 1902 law, following commercial treaties.
[d] Marks per head.
[e] 17 marks on pigmeat.
[f] 10 marks on red wine.
[g] Higher rates on wine of 14° proof and over.

Source: Reichsgesetzblatt.

by Count Caprivi. Caprivi, unlike Bismarck, had no agricultural ties: indeed he declared in a misguided moment that he possessed 'kein Ar und Halm' (no acre or blade of straw). He came under pressure from industrialists, who no longer had interests in common with agriculture. On the contrary, they now wanted not only cheaper foodstuffs to keep down costs, but greater access to foreign markets: this could only be achieved through tariff concessions on foodstuffs. The elections of 1890, moreover, brought gains to the left-wing parties which opposed protection because of its influence on the cost of living. Thus a number of factors were combining to bring about a change in tariff policy, and a revision of the tariff was necessitated in any case by the fact that several of the existing commercial treaties were due to expire in 1892.

Caprivi thus sought to conclude new commercial treaties in which Germany would obtain advantages for its exports of manu-factures in return for concessions on the agricultural tariff. The first treaty to be concluded was with Austria-Hungary; others, with Italy, Belgium and Switzerland, followed closely. The Austrian treaty lowered Germany's tariffs on wheat and rye from 5 to 3½ marks, with similar reductions in the duties on other grains. The treaty with Italy lowered German duties on wine, poultry, eggs and fruit.

These treaties were passed by the Reichstag only against stiff opposition. Shortly after they came into effect, grain prices suffered a sharp fall. This was due mainly to developments on the world market, but the tariff reductions were widely blamed. Discontent among farmers was intensified. In 1893, the Prussian landlords organized themselves in the Bund der Landwirte (Farmers' League),[1] which immediately demanded adequate tariff protection and fiercely opposed further commercial treaties. Also in 1893, new elections brought a recovery of the right-wing parties, many of whose candidates received effective support from the Bund.

Nevertheless, a treaty was concluded with Rumania in 1893 which confirmed the extension to Rumania of the reduced agri-cultural tariffs contained in the Austrian treaty. Well aware of Rumania's importance as an exporter of grain, the Bund der

[1] In fact the word 'Landwirt' suggests something more important than 'farmer' – 'landed proprietor' would be more exact. The choice of term reflects the nature of the organization.

Landwirte whipped up opposition, and the treaty was passed only by a narrow majority.

Still greater opposition was aroused by the Russian treaty of 1894, for Russia was an even more dangerous competitor than Rumania, and the treaty offered Russia the lower rates on agricultural products, as well as reductions in the duty on wood and free entry for certain other products. The German Emperor attached great importance to this treaty, because of his desire to preserve personal relations with the Czar. In a speech from the Throne he tried to placate the agriculturalists, promising to set up chambers of agriculture which would work to improve the credit system and relieve agricultural indebtedness (these were items in the programme of the Bund der Landwirte). Nevertheless the Bund petitioned the Reichstag to reject the Russian treaty. The conservative element in the Reichstag was now torn between its traditional loyalty to the Kaiser and his Government and its equally traditional ties with the landed class. For the time being, the Kaiser won, and the Russian treaty was passed by a bigger majority than the treaty with Rumania. Through the 'most favoured nation' clause, the reduced rates were now applicable to a long list of countries, including the United States and other grain-exporting countries.

Caprivi's position, however, had been steadily undermined by the agricultural opposition in the Reichstag and even in his Cabinet. He had received support from the Kaiser for the Russian treaty, but otherwise the Kaiser found it intolerable that his Government should have to rely on left-wing support for its commercial policy. Caprivi had been constantly sniped at by Bismarck in retirement. In October 1894 he resigned, and the leaders of the Bund had gained their first victory.

However, they found little consolation in Caprivi's successor. Prince Hohenlohe was a South German who had no sympathy with the Junkers and considered their demands excessive. He frequently made use of the argument that small holdings had no grain to sell and gained no benefit from the tariff.

In any case the damage, from the agriculturalists' point of view, was now done: the treaties were in force and could not be revised till the end of 1903. The Bund nevertheless set about organizing opposition in readiness for that time, and meantime supported vigorously a plan put forward by Count Kanitz (a Junker) for a government grain monopoly, which through import control would maintain certain minimum prices on the domestic market. These minimum prices would have been well above world market prices. The scheme was put forward several times in the Reichstag from 1894 to 1896, but to many members it appeared undesirable or impracticable, or both, and it was defeated on each occasion. The plan is nevertheless of considerable interest as the first attempt to set up a mechanism which at a later date was to become a vital part of agricultural support policies; it is discussed more fully in a following section.

Intensified protection – the 1902 tariff

As the time approached for the commercial treaties to be renewed, and in spite of a significant recovery in world agricultural markets, agitation by the agriculturalists was intensified. In its foreign policy Imperial Germany was aiming at expansion: it sought rearmament and a greater degree of economic self-sufficiency. The political climate thus became more favourable to agricultural protection. In 1900, when a proposal for increased naval expenditure came before the Reichstag, the agriculturalists seized the opportunity of bargaining their vote against a promise that the agricultural duties would be raised. Prince Hohenlohe was replaced in 1900 by Count von Bülow, who was more willing to grant increased protection to agriculture.

The preparation of the new tariff had begun in 1897. In 1901, a draft was produced which included substantially higher duties on all agricultural products as well as on many manufactured goods. The increases were not enough to satisfy the Bund der Landwirte, which demanded still higher duties on grains. The subsequent debate was long and fierce. Finally the Government succeeded in keeping the increases within approximately the limits proposed in the draft. The new tariff was enacted in December 1902.

For most grains it instituted maximum and minimum rates, the latter representing the lowest concession which the Government could make in commercial treaties. For wheat the duty was raised from 3·50 marks per 100 kg. to a maximum of 7·50 and a minimum of 5·50 marks; the increases for other agricultural products were equally large (Table 21). There were no minima to the rates on livestock products, which suggested to livestock producers that if concessions had to be made in future treaties, their products were those most likely to suffer.

The Government did in fact negotiate a new series of commercial treaties under which the minimum rates on grains became generally applicable. The duties on livestock products were cut by a third, a half or even more, and in several cases were finally no higher than after Caprivi's treaties. The new rates came into force in March 1906.

'Agrar- oder Industriestaat?'

It has been seen above that, in the 1870s and 1880s, the industrialists in Germany sought an alliance with the farmers in order to re-establish protection. The alliance, however, did not last. By the 1890s, German industry was in a much stronger competitive position; its further development was hampered both by relatively high wage costs, resulting from high food prices, and by protectionism in other countries, which in the case of the United States at least was in part a reprisal against German agricultural protectionism and could only be broken down by concessions in the German agricultural tariff. This was Caprivi's basic preoccupation. Though Bismarck constantly criticized Caprivi's trade policy, it seems likely that he himself, had he remained in power, would have seen the need to take similar action.

At the same time, there was growing preoccupation with the respective roles of agriculture and industry in the nation. While Germany's total population was growing fast, the agricultural population was falling. It was widely felt that the relative decline of agriculture was undesirable, for social and strategic as well as economic reasons. This question gave rise to much controversy.

Many persons feared that a nation exporting ever more manufactures and importing ever increasing amounts of food and raw materials would fall into a precarious situation. Widespread concern on this point seems to have begun around 1897, when Oldenberg stressed the dangers in a speech at the Evangelical-Social Congress in Leipzig. The argument reached its fullest development in a book by Professor Adolf Wagner, *Agrar- und Industriestaat* ('An Agricultural and Industrial Nation'), of which the first edition, published in 1901, was quickly exhausted. It is worth summarizing the analysis of this important work.

Wagner drew attention to the growing industrialization and to the associated rise in the urban population. This rapid development he regarded as harmful, firstly because it created a degree of specialization which, though it might have economic benefits, was socially undesirable: it 'makes the occupations of the people one-sided in the extreme, narrowing their outlook, limiting the scope of physical and mental education, removing all the advantages of comprehensive and varied national production'.[1] Secondly, the increased dependence on imports of food exposed the agricultural population to the vicissitudes of the world market and endangered their livelihood; the agricultural population was a traditional and essential part of the nation and should be preserved. Thirdly, this dependence on imported food endangered the nation's food supply: apart from the possibility of war, there was the risk of year-to-year fluctuations in the harvest, and in the long run it was not certain that world food production would always meet the needs of the rising world population. Further, increased food imports could only be paid for by increased exports of manufactures, and the prospects for this were doubtful since many countries, including the United States and Russia, were also becoming more industrial. It followed that:

> Adequate protection for agriculture, even if higher than the present level, is in the national interest: even if this means that the creation of an industrial nation is retarded, though not entirely prevented, it should thereby benefit the workers and the German economy as a whole, and perhaps also assist the demographic trend. The maintenance of a viable German agriculture signifies the preservation of the German people, both now and in the future.[2]

Wagner defended himself against the charge that he wanted a purely agricultural nation (as did some who shared his point of view). The question was one of degree: of ensuring the right 'mixture' of agriculture and industry in the nation. Agricultural protection should not seek to raise prices, but to prevent excessive falls in price and to ensure 'normal, average prices'. As a practical

[1] Adolf Wagner, *Agrar- und Industriestaat* (2nd ed., Jena, 1902), p. 33.
[2] Ibid., pp. 1-2.

proposition, Wagner considered that the agricultural duties should be considerably higher than those in force under the Caprivi duties, and that the increased rates of the 1901 proposals were about right.

It should be noted that Wagner's case had little to do with the need to protect agriculture in times of crisis: the original argument for protection had shifted to a much more sophisticated reasoning which saw protection as a basic long-term need.

Wagner's arguments, well presented and carrying considerable logical force, exerted much influence. They contained the seeds of most of the arguments which appear today in favour of support for agriculture.

A more moderate influence was exerted by the eminent economist Schmoller. In a comprehensive economic treatise in 1904, he included a chapter in which he criticized both the Free Traders and the Protectionists. The former, he said, over-emphasized the consumer interest and took too dogmatic a view:

> The main argument [of the Free Traders] is now as always the consumer's point of view: the complaint that protective duties raise the cost of goods. They overlook the fact that the interests of producers deserve equal attention.[1]

But Schmoller considered that the arguments of the Protectionists were equally weak. No country could do without trade. The argument that all economic sectors should have equal protection defeated itself: none would gain if everything were dearer. Sectors in decline should not be protected so much as rising ones, and raw materials not so much as end-products. The argument that agriculture must have tariffs if industry had them was irrelevant: agriculture needed tariffs to help it over the crisis caused by foreign competition: there should be tariffs sufficient to ensure that the agricultural population could survive, but they should not cause much increase in food costs or remove the stimulus to technical improvement.

Several other economists, including Conrad and Dade, felt that the unsatisfactory state of agriculture made it necessary to maintain protection, but that this should be only a transitional measure and should not prevent necessary structural adaptations.

---

[1] G. Schmoller, *Grundriss der allgemeinen Volkswirtschaftslehre* (Leipzig, 1904), Part II, p. 643.

The Free Trade school included Brentano, Dietzel, Lotz and Schäffle. They favoured increased industrialization of Germany and better international division of labour. They demanded that the tariff should be (gradually and cautiously) pulled down, if possible in the context of commercial treaties giving reciprocal concessions. A fairly full and clear statement of their position was given by Brentano.[1] He stressed the overall benefits of the division of labour and the importance of the law of comparative advantage, citing Adam Smith and Ricardo. He pointed out that even List and his followers were not in favour of protection as a permanent policy. German agriculture, in Brentano's opinion, had not made use of protection to facilitate a shift from grain, now unprofitable, to more economic lines of production: on the contrary, protection had been regarded as an inducement to expand production of grains. But no amount of protection could make German grains competitive with overseas production, because of the much higher cost of land in Germany.

The Free Traders made much of the argument that only a minority of the agricultural population – the large landowners – benefited from high grain prices. They also stressed the effects of protection on consumers: Brentano calculated that the duty on bread grains of 5·50 marks per 100 kg. meant that the average worker, with an average family, had to work thirteen days in the year simply to pay the duty.[2]

Moreover, the Free Traders failed to take account of the difficulties in adapting established farming patterns to the new situation. Their arguments were ineffective against the political strength of the agricultural movement. Though there was some popular agitation against 'dear bread', this never became a decisive force. The Free Traders had a smallish representation in the Reichstag among the Radicals, but on the whole did not exert great influence.

The Junkers and the Bund der Landwirte

The political action undertaken by the Bund der Landwirte from 1893 onwards must be counted the decisive factor in bringing about the reinforcement of agricultural protection. The Bund was

[1] L. Brentano, *Das Freihandelsargument* (Berlin–Schöneberg, 1901).

[2] L. Brentano, *Die deutschen Getreidezölle* (Berlin, 1910).

led by the Prussian landlords, and its primary objective was to secure better markets for the grain produced on the Prussian estates. It nevertheless succeeded in imposing itself as the sole representative of German agriculture. The small farmers seem to have been ready to accept the leadership of the Junkers, partly from habit, partly from an inability to see that their interests differed and to organize themselves separately, partly from a fear of rising Marxist elements which threatened to dispossess them. The Bund won the allegiance of many small farmers by promising increased duties on livestock products, though in fact the results of its action were much more favourable to the grain producers.

A close connection with the Conservative party gave the Bund der Landwirte a voice in the Reichstag. In elections it supported only those candidates who promised to vote as the Bund ordered on matters concerning agriculture. Its methods were at times unscrupulous. One contemporary writer, analysing the Bund's action, declared that 'Agrarian terrorism has thus, thanks to the feeble attitude of the Government, become one of the most dangerous phenomena in Germany's political life'.[1] Frequently the Bund made use of boycotts, in particular by forbidding its members to deal with traders who did not support its activities. In election campaigns it is said to have resorted to fraud and to have threatened political opponents with economic sanctions, even with physical violence. It was vigorously anti-semitic. Its propaganda was regularly diffused by the Conservative organs, the *Deutsche Tages-Zeitung* and the *Kreuzzeitung*, and by numerous local journals.

Through the Bund der Landwirte the Junkers constantly refused to give up anything of their established position, regardless of the effects on Germany's overall industrial and economic growth. They maintained their intransigence up to the First World War, opposing in particular a proposal for concessions to Russia on the grain tariff. The Vicomte de Guichen, in a paper delivered in 1917, aptly described the extent of their influence:

> The members of the distinguished German aristocracy, a considerable number of agriculturalists ... were the most reliable supporters of the Throne, the descendants of the

[1] C. Bürger, *Die Agrardemagogie in Deutschland* (Lichterfelde, 1911).

founders of the Empire. Would their Emperor take the risk of displeasing them, possibly of ruining them, in order to give satisfaction to the Russians? A cruel choice! This was in fact one of the most serious problems facing Germany, with an industry in full expansion asking only to conquer new markets, but with a great landed class insisting that there should be no departure, so far as agriculture was concerned, from a restrictive customs policy.[1]

The proposed grain monopoly

Reference has been made above to the proposals put forward from 1894 to 1897 by Count Kanitz, with the support of the Bund der Landwirte, for an import monopoly for grain. The proposal (subject to variations in its successive versions) was that [all imports of grain should be made on State account, and that the price at which the grain was resold on the domestic market should be the average of prices in the previous forty years. The profits made when import prices were below this level should go to a reserve fund, to be used for subsidizing imports on occasions when foreign prices rose above the price of resale] As prices in the mid-1890s were much lower than those which had prevailed during most of the previous forty years, the immediate result would have been to raise domestic prices very substantially above the world price and above their existing level.

The proposal aroused passionate interest in agricultural circles. Buchenberger, in a contemporary study of German agricultural policy, wrote:

Seldom has an agricultural programme attracted so much attention as the idea of nationalizing grain imports ... The proposal showed how, with apparently simple means, a certain and immediate remedy could be found for all the problems of the time – the intolerable situation of inadequate prices, falling rents, increasing indebtedness and impoverishment – and lead the way to a Promised Land safe from all fluctuations in prices.[2]

[1] Vicomte de Guichen, 'Le problème agricole allemand' (paper read on October 5th, 1917, to the French Société d'Economie Politique), p. 18.

[2] A. Buchenberger, *Grundzüge der deutschen Agrarpolitik* (2nd ed., Berlin, 1899), p. 240.

4

The proposal nevertheless encountered strong objections. It was opposed by Count Caprivi and his successor Prince Hohenlohe. The latter declared it to be an insidious and dangerous step towards Socialism, while the Social Democratic leader, Bebel, retorted that a measure to enrich one class at the expense of the community, and in particular of the workers and the poor, was anything but social. The Junkers however paid little attention to consumer interests, and the Prussian Minister of Agriculture declared in the Reichstag that the consumer had 'no right to get goods delivered to him below the cost of production' (the cost of production he had in mind being that which prevailed on Prussian estates).

The practicability of the scheme was also questioned. It would be difficult to determine an equitable minimum price. Millers preferred the higher-quality imported grain and would not necessarily pay more for home-produced grain. There would be technical problems in regulating supplies so as to avoid price fluctuations. Both supporters and opponents of the Kanitz plan drew the conclusion that, to ensure successful operation, control would have to be extended to domestic supplies. The objections to such far-reaching intervention by the State were at the time too strong to be overcome; but the essentials of the Kanitz proposals were introduced by the National Socialists in 1933 and maintained after the Second World War by the German Federal Republic.

The import certificate system

Import certificates were an arrangement devised to take account of some special features of the German grain trade; they provide a further illustration of the extent to which the interests of the Prussian grain-producers were catered for. It was a long-standing practice for Russian wheat and rye to pass through East German ports, and there to be mixed with the local grain, the quality of which was inferior and which thereby obtained an increased outlet. When duties on grain were revived in 1879, arrangements were made to enable this transit trade to continue: the re-export of foreign grain, or of foreign grain mixed with German grain, gave the right to import a corresponding quantity of grain free of duty.

This arrangement, however, did not cover another aspect of the grain trade, which was that East Germany sent most of its produce abroad, while West Germany imported the greater part of its requirements. Transport from East German ports by sea to Scandinavia was often cheaper than transport by rail to West Germany; further, West German consumers were used to a higher-quality flour than could be obtained from Prussian grain.

The opportunity for extending the system arose immediately after the passage of the commercial treaty with Russia in 1894, the justification being that producers required compensation for the expected increase in Russian competition. [Any exports of the major cereals, whether foreign or home-produced, now gave entitlement to a certificate which could be used to obtain exemption from duty on imports of grain.] Moreover, the import certificate was negotiable. Certificates obtained through the export of East German grain could thus be used to import grain into West Germany. The exporter could sell the certificate for its face value less only a small deduction for interest and transfer charges: he therefore received the export price for his grain plus nearly the full amount of the duty, and he had an incentive to export so long as the differential between the world price and the domestic price did not exceed the amount of the duty. The arrangement worked in effect as an export subsidy.

Initially, the certificate was valid only for importing grain of the same type as that which had been exported. However, under the Bülow tariff of 1902 this limitation was removed: the certificate was valid for importing any kind of grain. This enabled the system to be used for exporting German rye to Scandinavia and importing various kinds of grain, including feed grains, into West Germany.

As a result of the import certificate system, German exports of wheat and rye, which had been negligible since the 1880s, made a spectacular recovery from 1894 onwards. Moreover, the price level in East Germany was raised above the world price by approximately the amount of the duty and brought closer to the price on West German markets.

Considerable encouragement was thereby given to the production and export of grain – the trends are further discussed in the following section – and the value of the import certificates granted rose correspondingly: from 7 million marks in 1894 to 22 million in 1900 and 121 million in 1910. These amounts represented a loss of revenue which would otherwise have been obtained from import duties and were equivalent to a direct subsidy to producers and exporters. Even when exports of one kind of grain exceeded imports, as happened regularly for rye and occasionally for oats from about 1907 onwards, the system still operated owing to the possibility of using the certificates for importing other types of grain. Proposals were made to abolish this interchangeability, so that there would be no use for the certificates once exports were greater than imports; excess production would then be discouraged. However, no changes were made up to the First World War, and the system was revived to play once again an important role from 1925 to 1930.

German agriculture under protection

The measures of protection adopted in Germany from 1879 on did not prevent the fall in the world price of grain from being reflected on German markets: prices fell from 1879 onwards, and, after some recovery around 1890 with short harvests, they reached their lowest point in the mid-1890s. There was then a recovery lasting up to the First World War (Table 22).

The duties on grain certainly tempered the fall in price (see Figure 1 in Chapter 1) and seemed for a while at least to have restrained the growth of imports. Imports of wheat and rye, after beginning to increase in 1876, were checked in 1880 and did not rise again till the 1890s, helped by the reduction of duties under Caprivi's treaties (Table 23). With the rising population and hence the rising demand for bread, imports of wheat then increased very fast indeed up to the war. Imports of barley, mainly to feed the increasing numbers of pigs in West Germany, also expanded rapidly.

Perhaps the most striking feature of German agriculture during this period is that there was no contraction in the area under grain: indeed, the area sown to rye and oats expanded in the 1890s and 1900s (Table 24). As yields were rising under the influence of improved techniques, production of all grain – rye and oats in particular – expanded rapidly, doubling in the course of the thirty years 1880–1910 (Table 25). The tariff system gave a big advantage to rye as compared with wheat, for the duty on

Table 22

AVERAGE WHOLESALE PRICES OF MAJOR AGRICULTURAL PRODUCTS

(marks per 100 kg.)

	Rye	Wheat	Oats^a	Barley	Slaughter cattle	Butter
1860–9	20	15	14	15	..	..
1870–4	24	18	16	17	..	..
1875–9	21	17	15	16	..	..
1880–4	16	20	14	18	..	..
1885–9	14	17	13	16	94	..
1890–4	16	18	15	17	110	..
1895–9	13	16	13	13	115	228
1900–4	14	16	13	13	124	231
1905–9	17	20	16	14^a	141	238
1910–13	17	21	16	15^a	160	261

Note: The data prior to 1880 refer to the whole of Prussia, and are taken from Brentano, *Die deutschen Getreidezölle* (op. cit.). Subsequent data refer to Berlin, except that for barley till 1893 the figures refer to Magdebourg, and from 1894 for both barley and oats to Breslau; the source is the *Statistisches Jahrbuch für das Deutsche Reich*.

^{a} Feeding barley only from 1906 onwards.

.. Not available.

Table 23

AVERAGE ANNUAL TRADE IN MAJOR CROP PRODUCTS

(thousand tons)

	Rye		Wheat		Oats		Barley	
	Im-ports	Ex-ports	Im-ports	Ex-ports	Im-ports	Ex-ports	Im-ports	Ex-ports
1865–9	298	117	409	590	95	110	112	117
1870–4	626	125	365	432	175	110	119	100
1875–9	1,082	155	819	660	304	124	355	194
1880–4	732	15	535	82	265	33	321	95
1885–9	737	3	450	6	181	8	480	30
1890–4	630	10	946	16	208	5	799	9
1895–9	866	87	1,404	23	399	43	1,056	23
1900–4	804	168	1,891	162	420	139	1,165	35
1905–9	490	407	2,255	186	552	298	2,078	5
1910–13	418	830	2,419	363	564	445	3,037	3

Source: Statistisches Jahrbuch für das Deutsche Reich.

rye under the Caprivi treaties was the same as for wheat, and under the Bülow tariff it was only slightly less, whereas rye was much easier to grow on the soils and in the climate of East Germany.

The preference of consumers, however, was turning from rye bread to wheat. The increase in rye production, artificially stimulated by protection and above all by the import certificate system, was wholly out of line with the trend in demand. The result was that imports of rye fell after 1904, while exports increased enormously. Also under the influence of the import certificate system, Germany once again began to export wheat and oats on a substantial scale (Table 23).

Fortunately the encouragement given to grains did not prevent a large expansion of the livestock sector. Imports of livestock products increased fairly rapidly from the 1880s (Table 26), but with rising demand prices generally remained firm and even increased. The duties on livestock products may have contributed to the favourable price level, but generally the incidence of the duties was considerably less than in the case of grain and their influence on the domestic price was certainly less important. The number of cattle rose steadily, that of pigs multiplied (Table 27). The number of sheep, however, fell even more drastically than in France: in Germany too wool received no protection, in deference to the wishes of the manufacturers, and German consumers preferred pigmeat to mutton.

As has been mentioned above, the question of how many of the rural population actually benefited from protection was frequently debated in Germany at this time, and various calculations were made. The lack of precise data makes it difficult to resolve this question: however, it was reasonably supposed that holdings of less than 5 hectares got no benefit from higher grain prices and that only those over 20 hectares got a substantial benefit. In 1895 there were 4,252,000 holdings under 5 hectares, 999,000 holdings between 5 and 20 hectares, and only 307,000 holdings over 20 hectares. The average number of persons per holding was certainly higher on the larger farms, but the extra persons consisted mainly of hired labourers, whose benefit from increased farm prices must have been very indirect. The proportion of farmers deriving a clear benefit from increased grain prices therefore appears small indeed, in relation to the total agricultural

Table 24

AREA OF MAJOR CROPS

(million hectares)

	Rye	Wheat	Oats	Barley
1880	5·9	1·8	3·7	1·6
1890	5·8	2·0	3·9	1·7
1900	6·0	2·0	4·1	1·7
1910	6·2	1·9	4·3	1·6

Source: As Table 23.

Table 25

AVERAGE ANNUAL PRODUCTION OF MAJOR CROPS

(million tons)

	Rye	Wheat	Oats	Barley
1880–4	5·6	2·5	4·1	2·2
1885–9	5·8	2·6	4·5	2·2
1890–4	6·9	3·0	5·1	2·5
1895–9	8·4	3·5	6·3	2·8
1900–4	9·3	3·5	7·3	3·1
1905–9	10·2	3·7	8·2	3·2
1910–13	11·3	4·3	8·5	3·3

Source: As Table 23.

Table 26

AVERAGE ANNUAL IMPORTS OF MAJOR LIVESTOCK PRODUCTS

(thousand tons)

	Beef	Pigmeat	Butter	Eggs
1880–4	.... 15[a]		5	17
1885–9	.... 6		6	44
1890–4	.... 24		8	64
1895–9	.... 53		10	98
1900–4	.... 45		22	123
1905–9	15	10	39	136
1910–13	25	..	52	135

[a] Including poultry-meat, meat extract, etc., up to 1883.

.. Not available.

Source: As Table 23.

Table 27

NUMBERS OF LIVESTOCK

(millions)

	Cattle	Pigs	Sheep
1873	15·8	7·1	25·0
1883	15·8	9·2	19·2
1892	17·6	12·2	13·6
1900	18·9	16·8	9·7
1904	19·3	18·9	7·9
1913	21·0	25·7	5·5

Source : As Table 23.

population of some 18·5 million and the total population of
Germany of 52 million.

The depression undoubtedly caused a good deal of rural
distress, and indebtedness among the farm population became
serious. Owing to deficiencies in the statistics, it is not certain to
what extent farmers and farm workers were forced out of agriculture: the available data (Table 28) indicate a fall in the total
agricultural population but an increase in the active agricultural
population from 1882 to 1907. It seems certain, however, that
there was no mass exodus from the land, as in England.

The preoccupation with tariff policy did not entirely divert
attention from more constructive lines of action. An attempt was
made to deal with the problem of scattered holdings, and useful
results were achieved in some regions. The Prussian estates further
improved their high standards of cultivation. Germany led the
world in agricultural chemistry, and artificial fertilizers were
extensively used. Winter schools and continuation schools were
founded for the rural population. The Raiffeisen co-operative
banks greatly helped to solve the financial problems of the peasants
and came to act as collective purchasers of agricultural requisites.
Co-operative sales organizations – dairies in particular – made a
start. German agriculture was not unprogressive; but it was
producing too much of some commodities, and doing so too
expensively by comparison with overseas supplies.

From 1890 to 1913, the German national income grew at a rate
estimated at 2·9 per cent annually, which was faster than Britain,

Table 28

ACTIVE POPULATION AND TOTAL POPULATION IN AGRICUL-
TURE AND FORESTRY IN RELATION TO POPULATION IN ALL
SECTORS

	Active population			Total population		
	Agri-culture and forestry	All sectors	Agri-culture as % of total	Agri-culture and forestry	All sectors	Agri-culture as % of total
	millions		%	millions		%
1871	..	..	..	18·7	39·4	47
1882	8·21	19·0	43	19·2	45·2	43
1895	8·29	20·1	41	18·5	51·8	36
1907	9·88	26·2	38	17·7	55·8	32

.. Not available.

Source : As Table 23.

France and several other European countries, but lower than
Denmark, Sweden and the United States; German exports rose
by some 5·1 per cent annually – faster than almost any other
country.[1] It appears therefore that the protection given to
agriculture, though it kept up food prices, retarded the shift of
manpower to other sectors and impeded the conclusion of commercial treaties, was not an adverse factor strong enough to
prevent continued economic growth. However, it certainly did
not facilitate it; and the fact that more damage was not done can
probably be attributed to Caprivi's commercial treaties, and to
the dynamism of German industry.

---

[1] Cf. Angus Madison, 'Growth and fluctuations in the world economy,
1870–1960', *Quarterly Review*, Banca Nazionale del Lavoro, Rome, No. 61,
June 1962.

Chapter 5. Denmark

Evolution in Danish agriculture

Already before the Great Depression, Danish agriculture had achieved a standard of efficiency greatly exceeding that of other Continental countries. This was the consequence of peasant emancipation, of the favourable structure of agricultural holdings which resulted, and of an exceptionally high standard of rural education.

A feudal pattern had persisted in Denmark up to the late eighteenth century. A few hundred landlords owned three-quarters of the land, and most of the rest belonged to the Church or the Crown. The greater part of the lords' lånd was let out to peasants in return for services and for payment in kind or in cash. The peasants were legally bound to remain on the estate of their birth. They lived in village communities, the land they farmed being divided into three large fields (winter grain, spring grain and pasture, in rotation), and each peasant had strips in each of the fields.

In 1784 a new and enlightened Government, headed by Count Bernstorff with Count Reventlow in charge of agriculture, embarked on a series of important reforms with the object of creating an independent peasant class. The common field system was abolished and the separate strips rearranged into consolidated holdings. The peasants were assisted to buy their holdings by loans from a Government credit bank on favourable terms. They were encouraged to move out of the villages and live in farm-houses on their own land. The resulting change is well described in a passage by Dr Skrubbeltrang:

> The results of the Reform Period around 1800 were reflected in the Danish landscape ... The most visible result was the removal of farms from the villages and their dispersal in the open countryside. Farms and cottages moved into pastures and commons and took possession of them ... The three (more rarely four or five) large village fields had been broken up into more or less regular plots, as many as there were farms in the village ... If to these are added the numerous small cottage plots, we have a decentralised village presenting much the same picture as the Danish countryside today.[1]

Thus these early reforms, which were followed by others, laid down a pattern of small-to-medium farms, with the land conveniently grouped around the farm buildings. A law of 1819 prevented any tendency to split up the holdings, and laid down the dimensions to be regarded as a minimum for the support of a farm family. This favourable structure was preserved too by the custom by which the son (or daughter) best fitted to do so inherited the farm and compensated the other heirs in cash or by a mortgage on the property.

For agricultural labourers without land (cottagers), reform came later. Their compulsory service to landlords was abolished in 1848; a law of 1899 entitled them to State loans for the purchase of holdings.

These reforms in agriculture formed part of the general movement to effective democracy in Denmark. Various political reforms in the first half of the nineteenth century brought about a democratic structure in which the influence of the remaining large landowners was substantially curbed, and in which the mass of the peasantry had a voice and an influence unknown anywhere else in Europe. It is true that throughout the Great Depression of the 1880s and 1890s the Conservative party held office, and this was to some the extent the party of the big agriculturalists. But the Venstre (left) party, which began as a rural group and gradually became a people's party, held a big majority in the Volketing

[1] F. Skrubbeltrang, 'Agricultural Development and Rural Reform in Denmark', *FAO Agricultural Studies*, No. 22 (Rome, April 1953), pp. 60–1.

(lower house) for most of the time; its internal divisions prevented it from forming a Government until 1901, but it was able to exercise an effective check. Bearing in mind the disproportionate influence exerted in France and Germany by a dominating class of large landlords, the virtual absence of any such class in Denmark is a significant feature.

Rural education began early in Denmark. An Elementary Education Act of 1814 made schooling compulsory between the ages of six and fourteen. The famous Folk High Schools of Bishop Grundtvig began in the 1840s: by 1874 there were fifty such schools, with over three thousand pupils. The Folk High Schools aimed at providing education for students aged eighteen and upwards, mostly from farm families; the subjects taught were largely technical, but some academic courses were included. From 1868 the State provided grants to poor students; by 1900 about one student in three received a Government grant.

There was also an increase in the number of agricultural colleges, which had about a thousand students by 1900. The Royal Agricultural Society was active in spreading the latest knowledge of farming techniques; from 1845 on it held assemblies every few years. The Royal Veterinary and Agricultural College was instituted in 1858.

Thus by the depression, the Danish agricultural population had a high standard of both general education and technical agricultural knowledge. As a result, the Danish farmer was more willing and better able to embark on adaptations than his counterparts in other countries.

The adaptation to crisis

Before the advent of cheap overseas grain, Denmark herself was a major grain exporter. Indeed, grain was her most important export, though she also sent some butter, cheese, eggs and other livestock products to Britain and to Germany.

The fall in grain prices hit Denmark, as other countries, in the late 1870s; in the 1880s the decline for wheat in particular became acute; prices reached their lowest point in the mid-1890s, and there was a revival from about 1900 (Table 29). Livestock products were much less affected: for these, transport costs remained relatively high and restrained the growth in foreign

Table 29

PRICES OF MAJOR AGRICULTURAL PRODUCTS IN COPENHAGEN

	Wheat	Rye	Barley	Oats	Butter	Pig-meat	Eggs	Fat cattle
	kr. per hectolitre				kr. per 100 kg.			
1866–70	14	10	8	5	140	96	..	..
1871–5	14	10	9	6	166	104	..	..
1876–80	13	10	9	6	170	106	..	..
1881–5	11	9	8	5	180	110	79	110
1886–90	9	7	7	5	178	94	79	96
1891–5	8	7	7	5	188	96	88	99
1896–1900	8	7	7	5	190	88	91	87
1901–5	9	7	7	5	192	104	102	98
1906–10	10	8	8	5	204	116	110	100

.. Not available.

Sources : (1) *Statistisk Aarbog.*
(2) Danish Council of Agriculture, *Danemark – L'Agriculture* (Copenhagen, 1935) (for eggs and cattle).

competition. The prices of meat and livestock fell somewhat up to the end of the century, but the decline was much less acute than in the case of grain. A substantial improvement in the quality of Danish butter enabled its price to rise.

This difference in price trends gave an advantage to livestock production both directly, through the price of the product, and indirectly, in that feed grains and other feeding-stuffs could be imported very cheaply. Danish farmers saw the significance of this, and instead of supporting the price of grain through import duties they embarked on a fundamental transformation of their agriculture.

The challenge of overseas grain production had already been foreseen in the 1860s by enlightened agricultural leaders such as Edward Tesdorpf, the president of the Royal Agricultural Society from 1860 to 1888: Tesdorpf was a large landowner who introduced greatly improved farming methods on his own land, and used grain and fodder as the basis for intensive dairying. As a result of the encouragement given by such men to livestock production, the transformation of Danish agriculture was already well under way when the crisis came. The number of cattle – dairy

Table 30

NUMBERS OF LIVESTOCK

(thousands)

	Dairy cows	Other cattle	Pigs	Sheep	Poultry
1861	757	364	304	1,749	..
1871	808	431	442	1,842	..
1881	899	571	527	1,549	4,070
1893	1,011	695	829	1,247	5,856
1903	1,089	751	1,457	877	11,555
1914	1,310	1,153	2,497	515	15,154

.. Not available..

Sources: Landbrugsforhold i Danmark siden midten af det 19. Aarhundrede Statistisk Tabelvaerk, Femte Raekke, Litra C Nr. 4. København 1911). For 1914: Statistisk Aarbog.

cows in particular – was rising steadily; pigs were multiplying even more rapidly (Table 30). Only sheep, in common with the trend throughout Western Europe, were falling in numbers under the influence of overseas competition in wool. At the same time, livestock yields were rising enormously with improved methods:

Table 31

PRODUCTION OF MAJOR LIVESTOCK PRODUCTS

(thousand tons)

	Butter	Milk	Eggs	Pork and bacon	Beef
1871	36	1,082	8	39	..
1881	49	1,391	9	46	59
1893	75	1,945	15	72	68
1903	107	2,613	30	127	92
1914	143	3,574	48	217	123

.. Not available.

Sources: W. von Arnim, 'Die Landwirtschaft Dänemarks', Kieler Studien, 17, 1951; and Skrubbeltrang, op. cit.

between 1871 and 1914 the average annual output of milk per cow rose from 1,300 kg. to 2,700 kg. The output of livestock products thus rose in leaps and bounds: production of milk, butter, eggs and pigmeat trebled or more in this period (Table 31).

The adaptation was reflected in the use of agricultural land, which was increasingly devoted to the needs of livestock: the area under feed grains increased and there was a very big expansion in root crops (especially mangolds and swedes). The relatively small area under wheat was reduced still further, while the area of rye fluctuated but on the whole did not rise (Table 32).

Table 32

UTILIZATION OF AGRICULTURAL LAND

(thousand hectares)

	1876	1888	1896	1907	1912
Wheat	62	49	34	41	47
Rye	254	282	291	276	246
Feed grains	738	816	860	822	862
Total grains	1,054	1,147	1,185	1,138	1,156
Root crops	52	106	140	308	356
Legumes and pasture	888[a]	959[a]	994	799	743
Other crops	68[a]	61[a]	14	12	22
Fallow	248	262	251	225	200
Permanent grass	397	359	322	431	411
Total agricultural land	2,707	2,893	2,906	2,912	2,888

[a] Appears not to be fully comparable with data for subsequent years.

Source: For 1876 and 1888: as Table 30. For other years: Danish Council of Agriculture, op. cit.

Exports of livestock products began to expand rapidly as early as the 1870s (Table 33); in 1872 the value of these exports first exceeded that of grain; by the 1880s Danish exports of dairy products, meat and livestock were firmly established and Denmark had become an importer of all grain except barley.

Table 33

AVERAGE ANNUAL EXPORTS OF LIVESTOCK PRODUCTS

	Fat cattle	Pigs	Beef and mutton[a]	Pigmeat	Butter	Eggs[b]
	thousands		thousand tons			million score
1865/6– 1869/70	40	37			4	..
1870/1–1874	48	111	5		9	..
1875–9	81	186	5		13	..
			4			
1881–5	102	279	1	8	12	3
1886–90	102	131	1	24	24	5
1891–5	103	135	5	41	38	7
1896–1900	57	–	18	65	52	12
1901–5	73	–	24	76	70	18
1906–10	117	–	31	95	83	18

[a] Including offals.
[b] Net exports.
.. Not available.
– Nil or negligible.

Sources: Before 1880: Skrubbeltrang, op. cit.; after 1880: *Statistisk Tabelvaerk, Femte Raekke, Litra D.* (The two sources may not give fully comparable data.)

Agricultural co-operation

The development of co-operation was a distinctive feature of Danish agriculture and played a vital role in its transformation. The principle of co-operation had been established with credit associations founded in the 1850s and with retail co-operatives which first appeared in 1866. The effects of the crisis in the 1880s accelerated the movement.

The growth of livestock production necessitated arrangements for rapid and efficient processing and marketing. This was beyond the means of the individual small producer, but co-operation offered a solution. Co-operative dairies were the first to be formed: previously, butter-making had been left to the farmer's wife, but now butter was processed in bulk, by modern techniques (the centrifugal separator came into use around 1880). The skimmed milk was returned to the farms to be fed to pigs (hence the expression 'the pig hangs on the cow's tail'). Members of the co-operatives received an initial sum for their deliveries, plus a share of the eventual profits in proportion to their deliveries. From 1882, when the first of the co-operative dairies was founded, their number rose to 176 in 1886, 600 in 1890 and 942 in 1900; this represented an average of one for every other parish. This expansion of the dairies was indispensable to the increased output and improved quality of butter, and to the great development of exports.

In 1887 Germany suspended imports of live pigs on the pretext of disease control, and in subsequent years this restriction was reinforced, reducing Danish pig exports almost to zero from 1896 onwards (Table 33). The export trade in pigs had become very important to the Danish farmer, and this was a severe blow. It was essential to redirect production into bacon for the British market. This was achieved by the creation of co-operative bacon factories: the first was built in 1887, and by 1890 such factories existed in every part of the country.

Associations were formed also for the joint export of eggs. Other co-operatives were set up for the purchase of agricultural requisites, but this only became important after 1900. The importance of the various types of co-operative in 1900 is indicated in Table 34.

Table 34

AGRICULTURAL CO-OPERATIVES IN DENMARK IN 1900

	No. of societies	No. of members (thousands)	Annual turnover (million kr.)
Dairies and butter export societies	1,035	140	148
Bacon factories	26	60	35
Egg export societies	370	25	2
Purchase of feeding-stuffs	110	6	4
Total	1,541	231	189

Source: Danish Council of Agriculture, op. cit.

Danish agriculture after transformation

The adaptation to changed conditions through the shift to live-stock production did not prevent the effects of the crisis from being felt. As has already been seen, agricultural prices in general did not revive till around 1900. In the course of the depression, many farmers found themselves in difficulties: the burden of debt increased and many farms had to be sold. The price of agricultural holdings fell from a peak of about 4,000 kroner per hectare in 1880–4 to 2,400 kroner in 1895–9. Nevertheless, the population living by agriculture (including horticulture, forestry and fishing) rose from 889,000 in 1880 to 972,000 in 1901, and again to 1,004,000 in 1911. Since the total population rose from 1,969,000 to 2,757,000 over this period, the agricultural population was no longer quite so important as formerly.

The most important result was that Denmark emerged from the crisis with an agriculture adapted to the new situation, profiting from the opportunity of turning cheap grain into livestock products which were increasingly demanded as standards of living rose and which found a ready market in Britain.

Further, Danish farmers had built a highly efficient and integrated structure of production, processing, distribution and marketing, based upon a highly-developed co-operative system. This foundation made possible Denmark's development in the twentieth century as a great agricultural exporter, and enabled Danish agriculture to make an indispensable contribution to the economic growth of the nation as a whole.

Part II

The Crisis of the 1930s —
The Second Wave of Protectionism

Chapter 6.   General

The slump

During the First World War, farmers in both European and overseas countries benefited from high prices, which persisted for a few years after the war owing to the shortage of food supplies. But the reduction in soil fertility, the loss of livestock and of capital in the countries of continental Europe were gradually made up, and agricultural production recovered. Overseas production had expanded greatly during the war and afterwards continued to rise. In 1921 the increase in food supplies, combined with the effects of general economic depression, caused a sharp fall in prices. In subsequent years prices remained at a low level, and European farmers found themselves in difficulties. In many cases they had incurred debts during the period of prosperity, and repayments now constituted a heavy burden. Further, the costs of agricultural production – wage costs in particular – were rising, and a price 'scissors' began to operate to the detriment of agriculture. To increase their revenue many farmers sought to expand their output, but this only aggravated the fall in prices.

An improvement in the general economic situation brought a revival in farm prices in 1924, but this was of short duration: in 1926 depression set in again, and the pressure on agricultural prices was accentuated as production continued to rise. The output of grain in Europe rose well above the pre-war figure, and in overseas countries too the expansion continued (Table 35). Wheat

Table 35

PRODUCTION OF WHEAT

(annual averages, million tons)

	1909–13	1921–5	1925–9	1930–4	1935–8
WORLD	106·7	..	121·3	128·3	142·2
of which:					
U.S.A.	18·8	21·9	22·4	19·9	20·8
Canada	5·4	10·2	11·7	9·5	7·1
Argentina	4·0	5·5	6·6	6·6	6·2
Australia	2·5	3·5	3·7	5·1	4·4
Europe (excluding U.S.S.R.)	26·1	32·3	38·7	43·8	47·3
U.S.S.R.	20·6	..	21·5	25·2	37·3

.. Not available.

Source: League of Nations, *Statistical Yearbook.*

consumption meanwhile remained almost stationary. In 1928, exceptionally good harvests in Europe and overseas added to wheat stocks which were already heavy: by the middle of 1929, world stocks of wheat stood at 28 million tons, the equivalent of more than a year's exports by all exporting countries. The prices of wheat and other grains fell sharply.

Meanwhile, industrial production in the United States had been expanding rapidly, with great activity in the construction sector. By 1928 there were signs of saturation: wholesale commodity prices began to fall and the volume of new construction declined. Yet on the stock market there was a speculative boom: share prices soared without any relevance to the real earning power of the assets. This could not last while industrial activity was in decline, and the stock market suddenly collapsed in October 1929. The slump in the United States was rapidly communicated to other countries: prices fell, industrial output was drastically cut, unemployment rose.

The industrial countries sought to preserve their market for their own output, and the prohibitive duties of the Hawley-Smoot tariff in the United States (June 1930) set off a chain of tariff increases; 'beggar-my-neighbour' policies became the rule. As the depression deepened and the financial crisis became more acute,

PRICES OF MAJOR FOODSTUFFS (1927–29 = 100)

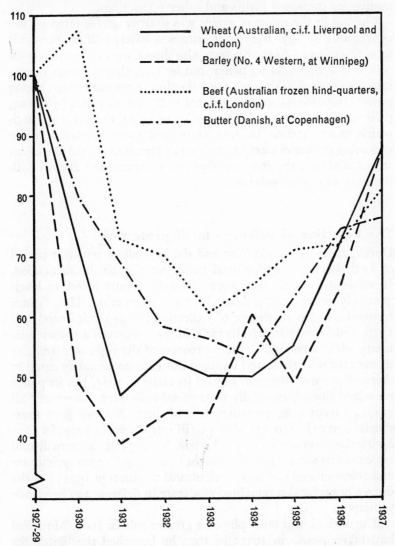

Wheat (Australian, c.i.f. Liverpool and London)

Barley (No. 4 Western, at Winnipeg)

Beef (Australian frozen hind-quarters, c.i.f. London)

Butter (Danish, at Copenhagen)

Source: International Institute of Agriculture, *International Yearbook of Agricultural Statistics.*

FIG. 2

the need to protect the balance of payments became the principal motive for increased tariffs and other restrictions.

The fall in the prices of grains was sharply accentuated by the depression: by 1931 the wheat price was barely half the pre-crisis level (Figure 2).[1] As the diagram also shows, the prices of livestock products at first held up better, but by 1931 they too were drawn into the depression through the reduction in consumer purchasing power. Importing countries reacted to the fall in prices by raising their tariff barriers and by a series of other measures through which their markets became more and more insulated, while exporting countries were in many cases forced to get rid of surplus stocks at almost any cost, and dumped their produce abroad with the help of export subsidies.

The first line of defence – tariff protection

During the First World War and the immediate post-war period of food shortages, agricultural tariffs were generally suspended. In subsequent years they were gradually reintroduced, at levels generally not exceeding those of the pre-war period. Thus France restored a moderate degree of protection in 1919, reinforced it in 1926, and in 1927 revised its tariff in the context of a commercial treaty with Germany. Germany recovered the right to determine its own tariff in 1925, and imposed duties approximately equal to those of pre-war. Belgium revised its tariff in 1924, but its policy remained liberal, especially where foodstuffs were concerned: all grains, except oats, remained free of duty. Norway gave some satisfaction to its farmers with a tariff introduced in 1927. In 1921 Switzerland revised its tariff. Austria, having lost the agricultural regions of its former Empire, sought to develop its own agriculture and reintroduced tariffs on agricultural products in 1924; but the degree of protection remained moderate in deference to free trade principles.

The agricultural tariff played a greater role in Italy. Mussolini had taken power in 1922; in 1925 he launched the 'Battle for

[1] In Figure 2 the quotations for Australian wheat in Liverpool and London have been used in preference to the price of wheat in the United States. The latter fell more steeply in the early stages of the crisis, but under the influence of the measures of support taken from 1933 on, it recovered more quickly than the world price.

Wheat'. In the early 1920s, about a third of Italy's wheat requirements were met from imports and these supplies accounted for a
large part of the total import bill. Increased wheat production
therefore seemed desirable both to achieve greater self-sufficiency
in food and to relieve the balance of payments. A big effort was
made to raise wheat yields through subsidies, technical advice and
propaganda; the major feature in the campaign was the increased
wheat price, achieved mainly through increases in the import
duty. The duty on wheat, suspended since 1915, was reintroduced
in 1925 at 7·50 gold lire per 100 kg., raised after the 1928 harvest
to 11 gold lire, and after further increases reached in August 1931
the level of 75 lire in current value, or approximately 19 gold lire;
at this rate the duty itself easily exceeded the price of wheat on the
world market.

When the crisis broke over European agriculture, agricultural
tariffs were raised as a first line of defence in both France and
Germany. They reached levels which in normal times would have
been prohibitive: with the fall in world prices, they came by 1931
to represent twice or even three times the world market price for
some products, in particular grains and sugar. Italy imposed
higher duties not only on wheat but also on other grains and on
livestock products. Belgium at first resisted the pressure, helped

Table 36

AVERAGE 'POTENTIAL' TARIFF LEVELS FOR FOODSTUFFS, AS
A PERCENTAGE OF EXPORT PRICES IN EUROPEAN COUNTRIES,
IN 1927 AND 1931

	1927	1931
France	19	53
Germany	27	83
Italy	25	66
Belgium	12	24
Switzerland	22	42
Austria	17	60
Sweden[a]	22	39
Finland	58	102

[a] Fruit and vegetables not included.

Source: H. Liepmann, *Tariff Levels* (London: Allen & Unwin, 1938).

by the fact that the fall in prices at first concerned mainly grains, which were of relatively small importance for Belgian agriculture; but in 1931 the fall in prices of livestock products necessitated increased protection. Several other countries raised their duties on agricultural products.

Table 36 shows calculations made by Liepmann of the average level of agricultural duties in 1927 and 1931. It should be recalled (cf. Chapter 1) that these figures represent the unweighted averages of duties on thirty-eight important foodstuffs, expressed as a percentage of the export prices of leading European exporting countries. The results cannot be regarded as precise, and it must be remembered that the increased incidence of specific duties reflects the decline in prices as well as increases in the duties themselves. It can however be seen that by 1931 the duties frequently amounted to half or even more of the export price.

The most spectacular development in the tariff field was Britain's conversion to protectionism in the autumn of 1931. The measures taken did not at first give any great benefit to British agriculture. In November 1931, fruit and vegetables were made subject to duty, and in February 1932 the Import Duties Act, which replaced the temporary legislation of the previous autumn, imposed duties on some agricultural products but left many of the most important ones free. Later in 1932, the application of new and revised duties in accordance with the Ottawa Agreements brought wheat and other products within the scope of the tariff. But since the produce of the Empire continued to enter free of duty, tariff protection remained of limited importance to British agriculture.

The second line of defence – non-tariff measures

At a time when exporters were prepared to sell at almost any price, tariffs, however high, were an ineffective means of protection. It became necessary to control imports more precisely and directly, and for this purpose a variety of new measures made their appearance.

The first of these, and one of the most effective, was the 'milling ratio' for wheat, sometimes too for rye: millers were legally obliged to use a certain minimum percentage of domestically-produced wheat in their grist. This device seems to have been invented by Norway in 1927; in 1929 both France and Germany adopted it; from 1930 onwards it became widespread in Europe and was applied in some non-European countries as well. It continued to be used up to the Second World War in many cases, and it was reintroduced by several countries after the war.

The ratio fixed between home-produced and imported grain could be made to reflect the market situation and the extent to which the authorities wished to promote domestic production; it could be varied from time to time. In practically all the countries which adopted this device, the proportion of domestic grain was increased as time went on: in some cases it reached 100 per cent, which amounted to prohibiting imports of wheat suitable for milling. Thus in France the proportion of domestic wheat was originally fixed at 97 per cent in December 1929; it was reduced slightly in subsequent years owing to reduced harvests, but was raised to 100 per cent in 1933. In Germany the proportion started at 30 per cent in 1929, but was raised to 97 per cent in 1931. In Italy it began at 75 per cent in 1931 and soon reached 95 per cent. In Sweden the proportion stood at 100 per cent in the 1934-5 crop-year. Even in the Netherlands the proportion was raised, from 20 per cent when the system was introduced in 1933 to 35 per cent in 1935. In 1938 Denmark too adopted a milling ratio for wheat of 50 per cent.

Milling ratios by their nature could be used only for bread grains, but they were only one of a family of 'linked-utilization' measures, by which in one way or another, a domestic product had to be used in connection with a foreign product. Such measures were applied not only to some feed grains and, in Germany, to a few other agricultural products, but also to various non-agricultural products (Italian cinemas were required to show one domestic film for every three foreign ones!). In some countries linked-utilization regulations were applied to two different products: thus several countries with butter surpluses, including the Netherlands and Sweden, required all margarine to contain a certain percentage of butter; in Denmark, margarine had to incorporate home-produced lard. Farmers producing alcohol from wine, sugar-beet or other products were sometimes helped by the compulsory inclusion of domestic alcohol in petrol.

A similar measure was the 'linked-purchasing' regulation. Latvia in 1931 required ten tons of home-produced sugar to be bought for every ton of foreign sugar imported, and enforced similar measures for wheat, rye and a few other products. The Government of Spain in 1935 obtained general authority to impose similar regulations. This device, although not of great importance before the Second World War, became one of the major instruments of Swiss agricultural policy when the *prise-en-charge* system was expressly provided for in the Agricultural Act of 1951 (see Chapter 11).

The most important of the new devices was the import quota. Import quotas had been used before the 1930s, but their purpose had been mainly, in connection with a commercial treaty, to guarantee to an exporting country a certain quantity of trade free of duty or at reduced rates. Tariff quotas of this kind were applied by Germany to meat from 1925 to 1930, and to cattle and butter in 1930. The first country to use quotas on a large scale as a means of protection was France: applied first in 1931 as an emergency measure to a few agricultural products, the system was extended in subsequent years to cover practically all agricultural products except wheat, and a number of manufactured goods as well; import quotas gradually became an integral part of French commercial policy. They were taken up to varying extents by other countries: Belgium was one of the first to introduce legislation to this effect, though it did not make full use of the system till 1933. In numerous other countries, import quotas were adopted as an element in measures of market organization: this was the case in Britain, Germany, the Netherlands and Italy. It has been estimated that in 1939 import quotas were being used on a large scale, mainly for agricultural products, by nineteen European countries and nine non-European ones.[1]

In several countries, import quotas came to be associated with import licence fees. The original object of these was mainly to recover some of the profits made by importers from dealing in a restricted market. Frequently, however, these fees came to have a protective function as a kind of variable import duty and served to eliminate differences between the world price and the domestic price; sometimes the import licence fee was higher than the duty provided for under the tariff. Cases in point were France, Belgium and the Netherlands.

[1] Margaret S. Gordon, *Barriers to World Trade* (New York: Macmillan, 1941).

A further step – intervention in agricultural markets

Of all the measures adopted to deal with the crisis of the 1930s, that which had the most significance and the greatest influence on subsequent developments was the attempt to organize domestic agricultural markets. This intervention was usually coupled with regulations concerning imports and, in some cases, exports.

The progression from measures of import control to more far-reaching intervention was particularly clear in FRANCE. Output of wheat had been rising fairly steadily and the initial measures of protection prevented the fall in world prices from discouraging this trend. A big harvest in 1932 saturated the market, and import controls were no longer adequate to maintain the price. Various measures were taken from then on, involving in particular government purchase of part of the crop at fixed prices and culminating in 1936 in the Office National Interprofessionnel du Blé, with the task of fixing the wheat price and ensuring that it was observed. The Office had monopolistic control over all foreign trade in wheat: it could regulate imports and subsidize exports. The other main commodity subjected to market organization in France was wine: here too the necessity arose in part because a surplus made import control ineffective. Measures of organization began in 1931 and were reinforced in 1934; they sought in particular to control the amounts marketed by producers and the period of marketing.

In BRITAIN, the wish to avoid restricting imports from the Empire meant that protection for agriculture had to take the form of marketing schemes, designed to strengthen producers' bargaining power, and subsidies. For wheat and sugar-beet, assistance was given by subsidies alone; in the former case, the market was left free and the subsidy was given through 'deficiency payments', reviving a device used in the First World War and destined to play an important role after the Second. Milk was supported by Milk Marketing Boards with the exclusive right to sell milk and fix prices, assisted by a government subsidy on milk sold for processing. Imports of beef were regulated by agreement with the main exporting countries, including Empire ones. The markets for bacon, potatoes and hops were supported by marketing schemes together with import controls; that for eggs through voluntary restrictions by exporting countries.

The crisis thus forced Britain to abandon its long-established policy of laissez-faire towards agriculture. DENMARK too was compelled, by the difficulties encountered on export markets and the consequent fall in farmers' returns, to abandon liberal practices. The special character of the measures taken reflects Denmark's situation as a large net exporter of the commodities in question. All cattle sold on the home market were subjected to a tax, and the proceeds were used to buy up low-quality cattle in order to raise prices. Taxes were imposed also on sales of butter for domestic consumption, and the proceeds were distributed among producers. A particularly far-reaching scheme, involving what was probably the first agricultural marketing quota in history, was devised for pigs.

The situation of the NETHERLANDS was somewhat similar to that of Denmark. The Dutch Government too was forced, partly by falling import prices but even more by the difficulties facing exports, to depart from tradition and to intervene on agricultural markets. Here again the complexity of the measures adopted reflects the problems involved in supporting the prices of commodities which are on an export basis. In a first phase, measures of support were applied to individual products according to needs : thus in 1931 wheat imports were regulated by a milling ratio and a target price on the domestic market, the latter maintained with the help of State subsidies. Subsidies were also paid for potatoes and sugar-beet from 1931. In 1932, as livestock products were drawn into the crisis, these too became the object of intervention : a Central Pig Office was set up to keep the number of pigs in line with market outlets and to operate an export and import monopoly for both live pigs and pigmeat. In the same year, a Central Dairy Office was formed with a monopoly of butter exports, and the domestic milk market was strictly controlled. In 1933 a Central Cattle Office was introduced; it sought to restrict cattle numbers by decreeing the slaughter of part of the herd. Fruit and vegetable producers, from 1931 on, began to hold back part of their supplies from the market in order to maintain a minimum price, helped by a State subsidy for the disposal of unsold stocks; in 1933 imports of fruit and vegetables were made subject to control. A second phase was reached with the Agricultural Crisis Law of 1933, which brought together all these separate regulations and provided a legal basis for subsequent action: the Government was given the right to designate 'crisis products' and to regulate production and all aspects of trade in such products. The Netherlands thus became one of the first countries to have an extensively planned organization of its agricultural markets.

SWITZERLAND was another country in which an attachment to liberal economic principles did not prevent recourse to a significant degree of market organization in agriculture. Even before the crisis, the Central Union of Swiss Milk Producers had been formed, controlling almost all marketed supplies of milk; also, from 1915 to 1929 the Government exercised a monopoly of the wheat trade. In 1929 this arrangement for wheat was replaced by Government purchase of domestic wheat and rye at guaranteed prices: millers were bound to take over this grain at prices fixed by the Government, but received compensation through the restriction of flour imports. In 1933 a special commission was set up to control imports of feed grains and other feeding-stuffs, and import levies were imposed in addition to customs duties, with the object of raising the price of fodder and discouraging the output of milk, already regarded as excessive. Though subsidies had to be given to milk production, an attempt was made to impose production quotas. Output of pigmeat too had increased rapidly and prices were falling: in 1935 limitations were imposed on the number of pigs that could be kept, and a scheme for directly restricting production was introduced.

AUSTRIA began in 1931 to regulate supplies to the cattle market, and imports were admitted only in so far as they did not endanger sales of home-bred animals. The milk market too was organized from 1931 on, and various measures were adopted for other products. In its trade policy Austria abandoned its liberal principles and began to draw up trade agreements in which the 'most favoured nation' clause was replaced by reciprocal agreements on preferences and quotas: arrangements of this kind were included in the Rome Protocols of 1934 between Austria, Italy and Hungary.

Various other countries adopted measures of a similar nature. NORWAY began to organize its agricultural market even before the crisis, with a grain monopoly set up under a law of 1926; from 1929 onwards a series of measures were taken, based mainly on sales co-operatives for the major products. SWEDEN in 1930 reinforced its milling ratio for wheat with Government purchases to support prices; organization of the dairy market and other measures were introduced in 1932.

Germany and Italy – agricultural policy in a totalitarian State

In Germany under National Socialism and in Italy under Fascism, agricultural markets were strictly regulated in accordance with general political aims and with an overall economic plan.

The National Socialist Government in GERMANY came to power in 1933 with a clearly-defined philosophy as to the role of agriculture in the nation. This philosophy formed an integral part of National Socialist thinking: its essential features concerned the social and racial importance of the farm population, the need to ensure fair prices to farmers and the importance of national self-sufficiency in food. In a remarkably short time German agriculture was organized in accordance with a prepared plan. The Reichs-nährstand (State Food Corporation) was set up in September 1933 to organize all aspects of food production and distribution and to regulate markets and prices. Full control of the volume and prices of imports was vested in the Reichsstellen (State Boards) which were set up for all important commodities from April 1933 onwards: the Reichsstellen could also buy and sell on the domestic market and operate buffer stocks. Under this system imports were drastically reduced, and the manipulation of supplies enabled prices to be stabilized and raised well above the level to which they had fallen in the crisis. The attempt to raise production nevertheless had only limited success, and at the outbreak of war Germany was still by no means self-sufficient in food.

In Fascist ITALY too, economic policy came to involve a high degree of central planning in agriculture as in other sectors. This, however, occurred over a period of years, and was never so thoroughly applied as in Germany. Mussolini did not develop the elaborate racial theories of the Nazis, but like them he regarded agriculture as a basic element in national well-being and saw in the agricultural population a source of strength in wartime. His agricultural policy too was dominated by the desire for self-sufficiency and was intimately linked with his object of raising Italy to the status of a Great Power: this involved promoting the increase in population by all possible means, which made increased food production all the more necessary.

Mussolini's agricultural policy meant an enormous effort to lift Italian agriculture out of technical backwardness and economic depression. Great emphasis was laid on the policy of *bonifica integrale* (integral land reclamation), initiated by a law of 1928 which ordered the improvement of all unused but cultivable land. The early stages of the Battle for Wheat have already been described. After a slow start, considerable success was achieved in raising yields and output; at the same time the increase in price resulting from the import duty reduced wheat consumption, and after a large harvest in 1932 imports were reduced to a low level. This, however, meant that the import duty was no longer so effective in raising the domestic price, and other measures became necessary. A milling ratio was introduced in 1931: at first 75 per cent of domestic wheat had to be incorporated in the flour; soon afterwards the ratio was raised to 95 per cent. Then, however, the situation changed; the 1934 harvest was small and the milling ratio was suspended; moreover, the Abyssinian War of 1935–6 contributed to an increase in prices. In 1935 a target price system was introduced with the object of restraining price increases. This proved ineffective, and was replaced the following year by a system under which wheat could be sold to the mills only by authorization and at fixed prices. After the end of the Abyssinian War, a full State monopoly was instituted: growers were bound to deliver their wheat at fixed prices, and imports were directly controlled by organizations responsible to the Ministry of Agriculture.

Though the Battle for Wheat largely achieved its immediate object, the excessive emphasis placed by Italian policy on wheat had questionable results. It helped the larger farmers and landowners, but not the peasants. It stimulated wheat at the expense of other products more needed and better suited to Italian conditions. It made only a limited contribution to the balance of payments, for with the low level of world prices, wheat could have been imported cheaply; moreover, the rising demand for livestock products had to be met by increased imports.

It is worth noting that the agricultural policy adopted in another totalitarian State, JAPAN, was closely analogous to those of Germany and Italy. Here too, nationalist aims involved belief in the agricultural population as a vital element in the nation: the Imperial Agricultural Society declared that the farming community was 'the backbone of the nation, the source of its military strength and the guardian of traditional virtues against alien

5

influences'.[1] In Japan too, increased food production with a view to self-sufficiency became a major aim, and an extensive system of control over agricultural production and markets was set up.

Factors contributing to the growth of intervention

The economic crisis which began in 1929 was thus the cause of a second convulsion in agriculture: following the collapse of agricultural prices on the world market, traditional patterns of agricultural production and trade were transformed and official policies towards agriculture underwent a basic change. In countries where agriculture already received protection, as in France, Germany and Italy, the tariff structure was reinforced by a series of new and far more drastic measures, while countries such as Britain, Denmark, the Netherlands and Belgium abandoned their traditional policies of free trade and began to support their farmers in a variety of ways.

This growth of intervention took place with remarkably little opposition: there was far less controversy than during the Great Depression of the nineteenth century. Protection was being given to industry in an effort to ward off unemployment, and similar assistance could hardly be refused to agriculture. In the face of the crises, academic theories of free trade were irrelevant. Governments did not want to be accused of raising food prices, but it was difficult to criticize measures which sought merely to restrain the fall in prices.

Many of those who accepted the change, however, did so in the expectation that the new measures would be temporary, and could be relaxed when economic conditions returned to normal. In fact the opposite happened: measures of support remained and were even reinforced in the course of the 1930s. To some extent, this was necessitated by the fact that world prices continued low till the middle of the decade. However, the various measures of intervention were themselves an important cause of the persisting difficulties on the world market: import restrictions and export subsidies were constantly limiting demand, raising supply and depressing prices, and thus perpetuating the need for their own existence. The cumulative effects of separate national protectionist

[1] Quoted by G. C. Allen, *A Short Economic History of Modern Japan* (London: Allen & Unwin, 1946), p. 110.

policies were scarcely understood, and the climate of opinion was not yet ripe for the international action which alone could have reconciled these divergent interests; this point is further discussed in the last section of this chapter.

Other factors contributed to the willingness of governments and the public to help agriculture. There was a growing awareness that agriculture was not like other industries: that it was particularly subject to fluctuations in supplies and prices, and that a large number of producers acting individually were helpless in the face of market disequilibrium. This realization contributed to the introduction of marketing schemes, in Britain in particular, the object of which was as much to reinforce the farmers' position on their own market as to protect them against foreign competition.

Added to this problem of market disequilibrium was the old argument about the social value of the farming community. This concept appeared in an extreme form in the racial theories of National Socialism, but it was present to varying extents in most countries. It was particularly important in Switzerland, where the rural population of independent farmers appeared as an essential element in the democracy and a bulwark against Socialist tendencies in the urban working population; on several occasions in the 1920s the farmers were instrumental in breaking industrial strikes.

The other old argument, concerning the strategic importance of a large food supply, gained considerable force from the experience of food shortages during the First World War and from the preparations for the Second. Thus in Germany, Italy and Japan, the need for self-sufficiency in food was an integral part of nationalist policies. In Britain, responsible opinion pointed out that a policy of self-sufficiency in peacetime could actually damage the economic strength of the nation in war, and there was little deliberate effort to raise food production till close to the outbreak of war.

The increased support for agriculture owed much to the activities of farm organizations. In France there was a big increase in the number of such organizations and in their influence; the initiative passed from the old Société des Agriculteurs de France to a right-wing syndicalist movement, which in 1934 and 1935 combined its action with a rural movement dominated by Fascist tendencies, forming the Front Paysan. In Germany, the Prussian landlords continued to be influential in the Weimar Republic;

moreover, on a number of points – particularly concerning the importance of agriculture for the nation's military strength – they had views in common with the National Socialists: they concluded an alliance with the Nazis in 1931 and their position was to a large extent respected under the Nazi regime. In Britain, the old Central Chamber of Agriculture, together with the newer and more vigorous National Farmers' Union, publicized farmers' views, though their influence at this time was somewhat limited.

In spite of all the action that was taken, surprisingly little thinking was done in most countries into the needs of long-term agricultural policy. In the early stages of the economic crisis, measures of assistance were improvised in response to the emergency; afterwards, these measures were reinforced in various ways. But in most cases, no official policy was evolved as to the place of agriculture in the economy: basic questions as to how much food and what kinds of food should be produced at home, how big the agricultural population should be, what level of farm income was justifiable, were scarcely considered. This lack of a clearly-defined policy was particularly evident in Britain. In France, the instability and short life of the various governments during this period put a consistent agricultural policy out of the question. Even in Italy, where agriculture played a large part in official thinking from 1925 on, the obsession with wheat production blinded the policy-makers to the overall economic problems of agriculture. It was only in Nazi Germany that the role of agriculture was clearly defined in relation to overall political and economic aims, and that the resulting policy was consistently and effectively applied; but the aims in question were to reinforce the power of a single nation and the interests of other countries, in agriculture as in other respects, were disregarded.

Some consequences for prices, production and trade

Perhaps the most striking outcome of this period in which the countries of Western Europe intervened in a variety of ways to support their agricultural markets was the resulting divorce between the trends of world prices and those of prices received by producers in importing countries.

Figure 2 has shown the extent of the collapse in the world grain market in 1930 and 1931, and the later but still drastic fall in the

WHEAT PRICES (1927-29 = 100)

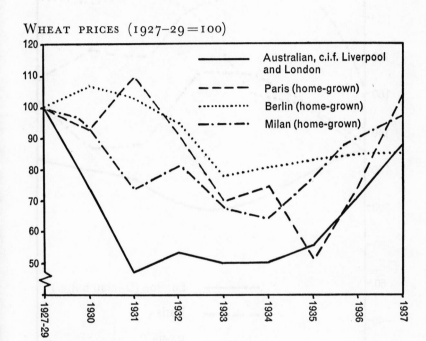

Source: International Institute of Agriculture, *International Yearbook of Agricultural Statistics.*

FIG. 3

BUTTER PRICES (SHILLINGS PER CWT.)

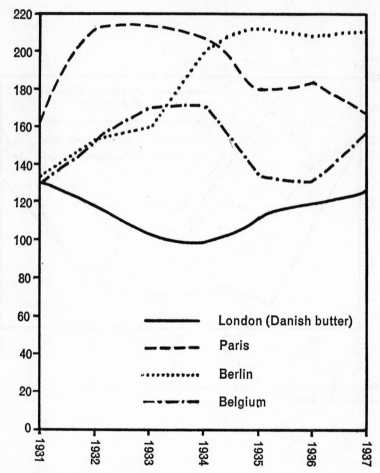

Source: Statistics of the Commonwealth Economic Committee.

FIG. 4

world prices of livestock products. It was not till 1933 or 1934 that a recovery took place, and even by 1937 prices were still well below the pre-crisis level.

In most of the European importing countries, producers were to a considerable extent insulated from the fall in prices. Developments for wheat are shown in Figure 3. It can be seen that the fall in the world price in 1930 and 1931 was not at all reflected in the domestic price in France and Germany, and in Italy was reflected only in part. Subsequently, the wheat price in France fell under the influence of large domestic harvests rather than of the low world price; it recovered in 1936 and by 1937 was slightly above the pre-crisis level. In Germany the price declined from 1931 to 1933; afterwards, the strict controls instituted by the Nazi regime enabled a stable and slightly rising price level to be maintained. In Italy the price recovered by 1937 to nearly the pre-crisis level.

The butter prices shown in Figure 4 need to be interpreted with some care: since the quotations in different currencies have been converted into shillings on the basis of current exchange

Table 37

CROP PRODUCTION AND LIVESTOCK NUMBERS IN WESTERN EUROPE

	Unit	1924–8[a]	1929–33[a]	1934–8[a]
Wheat	million tons	24	29	30
Barley	,,	10	11	11
Potatoes	,,	78	89	94
Sugar	,,	4·2	4·8	5·0
Wine	million hectolitres	131	127	131
		1928	1933	1938
Cattle	millions	87	90	92
Pigs	,,	52	59	59

Note: It has been necessary to adapt data given by the source for the whole of Europe: as information is not available for all countries, the results include small amounts for certain Eastern European countries.

[a] Annual averages.

Source: International Institute of Agriculture, *Les Grands Produits Agricoles* (FAO, 1948).

rates, the result reflects changes in the exchange rates as well as changes in domestic prices. Thus the apparent increases in the French and German prices from 1931 to 1933 are a consequence of the devaluation of sterling – in fact the domestic prices fell to some extent. This diagram does show nevertheless that after about 1935, when most of the exchange rates had more or less settled down, there remained a very substantial price differential between Danish butter on the free London market and home-produced butter in Germany and – to a lesser extent – in Belgium. The high French price from 1932 to 1936 is to some extent a reflection of the overvaluation of the franc during this period, but even after the drastic devaluation of 1937 the French butter price remained well above the London price.

As a result, agricultural producers in most European countries, though they by no means escaped the crisis, were spared its worst effects. Farm output was not discouraged: rather the reverse. As Table 37 shows, the production of most major commodities in Western Europe increased in the course of the 1930s; the expan-

Table 38

WORLD EXPORTS OF FOOD, BY COMMODITY

	Current value		Unit values[a]		Volume index[b]	
	1929	1937	1929	1937	1929	1937
	$ million		1913 = 100		1913 = 100	
Cereals	2,050	1,526	107	88	107	98
Sugar	719	432	84	62	185	152
Livestock products	2,132	1,557	137	114	135	118
Fruit and vegetables	872	660	105	69	185	214
Coffee, tea, cocoa	946	653	123	79	139	149
Oil-seeds and fats	1,109	882	92	68	161	171
Other food and drink	626	541	..	..	..	..
Total	8,456	6,251	113	85	136	133

[a] Weighted average of unit values of the various items in each group.
[b] Current value deflated by indices of unit values.

.. Not available.

Source: P. Lamartine Yates, *Forty Years of Foreign Trade* (London: Allen and Unwin, 1959).

sion in wheat was particularly large. The numbers of livestock also continued to rise.

At a time when the general reduction in purchasing power was depressing consumption and when prices often were not allowed to fall sufficiently to offset this decline, the increasing trend in home production could only mean a cut in imports. Thus the fall in prices on the world market was accentuated and the volume of trade reduced.

It appears from Table 38 that the value of world trade in food-stuffs as a whole was less by about a quarter after the crisis, in 1937, than in 1929 (total world trade fell by just over 20 per cent in value). Both the volume and the unit values of trade had fallen for the products of the temperate regions – grains and livestock products – as well as for sugar, which also competed directly with European agriculture. On the other hand, trade in tropical and semi-tropical products – coffee, tea, oil-seeds, certain fruits, etc. – increased in volume, though it suffered a serious fall in prices.

Table 39 shows in greater detail the developments in trade for some important 'temperate' foodstuffs, in terms of quantity, and indicates the effects on various exporting countries. The decline in the wheat trade mainly affected the United States and Canada; Argentina and Australia did not do so badly. Poland and the countries of South-East Europe managed to increase their exports of wheat and rye during and after the crisis, thanks in part to preferential treatment by France and, more important, to the close commercial links established with Germany after 1933. Trade in barley and oats also declined; the only type of grain for which trade expanded was maize, this expansion being accounted for by imports into Britain (where no maize is grown). Trade in sugar fell, and the pattern shifted: the traditional exporters – Cuba and the Dutch East Indies – lost heavily, while the dependencies of the United States – Philippines, Hawaii and Puerto Rico – together with the countries of the British Empire were enabled by preferential arrangements to increase their trade.

Exports of livestock, of which cattle and pigs were the most important, suffered badly. Britain reduced its imports from the Irish Republic (largely as a result of the trade war between the two countries from 1932 to 1938). Austria, which had been the world's largest importer of pigs, mainly from East and South-East Europe, cut its imports drastically; Germany too reduced its

Table 39

EXPORTS OF MAJOR AGRICULTURAL PRODUCTS, BY COUNTRY
OF ORIGIN (ANNUAL AVERAGES)

	1924–8	1929–33	1934–8
WHEAT AND RYE	million tons		
N. America	14·4	9·5	6·2
Argentina	4·1	4·2	3·5
Australia	2·5	3·4	2·8
E. and S.E. Europe[b]	1·4	1·8	1·9
Others	3·4	4·9	4·2
World	25·8	23·8	18·6
SUGAR	million tons		
Cuba	4·4	3·2	2·6
Dutch E. Indies	2·1	1·8	1·0
Philippines, Hawaii, Puerto-Rico	1·7	2·4	2·5
British Empire	0·5	0·8	1·2
Others	4·3	4·4	4·1
World	13·0	12·6	11·4
CATTLE AND PIGS	thousands		
Ireland	984	1,056	757
Denmark and Netherlands	342	218	252
E. and S.E. Europe[b]	1,715	1,335	1,045
Others[c]	2,302	2,026	1,986
World	5,343	4,635	4,040

[a] Including flour in grain equivalent.
[b] Poland, Rumania, Hungary, Yugoslavia, Bulgaria.
[c] Consisting largely of exports of pigs from China to Hong Kong and

imports from Denmark and the Netherlands during the worst of
the crisis, but in 1934–8 this trade partly recovered. As for beef
and mutton, of which Britain was by far the largest importer,
the striking feature was the displacement of South American
supplies by Australia and New Zealand, as a result of preferential
arrangements for the latter. Germany ceased to be a major beef
importer. For bacon, import quotas in Britain reduced trade from
almost all sources except Canada, which benefited from a particularly large quota. Trade in pigmeat (other than bacon, ham and
lard) suffered a decline, with reduced imports by France and
Germany in particular: exports by Denmark and the Netherlands,

TABLE 39—*continued*

	1924–8	1929–33	1934–8
BEEF AND MUTTON	thousand tons		
Argentina, Uruguay, Paraguay	1,042	841	853
Australia and New Zealand	218	196	221
Others	276	254	212
World	1,536	1,291	1,286
BACON, HAM, LARD	thousand tons		
Denmark and Netherlands	254	382	225
U.S.A.	170	74	32
Canada	41	15	70
Others	87	131	101
World	552	602	428
OTHER PIGMEAT	thousand tons		
Denmark and Netherlands	50	29	9
E. and S.E. Europe	32	11	28
U.S.A.	41	32	23
Australia and New Zealand	4	12	37
Others	40	43	35
World	167	127	132
BUTTER	thousand tons		
Denmark and Netherlands	177	196	199
Australia and New Zealand	113	183	240
Others	169	189	177
World	459	568	616

of cattle from Mexico and Canada to the U.S.A.
Source: International Institute of Agriculture, *Les Grands Produits Agricoles* (FAO, 1948).

especially the latter, were severely hit. On the other hand, Australia and New Zealand were able to increase their exports of pigmeat to Britain. For butter there was a similar development: Germany reduced its imports in 1934–8, while those of Britain increased, and as a result exports by Denmark and the Netherlands remained at about the same level while those of New Zealand and Australia more than doubled as compared with 1924–8. In cheese too, New Zealand and Australia gained at the expense of Denmark and the Netherlands.

Thus, in this period when trade in 'temperate' foodstuffs in general was declining, the exporting countries which did least badly were those able to get preferential treatment from a major importing country: the American sugar-exporting colonies from the United States, to some extent South-East Europe from Germany and France, and above all the British Empire from Great Britain. France, Belgium and the Netherlands also gave preference to their overseas territories; this however – apart from wine and wheat from French North Africa – mostly concerned tropical and semi-tropical products. On the other hand, the agricultural exports of Denmark and the Netherlands suffered from increased protection in neighbouring countries and from discrimination against them in Britain; those of the United States suffered from the general slump in grains and from import restrictions both on grains and on pigmeat; and those of Argentina and other South American countries suffered from the preferential treatment given to Empire meat on the British market.

Reactions in agricultural exporting countries

Agricultural exporting countries were forced by their difficulties to take a number of measures to assist their farmers. Those which were adopted in Denmark and the Netherlands have already been described. The remainder do not fall directly within the scope of this study, but may be referred to briefly.

The countries of EAST AND SOUTH-EAST EUROPE were in a particularly difficult position. These were mostly poor countries where agriculture predominated; the peasant population was often living on a bare subsistence, and there was little possibility for support by the rest of the community. These countries – Bulgaria, Hungary, Poland, Rumania and Yugoslavia – made an attempt to co-ordinate their exports and to obtain preferential treatment from the countries of Western Europe; several conferences were held to this end, starting in July 1930. Other exporting countries, however, objected strongly to the idea of preferential treatment for their competitors, and not much was obtained. During 1931 some preferential tariff agreements were negotiated, in particular by France with Hungary, Rumania and Yugoslavia: these agreements provided for the reimbursement by France to the exporting countries of a part of the duty on wheat. Germany also offered preferences on grain to Hungary and Rumania, but this idea had to be given up because of the objections raised by countries entitled to 'most favoured nation' treatment by Germany; however, at a later stage, the National Socialist regime entered into close trading links with South-East European countries, from which they derived a limited benefit.

The UNITED STATES naturally became extremely concerned at the prospects, especially for its wheat exports, as the following passage indicates:

> Western Europe aims to raise more wheat. Central Europe seeks preference in the wheat markets of Western Europe. The Dominions of the British Commonwealth seek preference in the wheat markets of Great Britain. Great Britain, Holland, Belgium, and France extend preferences to their colonies for feeding-stuffs. In order to effectuate quotas and preferences, intricate internal regulations and extensive interstate barters become necessary. Russia, Argentina and the United States stand outside the charmed circle.[1]

In 1933 the U.S. Senate considered an important document on 'World trade barriers in relation to American agriculture', which stressed the extent to which farm prices in the United States had been affected by the fall on the world market.[2]

Unlike most other agricultural exporting countries, the United States had the financial means to come to the rescue of its farmers. The emphasis was laid at first on Government-financed stockpiling operations to relieve the market, but this effort proved largely unsuccessful. In the context of Roosevelt's 'New Deal', the Agricultural Adjustment Act of 1933 provided more effective and far-reaching legislation: it aimed to restore the balance between production and consumption and to give farmers 'parity' prices. Payments were made to farmers for reducing their acreage of wheat, maize, cotton and tobacco; pigs in excess supply were purchased by the authorities and slaughtered. The Commodity Credit Corporation was instituted to buy and sell agricultural commodities, making 'loans' to farmers on the security of the commodities delivered. Surplus stocks were disposed of in various ways at home and abroad.

In CANADA too, early efforts to help wheat growers consisted

---

[1] In the cover note to 'Economic nationalism in Europe as applied to wheat', *Wheat Studies* (Food Research Institute, Stanford University), February 1932.

[2] Senate Document No. 70, 73rd Congress, 1st Session, 1933.

mainly of stockpiling operations. The Canadian Wheat Pool was formed in 1924, and received government support from 1929. As in the United States, the mounting burden of surplus stocks necessitated a change in policy: in 1935 the Wheat Board was established to buy grain from producers and to sell on world markets with the help of export subsidies.

ARGENTINA and AUSTRALIA lacked the means and the facilities for storing grain. The Argentine Government bought a large part of the exportable surplus from producers and sold it on the world market, usually at a loss. In Australia, the Commonwealth Government made grants to the individual States for distribution to farmers; it did not subsidize wheat exports directly till 1938.

Export subsidies became common in a number of other countries as well. SOUTH AFRICA began in 1931 to subsidize exports of processed foodstuffs and sugar, and later extended subsidies to beef and mutton. The IRISH REPUBLIC tried through export subsidies to counter the increased duties imposed by Britain in the course of the trade war. Even NEW ZEALAND began to subsidize its dairy exports in 1936.

An interesting picture of the increase in intervention in both importing and exporting countries is given in a diagram by G. Mackenroth (Figure 5). This shows the percentage of agricultural trade which was 'directly or indirectly' affected by 'state measures of control or guidance' other than tariffs, in thirty-two countries accounting for 80–90 per cent of world trade in foodstuffs. It appears that this percentage grew from about 5 in 1929 to 55 in 1934; moreover, intervention apparently took place in exporting countries to approximately the same extent, and at approximately the same time, as in importing countries.[1]

[1] G. Mackenroth, an untitled contribution to a discussion on 'International Trade in Relation to Agricultural Development', *Proceedings of the Fifth International Conference of Agricultural Economists* (London: O.U.P. 1939). This calculation, of course, reflects only the existence or non-existence of a measure – not the extent of its effect upon trade. On the latter score, there is no doubt that import restrictions were by far the greater influence, and that they were often the cause of measures applied by exporting countries. It should also be noted that the diagram may be misleading in suggesting that measures were applied simultaneously in importing and exporting countries: a lag of some months between one measure and another might not show up in the calculation.

PERCENTAGE OF WORLD TRADE AFFECTED BY MEASURES OF INTERVENTION

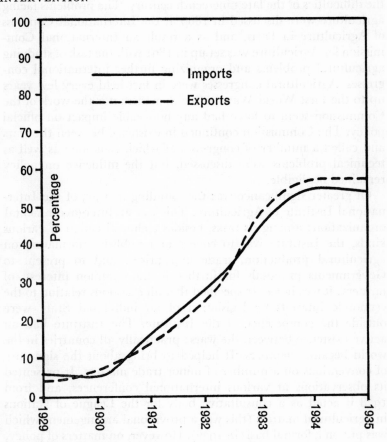

Source: Mackenroth, op. cit.

FIG. 5

The failure of international action

With the exception of the Brussels Sugar Convention of 1902, by which sugar exporting countries agreed to refrain from export subsidies, there had been no effective international action during the difficulties of the late nineteenth century. The problems facing agriculture were discussed in 1889 at the International Congress of Agriculture in Paris, and as a result an International Commission for Agriculture was set up in 1891 with the task of studying agricultural problems and organizing further international congresses. Agricultural congresses were in fact held every few years up to the First World War, but neither these nor the work of the Commission seem to have had any noticeable impact on official policy. The Commission continued in existence between the wars and called a number of congresses at which economic as well as technical problems were discussed, but the influence on policy remained negligible.

Of greater significance was the founding in 1905 of the International Institute of Agriculture. This was an intergovernmental organization; among its tasks, besides technical action of various kinds, the Institute was to collect and publish information on agricultural production, trade and prices, and to present to Governments proposals for furthering the common interests of farmers; it was however specified that all questions relating to the economic interests or legislation of an individual State were outside the competence of the Institute. The Institute had an active existence between the wars; practically all countries in the world became members. It helped to bring about the signature of conventions on a number of minor trade matters. It presented its observations at various international conferences, and from 1928 it acted as a consultative body for the League of Nations in agricultural matters (this was a provisional arrangement which was put on a formal basis in 1932). However, on matters of policy, and in particular on problems of international trade in agricultural products, its influence was, at the most, indirect.

The League of Nation's interest in agriculture began with the International Economic Conference of May 1927, which called for a halt to the rising wave of tariffs, and discussed the problems of agriculture on the basis of a long report submitted by the International Institute of Agriculture. In January 1930 the League

called a meeting of agricultural experts, and its Economic Committee subsequently reported that the economic work of the League
could not succeed unless it gave due attention to the needs of
agriculture. The next year the Economic Committee produced a
detailed report on the agricultural crisis, which laid stress on the
growing gap between prices paid and prices received by farmers,
and declared that the crisis was being aggravated by the numerous
restrictions on imports and aids to exports. At the Assembly of the
League in 1934 there was a long discussion of the problems of
agriculture, and as a result, in 1935, the Economic Committee
issued a further study on the evolution of agricultural protectionism. This report – a comparatively short one – made a penetrating
analysis of the current problem which deserves attention. It began
by pointing out that around 1925 the recovery of agricultural
production in countries affected by the war had upset the balance
of supply and demand and started a decline in agricultural prices,
which since 1930 had become acute. Exporting countries had been
able to do little to help themselves except build up stocks.
Importing countries, however, had resorted to far-reaching
measures of protection:

> On the other hand, agricultural producers in the importing
> countries with a shortage of crops were obliged to appeal to
> their Governments and to national solidarity in order to
> escape the contagion. This means they have used, and
> abused: the introduction of duties two or three times higher
> than world prices, ever stricter rationing, the progressive
> reduction to close upon vanishing-point of the proportion of
> foreign products admitted in the various preparations,
> bounties for production, export bounties, 'schemes', mono-
> polies and various other forms of planned economy.

These measures had disrupted trade, and protectionism had
proved contagious:

> The consequence of all these measures, applied more particu-
> larly by the big industrial countries, was naturally a big-scale
> reduction, amounting in some cases to the total exclusion, of
> agricultural imports, and that more particularly in the case
> of products – such as wheat, meat and butter – playing a
> fundamental part in the economic life of the producing

countries ... This situation, taken as a whole, represents a
defensive reaction, often violent and incoherent, but in the
main comprehensible, against the dangers of an unprecedented economic depression.
Had it achieved its object, it would be difficult indeed to
criticize it; but facts are to hand which prove that this
exaggerated policy of protectionism, spreading from one
country to another, is tending to prolong the depression which
it was designed to combat and to prejudice the interests of
the classes that it aimed at protecting.[1]

The attempts by the League to combat the rising tide of
protectionism met with only limited success. Already in 1929 the
Assembly discussed proposals for a 'customs truce', and in
February 1930 a conference was held to work out this idea; a
Convention was drawn up, but was never put into effect. A further
attempt was made at the London Conference in June 1933: all
delegations agreed that trade barriers should be reduced, but this
agreement was hedged around by reservations and no concrete
results could be obtained. In the autumn of 1936, the declaration
by the United States, Britain and France expressing the intention
of these three countries to safeguard the peace and restore order to
international relations was favourably received by the Assembly of
the League, and the improvement in the economic situation at
that time did permit some reductions in tariffs and an easing of
quantitative restrictions. The Economic Committee, in a report
to the Assembly the following year, drew up a plan for restoring
normal economic relations. But the threat of war then began to
dominate the international scene, causing countries to expand
production by all possible means and making impossible any
further action to liberalize trade.

The effort, already referred to, by the countries of East and
South-East Europe to obtain preferential treatment from Euro-
pean importing countries attracted much attention at the time.
It was helped by the idea of a European Union put forward by
French delegates at the 1929 Assembly of the League, and was
discussed at a number of conferences held under the auspices of

[1] League of Nations, Economic Committee, *Considerations on the present
evolution of agricultural protectionism* (Geneva, 1935), pp. 6–7. The document was
apparently drafted in French and the official English version, quoted here,
is less satisfactory.

the League. In particular, the Stresa Conference of September 1932 was devoted to this question : it led to a recommendation that limited tariff concessions should be given to the countries concerned and to a financial plan for measures to stabilize the grain market. However, the financial arrangements – on which the other provisions depended – could not be put into force, and the scheme had little practical result.

One of the few agreements put into force during this period was the first International Wheat Agreement, in April 1933. This was a two-year agreement in the first instance. Exporters undertook to limit their exports to certain quotas, and in the second year to reduce wheat production by 15 per cent; however, Russia and the Danubian States did not commit themselves. With regard to importing countries, it was recognized that domestic policies could not easily be changed : still, these countries agreed to take no action which would increase their wheat output, to adopt measures to raise wheat consumption, to reduce tariffs if the price on the world market rose above a certain level for sixteen consecutive weeks, and to accept as desirable a relaxation of import restrictions if prices did in fact improve over a period of a year. An International Wheat Committee was set up in London to administer the Agreement.

Perhaps the most remarkable thing about this Agreement is that it was reached at all : it was the first international agreement of any significance affecting a major foodstuff, with the exception of the Brussels Sugar Convention of 1902. However, it was not a success. Importers did not undertake to import any specified amount, and as prices continued to fall, their obligation to relax import restrictions was not called upon. Further, most exporting countries did not take the necessary steps to reduce production : in the United States, Canada and Australia, the area sown to wheat in 1934 was only slightly less than in the previous year, while Argentina increased her wheat area and shipped more wheat than her quota allowed. It proved impossible to reach an agreement on export quotas for the 1934–5 season, or on acreage controls for the 1935 crop; as a result the Agreement was terminated in 1935, and only a Wheat Advisory Committee continued to function up to the war.

Sugar was also the object of an international agreement, more far-reaching than the 1902 Convention. The first step was the

Chadbourne Agreement of May 1931 between seven exporting countries (later joined by two others), which agreed upon export quotas to maintain a stated world price. Importing countries, however, continued to promote their own production, and trade fell even more than had been foreseen; moreover, the United States gave preference to its own colonies, Britain to the British Empire. The Chadbourne Agreement expired in 1935. In 1937 the International Sugar Agreement came into force, for a five-year period: it covered most of the exporting countries as well as some large importers, including the United States and Britain: the United States undertook not to reduce its imports below the 1937 level, while Britain agreed to limit home production to a stated amount and also to limit sugar exports by the British colonies; Australia and South Africa also agreed to limit their exports. This formed the basis of a more effective arrangement, which however did not have long to operate before it was overtaken by the war.

The question arises why international action had so little success in restoring balance to agricultural markets and in curbing the growth of mutually-defeating measures of intervention by individual countries. The secretariat of the League prepared many excellent studies, numerous conferences were held, and many admirable resolutions were passed. Yet the effects on national policies remained marginal. In an interesting report published in 1942, the League itself set out to explain why its efforts to solve the problems of world trade had failed:

> We have noted with what circumspection and with what scant results autonomous tariff reduction was recommended. This was due to the fact that, while each country believed that the tariffs imposed by others were damaging to it, it believed that its own were an asset not readily, certainly not gratuitously, to be sacrificed. There was, that is, no general belief that each extension of the division of labour would bring about an economy in production and hence an increase in welfare, or that each country must gain, even if the degree of gain varied, from a general reduction in trade barriers.[1]

[1] League of Nations, *Commercial Policy in the Interwar Period* (Geneva, 1942), p. 131.

As the report of the League observed, the basic difficulty had been that trade barriers could not be reduced while depression and unemployment prevailed. Many statesmen, when in Geneva, approved liberal policies of long-term value, but when they returned to their countries they were compelled to take an opposite course in accordance with immediate needs. The emphasis on the 'customs' truce' was therefore misplaced: the only effective policy would have been to take joint action against depression. But the League of Nations was unable to intervene in matters then regarded as domestic policy.

Chapter 7. The United Kingdom

The First World War and its aftermath

Britain entered the First World War with no prepared plan for raising food production. In the early stages, farmers were advised to grow certain crops but they were not given any special financial inducement to do so. In July 1915 a Food Production Committee under Viscount Milner reported that if increased wheat production was required, farmers would need to be guaranteed a minimum price over a period of years. (It suggested that this minimum should be implemented by payments to make up the difference between the guaranteed price and the average price in the harvest year – this seems to be the first mention of a system of 'deficiency payments'.) In August, however, the Government announced that it did not intend to introduce price guarantees: the harvest in Britain as well as in America promised to be large, and the German submarine campaign seemed to be on the wane.

Farmers therefore made no special effort to raise production. The numbers of livestock were practically unchanged. In 1916 the wheat acreage declined and the total arable area fell below the pre-war level; the harvest was poor. But the submarine campaign intensified. In December 1916 a new Government had to take careful stock of the food situation: it decided to stimulate an increase in the home supply of grain and potatoes. A Food Controller was included in the Government, and a Food Production Department was formed. County Agricultural Executive

Committees were set up, with powers to compel ploughing of grassland and to take possession of badly-cultivated farms. The new President of the Board of Agriculture, R. E. Prothero (afterwards Lord Ernle) had been a member of the Milner Committee, and he now decided to adopt the recommendations of the Committee: a scheme of guaranteed prices for wheat, oats and potatoes was announced in February 1917, followed in August by the Corn Production Act, which guaranteed minimum prices for wheat and oats on a declining scale up to 1922.

These measures encouraged a considerable expansion of the ploughed area in 1917. Market prices were in fact above the guaranteed minima, but the existence of the guarantees gave the farmers confidence. The events of 1917 proved how necessary the change in policy had been. Attacks by submarines reached a peak and shipping problems became acute. In 1918 a crisis in food supplies was avoided only by a further expansion in the crop area and a large harvest. It was estimated that by the end of the war British agriculture was feeding the population for the equivalent of 155 days in the year, as compared with only 125 days at the outbreak of war.[1]

By 1918 extensive control had been established over food supplies: all essential foodstuffs, both imported and home-grown, were bought or requisitioned by the Food Controller at fixed prices; importers, manufacturers and distributors became in various ways the agents of the Controller.

The war had thus necessitated a reversal in the traditional policy of laissez-faire towards agriculture. When it ended, there was much discussion as to the policy which should be followed in peacetime. A Royal Commission was appointed to inquire into the 'economic prospects of the agricultural industry'. It reported in 1919, but its members reached opposite conclusions. A majority of twelve pointed out that farmers were anxious about their future: the costs of arable farming had become very high, with wages in particular rising, and there was a fear that world prices would fall. Farmers generally were prepared to do without guarantees if they were freed from all control, but if the Government decided that production should be increased, it was under an obligation to provide a financial guarantee. These twelve members recommended that price guarantees for wheat, barley and oats should

[1] T. H. Middleton, *Food Production in War* (Oxford, 1923).

be maintained for at least four years. A minority of eleven, however, disagreed: they thought that there was no risk for some years to come of grain prices falling to an unremunerative level. Already the financial situation of agriculture had improved. They were not convinced that it was necessary to maintain agriculture on a wartime basis; the foreign exchange situation could be improved by raising exports rather than by decreasing imports. They concluded that:

> We have seen no evidence that will enable us to conclude that the financial position of the country can be improved by embarking on a policy involving the expenditure of public money in diverting agriculture into uneconomic fields.[1]

The Government, faced with increasing insistent demands from farmers for some sort of policy, introduced an Agriculture Act in 1920. This in effect extended and reinforced the Corn Production Act: guaranteed prices were to continue indefinitely, and the level of the guarantees for wheat and oats was raised.

But the Government soon had cause to regret the liability it had incurred. The following year the price of grain fell steeply, and the cost of supporting the guarantees amounted to over £18 million. This appeared excessive, and the Government abandoned its year-old policy. In August 1921 the price guarantees were repealed.

Farmers now found themselves in serious difficulties, with on the one hand falling grain prices and on the other rising wages and other costs. The Government's act of 'betrayal' had far-reaching consequences. In the years to come, more and more land was returned to grass: the arable area fell even below the level of 1914. Many farms were neglected, their capital equipment was allowed to deteriorate and farm labour again began to move into industry. Once again, agriculture was in decline.

The 1920s

Through most of the 1920s, the general price trend was downwards, interrupted only by periods of relative stability from 1923 to 1925 and from 1927 to 1929. Throughout this period, British

[1] Royal Commission on Agriculture, Interim Report (Cmd. 473, 1919), p. 10.

agriculture was feeling the effects of overseas competition. Wheat-exporting countries were raising their output; the invention of chilling made it possible for the Argentine to send meat which could compete with all but the best British qualities; New Zealand enormously expanded her trade in meat and dairy produce; Denmark was shipping more butter, eggs and bacon; and fruit was being sent in increasing quantities from North America at times when it competed directly with the output of British horticulture. The only course for the British farmer was to concentrate on products, such as milk, eggs and fresh vegetables, for which he enjoyed a naturally sheltered market.

The Governments of this period held almost without exception to the policy of laissez-faire. The only direct measure of financial assistance to farmers was the subsidy on beet sugar, introduced in 1924. This subsidy stimulated a rapid expansion in the area under sugar-beet (from 22,000 acres in 1924 to a peak of 396,000 ten years later) and in the number of sugar factories.

There were some departures from strict free trade principles, but none that was of any importance for agriculture: the 'McKenna' duties on certain luxury goods, introduced in 1915, were maintained after the war, and the Safeguarding of Industries Act of 1921 introduced duties to protect certain 'key' industries. In the 1919 Finance Act, the principle of Imperial Preference was applied by Britain for the first time, a rebate on the existing revenue duties and on the McKenna duties being granted to Empire goods. At the Imperial Economic Conference of 1923, the Conservative Party announced its support for a much more extensive policy of protection and Imperial Preference, but at the general election of the same year, fought largely on this issue, the electorate showed itself still hostile to the idea. By 1929, Britain's policy was still essentially that of free trade, and agricultural products were subject only to certain revenue duties. There was thus little scope for Imperial Preference; sugar was almost the only item where preference had a marked effect in favour of the Empire.

The crisis – Britain abandons Free Trade

In the absence of any measures of protection, the crisis which began in 1929 had an immediate and severe effect on British agriculture. The fall in world grain prices was reflected on the

British market, and as other European markets were more and more closed by measures of protection, Britain became the object of large-scale dumping. In October 1931 the volume of food imports was 35 per cent above normal: besides grain, imports of dairy produce, meat and other products increased.

General economic depression added to the difficulties of agriculture: Britain's exports fell, industrial unemployment grew and consumer purchasing power was reduced. No effective policy was devised for reviving the economy, and the emphasis was laid on measures of protection against imports.

The Labour Government in power at the onset of the crisis resigned in August 1931. The National Government which took its place was a coalition dominated by Conservatives, who urged that a comprehensive tariff system should immediately be adopted. In November the Government obtained authority to impose duties up to a maximum of 100 per cent on a large range of wholly or partly manufactured goods; at the same time, protection was given to horticulture. These emergency measures were replaced in 1932 by the Import Duties Act, which has remained the basic instrument of the British tariff. It imposed a general tariff of 10 per cent *ad valorem*; however, certain major foodstuffs and raw materials – including wheat, maize, meat, livestock and wool – were exempted from duty. An Import Duties Advisory Committee was set up, which could recommend changes in the duties. Further, the Government was authorized to admit goods free or at reduced rates of duty from specified foreign countries, or on the contrary to double the rate on goods from countries which discriminated against British products.

Imperial Preference

Protection in Britain could not take the same course as in other countries. The question of how to treat Empire goods – most of them agricultural – was immediately raised. Negotiations were held at Ottawa in 1932 between Britain and the Dominions, and as a result Britain made a series of important concessions which were shortly afterwards put into effect by the Ottawa Agreements Act:

1. The exemption from duty of Empire goods, already provided for under the Import Duties Act, was confirmed.

2. New or increased duties were imposed on imports from foreign countries which competed with Empire produce: these included a new duty on wheat and revised duties on butter and cheese, certain fruits and various other products.

3. A guarantee was given that the existing 10 per cent margin of preference on certain products would not be reduced.

4. Special preferences on certain other goods from the Empire (including sugar, wine, coffee, tobacco) were guaranteed.

5. An undertaking was given that imports of meat from foreign countries would be controlled.

In granting these concessions, the British Government made two main reservations: firstly, the new duties on foreign wheat and certain other products could be removed at any time if Empire supplies proved inadequate (this provision was never called into force); and secondly, the Dominions were to be given an expanding share of meat imports only in so far as this was consistent with the development of British production. Also, Britain reserved the right, in the interests of home producers, to review after three years the preferences for dairy products, poultry and eggs. The principle underlying the Government's policy was that home producers should have first claim on the market, Empire producers second and foreigners last.

The advantages which Britain obtained from the Ottawa Agreements consisted mainly of increased preferences for British exports and assurances that protection against British goods would not be excessive.

The Irish Free State did not benefit from the Ottawa Agreements. On the contrary, in July 1932, following a financial dispute between the two countries, Britain imposed extra duties on Irish goods, most of which were agricultural products. Britain also prohibited imports of Irish beef and veal and restricted imports of Irish cattle. This discrimination was brought to an end in 1938, and subsequently Irish produce was admitted on the same terms as Empire goods.

Also in 1932, assistance was given to the sugar industry in the West Indies through increased tariff preference for all Colonial sugar (that from the Dominions continued to get the existing rate of preference), together with an extra preference for defined quantities of sugar from specified Colonies in the West Indies.

Support for British agriculture

All these measures concerning trade gave little benefit to British agriculture. By the time when farmers in most other European countries were sheltering behind high tariffs and strict import controls, Britain's farmers were still exposed to the full blast of competition from the Empire, and even imports of agricultural products from foreign countries were subject only to relatively low duties. Lord Astor and K. A. H. Murray observed in 1933:

> The Ottawa Agreements must have made it plain, if it was not so evident beforehand, that British farming cannot expect much relief at the hands of Members of Parliament representing the urban voter. The British delegation set out to seek a freer market for the United Kingdom exports, and these exports are not agricultural products. It has also been made evident that if import concessions are to be made to the Dominions, these concessions must be made in those imports which form the bulk of the Dominions' trade, i.e. in agricultural products.[1]

Besides these considerations, the traditional policy of cheap food was still an important factor; particularly in a period of acute depression, the Government was reluctant to take measures which might be held to raise the price of foodstuffs.

The attempt to help British farmers took the form of a series of measures from 1931 onwards on a commodity-by-commodity basis. These measures were applied piecemeal: they did not correspond to any deliberate policy for agriculture as a whole nor to any agreed priorities for different products. They involved subsidies, marketing schemes, import restrictions and various combinations of these. Thus for wheat and sugar-beet, assistance was given by subsidy alone; for milk, by a marketing scheme and by subsidy; for beef and cattle, by restriction of foreign imports and by subsidy; for bacon, potatoes and hops, by marketing schemes combined with import control; for eggs, by voluntary restrictions applied by exporting countries.

The marketing schemes were based on the Agricultural Marketing Acts of 1931 and 1933; the second of these also provided the

[1] Viscount Astor and K. A. H. Murray, *The Planning of Agriculture* (London, 1933), p. 136.

authority for import controls. The 1931 Act was introduced by the Labour Government and represented a first attempt to deal with the crisis: the Government was not prepared to make a radical breach with free trade, and marketing reform seemed to provide an attractive alternative. This Act enabled a 'substantial' majority of producers in any branch of agriculture to adopt a marketing scheme, subject to approval by the Minister of Agriculture and by Parliament; the scheme then became binding upon all producers. The marketing scheme could involve the enforcement of minimum and maximum prices and other regulations, but the 1931 Act made no provision for controlling imports. This loophole was filled by the Act of 1933, which declared that if a satisfactory marketing scheme was evolved for any product, the Government would regulate imports; under the marketing scheme itself, the quantities sold by any registered producer could be regulated. With this extension of powers, marketing schemes began to look more attractive and, before long, schemes were in operation for milk, bacon, potatoes and hops.

The arrangements for the major products are described in the following paragraphs.

WHEAT. In 1932 a Wheat Act was passed, which reintroduced guaranteed prices on lines similar to those followed at the end of the First World War: producers were to be ensured an average price of 10s. per cwt. for millable wheat by means of a deficiency payment making up the difference between the average market price and the guaranteed price. To discourage undue expansion, full payment was to be made only for an output up to 27 million cwt.: in excess of this, the rate of subsidy would be proportionately reduced. Finance for the subsidy was obtained from a levy on all flour, whether from home-produced or imported wheat. The scheme was made possible by the fact that home supply formed a small proportion of the whole.

Market prices in subsequent years were generally well below the guaranteed price of 10s. per cwt.: subsidy had to be paid at rates varying, from 1932 to 1936, between 3s. and nearly 5s., and the annual subsidy bill reached £7·2 million in 1933/4.

The result was to give a considerable stimulus to wheat cultivation: area and production rose, largely at the expense of oats; till 1937, oats and barley did not benefit from a price guarantee. The system was criticized for encouraging expansion in areas not well suited to wheat. Although in 1932 wheat constituted only about 5 per cent by value of gross agricultural output, it was still regarded by many as a vital crop, and the special support it received owed a good deal to this – almost sentimental – attachment. Lord Astor and B. S. Rowntree, in their important work on British agricultural policy, wrote:

> Bread is the staff of life; wheat makes bread; therefore, [it was supposed that] wheat must be the most essential foodstuff and its production should be safeguarded. It was also supposed (quite erroneously) that wheat was the cornerstone of British agriculture, and that any measure which stimulated wheat production would not only feed the people but would stimulate agriculture as a whole.[1]

Astor and Rowntree considered that the support given to wheat, instead of merely countering the instability of world markets, had come to operate as a permanent subsidy. But:

> On general economic grounds it would be unwise to give permanent artificial encouragement to wheat production in this country. Wheat can be grown overseas far more cheaply than in Great Britain; it is pre-eminently a crop suited to large-scale farming methods which we cannot conveniently imitate; it is a commodity which enters largely into inter-Imperial trade.[2]

SUGAR-BEET. The subsidy granted in 1924 was intended to disappear in ten years: by then, it was hoped, the sugar-beet industry could stand on its own feet. This expectation was not fulfilled. A considerable expansion took place and costs of production were reduced; meanwhile, however, some spectacular improvements were made overseas as a result of which the cost of producing sugar from sugar-canes fell to less than two thirds that of producing from beet. When the ten years were up, the Government appointed a committee to inquire whether the industry could be made self-supporting. Two members of the committee recom-

---

[1] Viscount Astor and B. S. Rowntree, *British Agriculture – The Principles of Future Policy* (London: Longmans, 1938), pp. 82–3.
[2] Ibid., p. 88.

mended that the subsidy should be brought to an end, the third disagreed. The Government decided to maintain the subsidy, but under new arrangements. The resulting Sugar Industry Re-organization Act of 1935 provided for continued assistance, but the quantity of sugar eligible for support was limited; also, the sugar factories, which had been making considerable profits out of the subsidy, were amalgamated into the British Sugar Corporation, and the whole industry was subjected to an independent Sugar Commission which was to determine the rate of subsidy.

MILK. Milk Marketing Boards were set up at the end of 1933 in an attempt to place farmers in a better bargaining position. All milk had to be sold through the Boards, which were empowered to fix wholesale prices. The main problem concerned the market for processing, for while milk for direct consumption enjoyed a natural protection against imports, the price of milk products had fallen sharply under the influence of imports. However, restrictions on imports of dairy produce from the Dominions were precluded under the Ottawa Agreements, and the Dominion Governments turned down a suggestion that they should reduce their exports of butter and cheese on the understanding that imports from foreign countries would also be cut. The British Government was forced to guarantee a minimum price for milk sold for manufacture.

BEEF AND CATTLE. Owing to the importance of supplies from abroad, the British meat market was very much exposed, and the substantial fall in prices caused a crisis in the British cattle industry. Britain had agreed at Ottawa not to reduce supplies of meat from Australia and New Zealand until the end of June 1934, nor to impose a duty on Empire produce before 1937. Moreover, in an agreement with the Argentine in September 1933, Britain undertook to reduce imports of chilled beef only if this became necessary to ensure remunerative prices, and then subject to limitations.

Within these limits, an attempt was made to restrict imports of chilled beef from foreign countries, starting in 1933. As a result, imports from the Empire increased substantially; a voluntary agreement for restricting them was reached in 1935. Rather more severe restrictions were imposed on frozen beef:

supplies from foreign countries were progressively reduced till by the end of 1934 they were limited to 65 per cent of the 1931/2 level. In 1937 the task of regulating imports was passed to an International Beef Conference, in which British producers, Empire countries and foreign exporting countries were represented: quarterly import quotas were determined for chilled, frozen and canned beef. In 1938, mutton and lamb were brought within the scope of the Conference. As has already been mentioned, imports of beef from the Irish Republic were prohibited after 1932, while Irish cattle were subjected to a quota and to a prohibitive duty.

None of these measures succeeded in making prices profitable to British producers, largely because they were inadequate to restrain the growth in competition from the Empire. The Government therefore introduced subsidies on cattle in 1934, in the form of a flat rate paid irrespective of market prices. At the same time, duties were imposed on all foreign imports of beef and veal.

BACON. By the beginning of 1932, pig producers were in a critical position. The general fall in prices was superimposed on a cyclical downward movement. A reorganization committee recommended a system of contracts and quotas, with the aim of increasing British production at the expense of foreign supplies. It was decided to stabilize the total supply of bacon and ham at 10,670,000 cwt. annually (this was the estimated average annual supply from 1925 to 1930). Home producers were to have preference in filling this amount: imports would be allowed only so far as necessary to make up the difference. In November 1932, voluntary agreements were reached by which eleven foreign countries undertook to restrict their exports to Britain.

Minimum prices for home supplies of bacon were fixed from time to time. The initial price offered was so attractive, in relation to the alternative market for pork, that there was a big increase in supply. It was decided to restrict imports still further: as Denmark objected, this had to be done on a compulsory basis by an order of November 1933 which prohibited the import of bacon and ham, except under licence, from any foreign country sending more than 400 cwt. a week to Britain. Imports from foreign countries were cut by about half, and Denmark in particular was severely hit. However, the scheme was administered through export licences issued through the Governments of the exporting countries: as a result, the foreign suppliers obtained almost the whole of the increased price resulting from the restriction. The price of British bacon rose relatively little, because of its inferior quality as compared with Danish bacon. No restrictions were imposed on Empire countries, but it was agreed that Canada could supply up to 2·5 million cwt.: this was about ten times Canada's previous exports (it was rumoured that an extra nought had been added by mistake). The result was a rapid increase in Canadian exports.

The import restrictions were relaxed in 1938 under the Bacon Industry Act, and instead a system of subsidies for pig producers was introduced.

Trade agreements

After the introduction of import duties, Britain entered into tariff negotiations with a number of countries, and in subsequent years several trade agreements were signed. However, in negotiations with countries whose exports were mainly agricultural, Britain was generally unable to offer concessions without breaking a pledge to one or another of the Dominions as regards the maintenance of a minimum margin of preference. The agreements thus brought about little reduction in import duties in general, and in particular had little effect on the agricultural duties.

In the agreement with Denmark in 1933, Britain agreed to import bacon and hams free of duty, and guaranteed that the duties on eggs and other products would not be raised above specified levels. However, Britain reserved the right to impose quotas on Danish bacon in connection with domestic marketing schemes; subsequent developments have been described above.

An agreement was also reached with the Argentine in 1933, in which Britain gave the guarantees concerning trade in beef which have already been discussed. Britain also undertook to admit meat and maize free of duty, and guaranteed maximum tariff rates for wheat and other products.

The most important agreement reached during this period was with the United States; it was signed in November 1938 and came into force the following January. Britain gave a wide range of concessions on agricultural products, removing entirely the duty on wheat, guaranteeing continued free entry for maize, reducing

6

the duty on rice and removing that on lard, guaranteeing the existing duties on pigmeat and granting an increased quota for hams. Further, the duties on a number of fruits and vegetables were to be reduced during the months when U.S. exports took place, and those on certain canned fruits and fruit juices were removed or reduced. There was to be continued free entry for cotton and no increase in the existing margin of Imperial Preference for tobacco.

The controversy over protection

The reversal of Britain's traditional policy of free trade did not take place without much heart-searching. As late as the autumn of 1931, a self-appointed committee of eminent economists, headed by Sir William Beveridge, pronounced themselves uncompromisingly against protection in any form and for whatever purpose, basing themselves squarely on the classical argument for free trade. The work in question included a chapter on agriculture by Professor Lionel Robbins, in which he conceded that a tariff on wheat would for a short time benefit the wheat farmers, who were the most severely hit by the crisis. But before long rents would rise, wages too might absorb part of the increased profit, and competition between the farmers would bring prices down again.

> Eventually equilibrium would be established with wheat farmers making no more than was being made elsewhere, a greater proportion of the food supply produced at home, and a national income smaller than it would have been by the extra cost of raising that much more wheat at home rather than procuring it abroad by way of exchange.[1]

This book was one of the most forthright and closely-reasoned statements of the free-trade position ever produced in Great Britain. Yet within a few months all its recommendations had become a dead letter, as the Government resorted to protection and Imperial Preference. It would be hard to demonstrate more conclusively the futility of abstract economic reasoning when the livelihood of much of the population is at stake and strong political

[1] Sir William Beveridge and others, *Tariffs: The Case Examined* (2nd ed., London, 1932), pp. 156–7.

forces are at work. Ten years later, Benham, who had been one
of the co-authors of Beveridge's book, lamented in the following
terms:

> Free trade would almost certainly have come in Great Britain
> in the nineteenth century if no abstract reasoning had ever
> been advanced in its favour, and all the economists – who,
> after all, are the specialists in this subject – were quite power-
> less to stem the tide of protection during and after 1931. It is
> a sad thought.[1]

Indeed, no Government in 1931 and 1932 could ignore the
problems of depression and unemployment or turn a deaf ear
to the many groups of producers clamouring for assistance.
Measures other than tariff protection could no doubt have been
taken, but Keynes had not yet written his General Theory and
there were sufficient voices laying blame on imports and dumping
for the Government to direct its attention that way. Moreover,
the Empire enthusiasts were out in force and now enjoyed much
greater influence within the Government than they had done at
the turn of the century. As for agriculture, the Central Chamber
of Agriculture and the National Farmers' Union were agitating
strongly for tariffs.

The unemployment problem influenced the action taken with
regard to agriculture. The idea was going round that a large-scale
programme for settling workers in small holdings could do much
to relieve unemployment, and in 1930 the Labour Government
introduced a Land Utilization Bill with this in mind. The old
argument about keeping work at home was also much in evidence:
if food were produced at home instead of being imported, it was
thought that there would be more work for farmers and at the
same time a larger market for home industry. Highly optimistic
estimates were put forward as to the proportion of food that could
be produced at home. On the other hand, Professor Robbins, in
the work already referred to, pointed out tersely that if the object
was to raise employment, it would be preferable to choose an
industry where wages were relatively high and not one such as
agriculture where they were exceptionally low. Several authorities,
in particular Astor and Rowntree, stressed the danger that by

[1] F. Benham, *Great Britain under Protection* (New York: Macmillan, 1941),
p. 24.

cutting down food imports Britain might injure the capacity of other countries to buy British manufactures.[1]

Much was heard also about the need for a 'balanced economy', by which was meant a higher proportion of people on the land. There was talk of the advantages of rural life, of better health and morality and so forth. Opponents of this view were quick to point out that those who talked this way usually did not live on the land themselves.

Emphasis was laid too on the need to secure food supplies: the dangerous experience of the First World War was often recalled. The counter-argument was that strength in war depended on many factors besides food supply, which could be harmed by a policy of agricultural self-sufficiency in peacetime: such factors included the nation's overall economic and financial situation, the size of its shipping fleet and the extent of activity in shipbuilding. Moreover, excessive cultivation of the soil over a long period could exhaust its fertility. To the exponents of these views, the best preparation for war seemed to lie in building up reserves of those foodstuffs that could be stored.

A basic difficulty for the advocates of protection was to reconcile the interests of British agriculture with those of Empire producers, while at the same time paying at least lip-service to the ideal of cheap food. A pamphlet written early in the crisis by Lord Beaverbrook and circulated by the 'Empire Crusade' was entitled, rather hopefully: *The Farmers' Crusade: How Empire Free Trade will help British Agriculture*. This was an unsuccessful attempt to have the best of both worlds. British farmers were promised Protection – i.e. against foreign imports – while consumers were promised Free Trade – i.e. in Empire products. The basic contradiction was scarcely concealed in the following passage:

> The policy of Empire Free Trade is in effect a new form of the Protection for British Agriculture which farmers have so long demanded ... The new policy of Empire Free Trade or Empire Protection [sic] is designed to give the same assistance to the farmer as the old, but at the same time to obviate the difficulty of dear food.

Another extreme statement of the case for agricultural protection, by Fordham, argued in favour of import controls to give the

[1] Astor and Rowntree, *The Agricultural Dilemma* (London, 1935).

British farmer the first claim on the home market, with the ultimate objective of reaching as near as possible to self-sufficiency in food. Fordham completely ignored the issue of Empire produce. He thought moreover that his proposals need not lead to increased food prices, mainly on the unlikely supposition that domestic production could be greatly increased at little or no extra cost per unit.[1]

Thus, while it was pointless and even cynical to reiterate laissez-faire principles in the face of obvious distress, the arguments of the Imperialists and Protectionists were often specious, sometimes absurd. The most important work on the problems of British agriculture at this time was that by Astor and Rowntree in 1938. This was based on sound economic reasoning, but recognized the difficulties with which agriculture was faced and the need for assistance in some form. The views of the authors with regard to wheat policy have already been mentioned. In general, they thought that protective action was justified to avoid the extremes of price fluctuations; thus they were in favour of a minimum price for wheat at a level approximating to 'normal' world prices. In their conclusions they expressed the view that the introduction of protection for industry gave agriculture a claim to a similar degree of State assistance, not merely as a matter of equity but because farming costs were raised by tariffs on manufactures. Nevertheless, they were firmly opposed to any policy of protection designed to promote the expansion of domestic agricultural output.

> We are convinced ... that those are profoundly mistaken who aim at effecting an expansion of British agriculture by further measures of protection against overseas competition, or by further subsidies for commodities which can be produced considerably more cheaply or more efficiently abroad. Our national interests in the maintenance of a large-scale international trade, the interests of the consuming population in the provision of cheap food, the interests of the British Dominions and Colonies as agricultural producers, the growing budgetary difficulties of the British Treasury, the complications of the structure of British agriculture itself, combine to render any such policy the height of unwisdom.[2]

[1] M. Fordham, *Britain's Trade and Agriculture* (London, 1932).
[2] Astor and Rowntree, *British Agriculture*, op. cit., pp. 441-2.

Consequences for agriculture and trade

Not surprisingly, in view of the nature of the measures taken, the market prices of most important foodstuffs remained low. In 1933 the overall agricultural price index (Table 40) reached its lowest point at 76 per cent of the pre-crisis level; it then recovered slowly, but even by 1938 it was only at 88 per cent. The inclusion of the subsidies on various products raises the overall index by only a couple of points. The subsidies, however, were important for wheat, where the market price (except in 1937) remained very

Table 40

AGRICULTURAL PRICE INDICES FOR ENGLAND AND WALES

(1927–9 average = 100)

	1930	1931	1932	1933	1934	1935	1936	1937	1938
CROPS	74	88	89	71	72	76	90	98	80
			(93)	(78)	(79)	(82)	(94)	(99)	(86)
of which:									
Wheat	80	56	56	49	47	51	71	90	59
			(74)	(94)	(89)	(85)	(91)	(96)	(94)
Barley	80	80	71	83	86	80	86	109	84
Oats	68	68	74	61	69	71	70	92	79
LIVESTOCK	97	81	75	75	78	75	78	87	86
					(78)	(77)	(80)	(88)	(88)
of which:									
Fat cattle	100	91	86	76	75	69	73	82	84
					(78)	(80)	(83)	(92)	(95)
Bacon pigs	104	74	63	70	77	70	78	83	84
Milk	95	82	84	84	88	85	85	94	100
					(89)	(88)	(87)	(95)	(102)
Eggs	91	77	72	71	68	72	78	83	85
ALL AGRICULTURAL PRODUCTS	91	84	81	76	77	79	81	89	88
			(81)	(77)	(79)	(81)	(83)	(91)	(90)

Note: Data in parentheses take account of subsidies for wheat, cattle and milk.

Source: Ministry of Agriculture and Fisheries, *Agricultural Statistics*, 1939.

low but the subsidized price approached the pre-crisis level. Livestock prices fell later than those of crops, but from 1931 onwards they did little or no better. The subsidized price of fat cattle remained well above the market price; on the other hand, the subsidy on milk for manufacturing made little difference to the overall milk price.

The effect of intervention was felt most markedly in the cultivation of wheat. Between 1932 and 1938, the wheat area in the

Table 41

CROP AREA AND LIVESTOCK NUMBERS IN THE UNITED KINGDOM

	1929	1932	1935	1938
AREA (million acres)				
Wheat	1·4	1·3	1·9	1·9
Oats	3·1	2·7	2·5	2·4
Barley	1·2	1·0	0·9	1·0
Roots, other crops and fallow	4·0	4·0	3·8	3·7
Temporary grass	4·6	4·6	4·4	4·0
Total arable land	14·3	13·6	13·5	13·0
Permanent grass	18·4	18·7	18·5	18·8
Total crops and grass	32·8	32·3	32·0	31·8
LIVESTOCK (millions)				
Dairy cows	3·4	3·6	3·8	3·8
Other cattle	4·5	4·7	4·8	5·0
Sheep	24·3	27·2	25·1	26·8
Pigs	2·7	3·6	4·5	4·4
Fowls	55·5	73·5	75·1	69·1

Source: Annual Abstract of Statistics.

United Kingdom as a whole expanded from 1·3 million acres to 1·9 million, while the area of most other crops declined and the total arable area fell from 13·6 to 13·0 million acres (Table 41). There was an increase in the number of dairy cows and other cattle, as well as in the number of pigs; poultry and sheep declined in numbers.

The gradual recovery of prices from 1933, and the help given through subsidies, provided some relief to farmers' incomes.

Agricultural wages were fairly well maintained even during the crisis, but the number of agricultural workers in Great Britain fell from 857,000 in 1930 to only 697,000 in 1938.

Perhaps the most striking result of the various measures of intervention was a shift in the pattern of food imports away from foreign countries in favour of the Empire. By 1938, as compared with 1927–9, total food imports from foreign countries had fallen

Table 42

INDEX NUMBERS OF THE VOLUME OF FOOD IMPORTS INTO THE UNITED KINGDOM

(1927–9 average = 100)

	Wheat and flour	Meat, incl. bacon	Dairy products	Eggs	Fruit	Vegetables	All food
1930	99	106	109	107	99	101	105
1931	110	117	123	104	120	156	117
1932	96	112	127	84	118	142	111
1933	103	101	133	76	107	87	107
1934	95	94	142	81	88	81	104
1935	92	92	137	84	111	88	103
1936	92	92	138	102	88	100	105
1937	89	95	136	103	85	86	103
1938:							
Total	92	95	138	114	107	79	106
Empire	129	142	158	63	217	130	143
Foreign	59	71	119	125	61	66	83

Source: K. A. H. Murray and Ruth Cohen, *The Planning of Britain's Food Imports* (Agricultural Economics Research Institute, Oxford), 1934, and supplements.

by 17 per cent in volume, while those coming from the Empire had risen by no less than 43 per cent (Table 42). This shift in the sources of supply was evident for all major foods except eggs, for which in any case trade consisted mainly of small amounts from Ireland. Overall, there was relatively little change in the volume of imports – an increase of 6 per cent. The only commodity for which total imports rose substantially was dairy products, where there was an increase of 38 per cent; total imports of wheat and meat were reduced. It thus seems that British trade policy, helped by other measures taken during this period (in particular the formation of the sterling area), succeeded in ensuring a larger market for the Empire while bringing total imports down to nearly the level which prevailed before the crisis.

THE UNITED KINGDOM

Chapter 8. France

The First World War and the 1920s

The war brought severe losses for French agriculture, both directly through the depletion of its livestock and the destruction of the battle areas (which included some of the most productive land in France) and indirectly through difficulties in preserving the fertility of the soil and in maintaining farm equipment. The greater part of the farm labour force was called into military service, fertilizer and fuel were in short supply, transport was lacking. Production of wheat in 1917 was less than half what it had been at the outbreak of war, and it was necessary to import, on the average, three times more wheat and flour than before the war.

'Protectionism is not a policy for wartime', wrote Augé-Laribé.[1] The existing duties on major foodstuffs were suspended early in the war to facilitate imports and to alleviate the rise in the cost of living. The State took over the purchase and distribution of foodstuffs; from 1916 to 1921 imports of grain and flour were carried out by an official body. The export of certain foodstuffs was prohibited. The preoccupation with keeping food prices down, combined with the mounting costs of agricultural requisites, tended to discourage output; incentives to production were granted only after some delay, and then not very systematically.

[1] M. Augé-Laribé, *La politique agricole de la France de 1880 à 1940* (Paris: P.U.F., 1950), p. 352.

In the period of reconstruction which followed the war, food was still short and there was fear of a continued rise in the cost of living. Protection was restored to agriculture only by degrees. In 1919 the pre-war tariff was reintroduced, with a system of co-efficients to take account of the increased price level; the coefficients applied to foodstuffs were relatively low. Various modifications were made to the tariff in subsequent years, particularly in 1926 when overall increases of 30 per cent were applied to the coefficients twice in the year. An attempt was made in 1927 to carry out a general revision of the tariff, but before this could be completed the Government revised almost half the items of the tariff in the context of a commercial treaty with Germany; the agricultural duties however were not affected.

Agricultural associations demanded greater equality of treatment with industry. The Confédération Nationale des Associations Agricoles complained in a pamphlet in February 1927 that 'since the war, our entire customs and economic policy seem to have been directed to one sole aim: that of developing France into a great industrial power, regardless of the interests of agriculture'; it maintained that the current tariff proposals would raise duties on industrial products above the pre-war level to a far greater extent than those on agricultural products.[1] In April 1927 a conference of agricultural associations demanded that agriculture and industry should be given equal tariff treatment. Industrial interests, on the other hand, opposed any increase in the agricultural duties and a bitter struggle ensued. In March 1928 the agricultural duties were raised, but the representatives of agriculture were not satisfied. In November 1929 the presidents of the Chambres d'Agriculture opposed the League of Nations project for a tariff standstill, declaring that this would merely confirm the inadequate treatment of agriculture. This view seems to have carried weight, since in February 1930 the French delegation to the League of Nations declared that France could not accept the project.

This preoccupation with tariff policy was overtaken by the crisis, in which tariffs alone proved an ineffective means of protection.

---

[1] Confédération Nationale des Associations Agricoles, *La nouvelle loi douanière* (Paris, 1936).

The crisis – tariffs and import quotas

In 1925 the French grain crop for the first time reached the level of the pre-war harvests. From about 1927 the pressure of supplies on the world market made itself increasingly felt. In the autumn of 1929 the crisis broke and the world grain market collapsed. The French harvest of 1929 was large, contributing to the fall in prices.

At the onset of the crisis, France was in a strong economic and financial position, and the general price level was at first relatively well maintained; the French market thus provided an attractive outlet for foreign supplies, while French exports encountered increasing difficulties.

The first reaction was to raise tariffs wherever possible. Most agricultural products were subject to the *loi de cadenas* of 1897, under which the Government was entitled to raise the duties on certain products without waiting for the approval of Parliament. The scope of this law was extended in 1929 and again in 1931, so that instead of covering only forty-six items it became applicable to almost all products competitive with French agriculture. This authority was used to raise the duties on wheat and most other grains, as well as those on some livestock products, wine, sugar and other foodstuffs. In many cases successive increases in 1930 and 1931 resulted in the duty being at least doubled from its previous level.

However, tariffs were found to be an inadequate method of protection. In the first place, it was feared that even bigger increases in the duties would be necessary to compensate for the fall in world prices; elections were due in 1932, and the Government did not want to be accused of raising the price of food. Moreover, some of the duties on agricultural products (including barley and most dairy products), and most of those on manufactured goods, had been consolidated in treaties since 1927 and could not easily be raised. The device of import quotas offered a solution. Import quotas had been used before by various countries, generally in connection with commercial agreements when tariff concessions were given for specified quantities of imports. France, however, was the first country to make systematic use of them as a means of protection.

The first import quotas, for timber and wine, were introduced by a decree of August 27th, 1931. Others followed in rapid succession: cattle, pigs, beef, pigmeat, butter and cheese on September 30th; mutton, poultry and eggs on November 10th; sugar on December 5th. In the course of 1932 sheep, potatoes, onions, fruit and barley were added to the list; in 1933 maize, oats, rye and margarine. Practically all agricultural products, with the important exception of wheat, thus became subject to quota. In a valuable contemporary study, Moroni commented:

> What in 1931 was only an emergency measure had gradually changed its character and become a method of protecting and organizing national production. Quotas were applied without limit, not only to products which constituted a direct threat to domestic production, but also to substitutes and derivations of these products. If the market for feed grains is in difficulty, imports of maize are restricted in order to divert demand to barley, rye and oats. Imports of bananas are restricted, because bananas may be a dangerous competitor for home-grown fruit. Once it had embarked on this course, it was difficult for the French Government to stop half-way, and at the present time [May 1934] all or nearly all agricultural products are subject to quota.[1]

Import quotas were at first regarded as a temporary expedient, but with the continuing instability of the world market they remained in force. The originally deficient techniques were gradually perfected (this point is further discussed in a later section) and quotas became a major instrument of economic control, extended from 1932 onwards to a considerable number of industrial goods. From about 1934 they were used as a weapon in commercial negotiations, concessions in the size of quotas being offered in return for advantages to French exports. The quotas, however, did not apply to imports from French North Africa or the colonies.

Special measures of protection were devised for wheat. The large harvest of 1929 caused serious difficulties: export possibilities were severely limited and substantial imports had been contracted for early in the year. The average price in 1929 was 135 francs

[1] P. Moroni, *L'agriculture française et le contingentement des importations* (Paris, 1934), p. 73.

per 100 kg. as compared with 152 francs the previous year. The import duty was raised from 35 francs to 50 francs in May 1929, and again to 80 francs a year later, but this was not enough to maintain prices. The main instrument of support was the law of December 1st, 1929, which authorized the Minister of Agriculture to prescribe the minimum percentage of domestic wheat which millers must use in their flour. This was fixed at 97 per cent in the first instance, but the proportion was changed from time to time in accordance with the market situation. Wheat from French North Africa was treated as domestic produce in determining the milling ratio, but special annual quotas were later applied to this trade. In addition to these measures, a law of April 30th, 1930, authorized action to build up wheat stocks and to spread the marketing of the crop over a longer period. As it turned out, the harvests of 1930 and 1931 were mediocre and the price revived to around 150 francs; manipulation of the milling ratio proved sufficient to balance supply and demand fairly satisfactorily.

State intervention in agricultural markets, 1933-1939

Even these perfected instruments for regulating imports were inadequate to maintain prices once domestic supplies themselves increased to the point of depressing the market. A growing need was felt for intervention on the domestic market as well as for import control. In a study of the agricultural crisis in France, Nogaro commented:

> Once the French home market had been isolated, through the policy of import quotas, from the world market, it was found that, for the majority of products, domestic production was fully sufficient to meet demand. As a result, the home market underwent a crisis similar to that of the world market, and from 1933 in particular French policy entered a new phase, that of 'organizing' the principal markets.[1]

Wine and wheat were the commodities most concerned in the new measures of market organization.

WINE. In 1931 wine began to be in excess supply, at least so far

---

[1] B. Nogaro, 'La crise de l'agriculture', *Revue économique internationale*, January 1936, pp. 23-4.

as the ordinary varieties were concerned, mainly as a result of rising imports from French North Africa. The average price per hectolitre fell from 183 francs the preceding year to 121 francs. A series of measures were taken from 1931 onwards. Originally, if total supplies exceeded 72 million hectolitres, producers could be compelled to deliver part of their output to the State Alcohol Office for distillation; also, part of the harvest could be blocked on the vineyards. The larger producers were forbidden to plant new vineyards, and high-yielding vineyards were taxed. In

Table 43

WINE: PRODUCTION, TRADE AND AVERAGE PRICES

	Production	Imports[a]	Exports	Prices
		million hectolitres		fr. per hectolitre
1925–8[b]	54·8	10·5	1·5	163
1929	65·0	12·0	1·4	154
1930	45·6	13·4	1·1	183
1931	59·3	15·9	·8	121
1932	49·6	14·1	·7	128
1933	51·8	17·5	·7	117
1934	78·1	12·8	·7	78
1935	76·1	12·6	·7	64
1936	43·7	12·9	·8	138
1937	54·3	12·5	·9	180
1938	60·3	16·3	1·0	169

[a] Mainly from Algeria.
[b] Annual average.
Source: Statistique Agricole Annuelle.

August 1931 import quotas were imposed, but imports from North Africa could not be restricted and continued to rise. After a bumper wine harvest in 1934, prices fell disastrously, reaching 64 francs per hectolitre in 1935 (Table 43). A complex marketing scheme was introduced, under which producers had to obtain permits to sell their wine, these permits being issued only in the amounts necessary to maintain a minimum price. Again, part of the output of the larger producers was blocked, and they could be obliged to sell part of their produce, at very low prices, for distillation. A decree of July 30th, 1935, provided subsidies for uprooting vines. In 1936 production fell, and by 1937 the average price was back to 180 francs.

WHEAT. The pressure on the wheat market was renewed in 1932 with a large harvest in both France and French North Africa; prices fell to an average of 117 francs per 100 kg. for the year (Table 44). In December 1932 the milling ratio was raised to 99 per cent, in April 1933 to 100 per cent, so that foreign imports were virtually excluded. In October 1932 the Government drew up a plan for subsidizing farmers willing to store part of their crop

Table 44

WHEAT: PRODUCTION, TRADE[a] AND AVERAGE PRICES

	Production	Imports[b]	Exports	Prices
	million tons			fr. per 100 kg.
1925–8[c]	7·6	1·3	·02	153
1929	9·2	1·4	·01	135
1930	6·2	1·1	·9	152
1931	7·2	2·4	·6	153
1932	9·1	1·8	·2	117
1933	9·9	·5	·2	106
1934	9·2	·5	·5	118
1935	7·8	·5	·9	75
1936	6·9	·4	·4	156
1937	7·0	·3	·1	189
1938	9·8	·4	·1	208

[a] Including flour in grain equivalent.
[b] Partly from Algeria.
[c] Annual average.
Source: Statistique Agricole Annuelle.

till the following harvest year, but most farmers preferred to sell even on a falling market. In January 1933 a law was passed authorizing the Government to purchase wheat at 109 francs, later at 115 francs, but the funds available were too limited for this intervention to make much impact. With the expectation of a further large harvest in 1933 (in fact it turned out to be a record), further measures appeared necessary. A law of July 10th, 1933, established a price of 115 francs as the legal minimum for all sales of wheat (the price on the world market by this time was only about 25–30 francs); this minimum was subsequently raised to reach 131·50 francs in July 1934. Those who did not observe the minimum were liable to heavy penalties, and at first the regulation was respected. Soon, however, the market became disorganized, as small mills bought wheat illegally below the minimum price while the larger ones, whose operations were more easily supervised, refused to purchase. The Government had to relieve the market by exports, with subsidies to reduce prices to the world level, and by 'denaturation' (rendering wheat unfit for human consumption and feeding it to livestock). To defray part of the heavy cost of these measures, levies were imposed on producers and millers. In December 1934 the legal minimum price was abolished (though temporarily retained for purchases by the Government): instead, the Government was authorized to block part of the harvest on the farms, to constitute stocks and to intensify export aids and 'denaturation'. Combined with the import duty, the milling ratio, acreage restrictions and other measures, this action constituted a very far-reaching intervention on the market. From 1933 onwards, imports were reduced to a low level, and with large exports in 1935 France for the first time in many years had net exports of wheat.

So far the various measures taken had mainly been improvised to meet immediate needs. The Popular Front Government which took office in June 1936 aimed at more systematic legislation, with the basic object of insulating the market from the forces of supply and demand. A law of August 15th, 1936, set up the Office National Interprofessionnel du Blé, with the task of fixing the wheat price and ensuring its observance. The Office had monopolistic control over all foreign trade in wheat and could decide on the measures necessary to absorb surpluses. A contemporary study by Maspétiol commented:

By the novelty of the solution which it brings to the French wheat problem, the recently-established Office has a significance which is not limited to this country nor to this commodity. The experience which is gained will be closely followed both by those who place their hopes in an extension of State activity in agriculture and by those who, on the contrary, would prefer an organization giving a flexible type of co-ordination and leaving the activities of trading and cultivation free.

In any case it would be a mistake not to appreciate the scope and importance of the initiative, which constitutes, among all the measures taken by the Government of M. Léon Blum, the greatest departure from the classical liberal economy. Moreover, in the mind of M. Monnet, the Minister of Agriculture who initiated the reform, this is only a first step, the principles of which are to be extended to the entire agricultural market.[1]

In fact the Popular Front Government of Léon Blum lasted in power for only a year, and the Office du Blé was to remain its only major contribution to a more systematic organization of agricultural markets. The 1930s were indeed marked by acute political instability: the regime was menaced by the rise of Fascism on the right and the counter-activity of the Communists on the left, and one Government succeeded another. In these circumstances a consistent agricultural policy was hardly possible.

The import quota system

In view of the important role which import quotas have since come to play, it is of interest to examine some of the problems which France encountered in the early stages. The following account is largely indebted to the excellent study of this question made by Moroni in 1934.

The original measures rested on a rather doubtful legal basis, but in the atmosphere of the crisis no one was inclined to quarrel over niceties of interpretation. Other countries too were more inclined to take similar steps themselves than to question the legality of the French move.

The techniques used were originally simple. The quotas were announced on a global basis, without any specification as to where the imports should come from or who should carry out the imports; the frontier was closed to imports from all sources as soon as the quota was declared filled. A difficulty arose over the treatment of goods in transit at the time the frontier was closed, but

---

[1] R. Maspétiol, 'L'Office Français du Blé', *Revue économique internationale*, June 1937, pp. 545–6.

this problem was dealt with in December 1931 by an announcement that goods would be admitted if proof were available that they had been consigned before the quota had been declared complete.[1] Problems arose also from the system whereby goods could be temporarily admitted into France free of duty: mills owning large stocks of grain imported in this way were liable to declare them officially for customs purposes just before the frontier was closed, and it proved necessary to restrict the use of temporary admissions.

A serious difficulty was the tendency for imports to flood in as soon as the quota was opened: frequently, as a result of delays in closing the frontier, the quota was exceeded in the first few weeks. An attempt to solve this problem was made in November 1931, when import licences were distributed to importers in relation to their past imports. This enabled a precise control to be exerted over the volume of imports.

However, there were difficulties in deciding who should get the licences, and it was found necessary to set up special committees of Government representatives, traders and producers to allocate them. Another solution tried was to hand over the administration of the quotas to the exporting countries. Besides relieving the French administration of the embarrassing task of allocating the licences, this served as a gesture to placate countries which were annoyed at the French restrictions. The exporting country was thus responsible for distributing licences between its exporters, and French customs offices would admit goods only if they were accompanied by the necessary authorization. Agreements to this effect were reached with a dozen countries early in 1932, concerning in particular cattle, meat, dairy products, fruit and vegetables. The foreign administration was expected to space out the exports over the period to which the quota applied and to ensure that traditional trade channels were used. The latter undertaking was not always respected: French importers were by-passed in a variety of ways. What was more serious was that the foreign firms possessing export licences were in a strong bargaining position and could extract a high price from French buyers. Another problem

---

[1] The story was told of a consignment of bulls from Czechoslovakia which arrived at the French frontier just after the quota for bulls was declared filled, but which, with the assistance of a veterinary surgeon, were admitted on the quota for bullocks!

was that some foreign countries, when they could not fill their quota, obtained supplies from elsewhere and sent them to France, concealing their real origin. French traders complained at these practices, and the Government was forced gradually to abandon this system and revert to the allocation of import licences.

French importers fortunate enough to obtain licences were generally able to make considerable profits. On the other hand, the restricted volume of trade meant that customs receipts were diminished. Consequently, in February 1933 taxes on import licences were introduced. These soon came to have an additional function: that of an extra – and variable – protective duty. The amount of the tax was often calculated so as to compensate for the difference between foreign and domestic prices, and in some cases the tax on a product was considerably higher than the import duty (Table 45). The taxes, moreover, were included in trade negotiations.

Table 45

IMPORT LICENCE TAXES AND IMPORT DUTIES ON MAJOR AGRICULTURAL PRODUCTS, IN 1934

(francs per 100 kg.)

Product	Tax	Import duty minimum	general
Cattle (live weight)	50	100	200
Pigs (live weight)	75	150	300
Beef and veal – fresh or chilled	100	175	350
frozen	100	90	180
Pigmeat – fresh or chilled	100	250	500
frozen	100	130	260
Eggs in shell	150	24	72
Butter	50	700	1,400
Cheese	300	100	200
Barley	25	22·50	45
Apples	125	7·50	15
Pears	175	20	40

Note : All licence taxes were established by a decree of May 12th, 1933, except apples and pears (December 28th, 1933) and cheese (March 30th, 1934).

Source : Moroni, op. cit.

Perhaps the most serious problem was the distribution of quotas between exporting countries. The global quotas which were used at first put the more distant countries at a disadvantage. In January 1932 quotas were allotted to each exporting country on the basis of its past exports. The difficulty here lay in deciding what years to take as the basis, especially in cases where trade had already been restricted in one way or another. The original basis was 1927–31, but within this period greater weight was given to the years 1927–9, which were regarded as more normal. For products to which quotas were applied after July 1932, the base period was the three years preceding the introduction of the quota.

This arrangement seemed fairly equitable, but it had the serious disadvantage of crystallizing the previous pattern of trade. It also hampered commercial negotiations, since countries whose quotas were fixed had no further restrictions to fear and nothing better to expect: they could even discriminate against French exports with little danger to themselves. On the other hand, good customers of France could not be given advantages on the French market. As a result, an important change of policy took place in September 1933: quotas became a subject for negotiation, and only a quarter of the total quota was now allocated on the basis of past trade. Agreements involving quotas were reached with a number of countries in the course of 1934. Other countries, however, objected to this procedure: Germany and Great Britain both retaliated against French exports and the existing trade agreements were denounced. Nevertheless, with the use of quotas as a bargaining-counter, the first phase in which they were simply a means of protection passed into a second phase in which they became an instrument of economic control, intimately linked with overall trade policy.

The justification of agricultural support

The crisis which began in 1929 was so acute and the effects of rising imports in the early stages were so obvious that there was little opposition to the measures of protection adopted. Free trade arguments would have appeared irrelevant in the circumstances, and in any case there was no strong body of free trade opinion, as there still was in Britain. Though there was some concern that the price of foodstuffs should not be raised, the question in the early stages at least was rather one of preventing a collapse in the market.

Responsible opinion at first stressed the exceptional nature of the situation and accepted protection through import quotas and other means as inevitable in the circumstances; the corollary of this view was that import restrictions should be relaxed once conditions returned to normal. This for example was the attitude taken in the first report of the Conseil National Économique on the trade problem in 1932: the Conseil criticized the quota system for its rigidity, but recognized that it was the only effective measure available. Augé-Laribé echoed widely-held views when he wrote in 1933 that 'removal of protection would make it practically impossible to practise agriculture in Europe, to the benefit of the new countries where the land is worked either by machines or by cheap labour' and concluded that France's economy had to be isolated until conditions on the world market improved.[1]

In fact, world markets were slow to recover, and in 1935 the Conseil National Économique observed that protection by tariffs and quotas was still necessary; however, efforts should be made to resume normal trade and quotas should now be used not to restrict imports but to permit a gradual increase.

However, the tendency – as has been seen above – was to a greater degree of State control both of imports and of domestic markets. This development was far from being unanimously accepted. Maspétiol, whose study of the Office du Blé has already been mentioned, regarded this innovation with disquiet. In an analysis of the import quota system, Long pointed out that quotas, once installed, tended to perpetuate themselves:

Protection prevents adaptation, and the lack of adaptation calls for protection. Consequently, unless the steps are re-traced – and this appears less and less likely because it becomes increasingly painful – protective measures follow one another. This explains why, some seven years after the first quotas were introduced, we now find the quota system firmly and widely embedded in the French economy.[2]

[1] M. Augé-Laribé, 'Nouveaux fondements du protectionnisme agricole', *Revue d'économie politique*, March–April 1933.
[2] O. Long, *Le contingentement en France* (Paris, 1938), p. 175.

Such criticism, however, was swamped in the rising tide of interventionism. The evolution that had taken place in general attitudes was reflected in a further report by the Conseil National Économique in 1939:

Agriculture in France plays an important role. It is an essential element in the economic and social balance. It is necessary that the nation as a whole should, even at the cost of some sacrifice, ensure to farmers a satisfactory income which will keep them on the land and enable them to raise their standard of living on an equitable basis.[1]

This was a significant passage: it was probably the first authoritative statement in France (the Conseil was responsible for advising the Government) of an income policy for agriculture. The Conseil, moreover, departed from its earlier, comparatively liberal views and advocated a comprehensive policy in which France would aim to obtain its supplies from its overseas territories, while the latter would as far as possible buy from France foodstuffs such as flour, butter and cheese. This would be achieved by mutual preferences, with imports from foreign countries restricted by tariffs and quotas except in cases where France and its territories could not attain self-sufficiency.

The experience of the 1930s left a permanent impression on French thinking about agricultural matters. After the war, Augé-Laribé wrote the following passage, which gives food for thought:

On account of the structure of her agriculture, of the devastation suffered by her best regions (which were repaired but slowly) and of the imperfect ways in which production and distribution are organized, France is a country of high costs: her market attracts competition from producers throughout the world who have an advantage in one respect or another. If France had not maintained her customs barriers (which she was not the first to use), if towards the end of the inter-war period, she had not resorted to the method of import quotas (which she did not invent), if in other words France had not taken the precautions necessary to attenuate – but not entirely to suppress – the import of goods which can be

[1] Conseil National Économique, *La politique agricole* (Melun, 1939), p. 17.

produced on her own soil, then French agriculture would
have ceased to exist.[1]

Augé-Laribé goes on to point out that after the First World
War France attached great importance to recovering a balance
between industry and agriculture: the war had demonstrated the
danger of dependence on imported supplies. The fact that home
produce cost more than imported was a secondary consideration.
Social reasons also were important, and the following passage
provides an insight into a widespread attitude to agriculture in
France:

> Agriculture occupies too large a place in the French economy
> for it to be quickly suppressed and replaced. Neither the
> factories nor the accommodation available in the towns would
> be able to absorb all those of the farm population who would
> be obliged by free trade to give up the cultivation of the soil,
> even if a large number remained to breed livestock or engage
> in specialized activities. France, though she is a country of
> revolutions, has a profound desire for stability; she likes to
> stick to her old habits. She lets some young enthusiasts embark
> on adventures (where they have had some success) but she
> wants a large number of her sons to cultivate the land on
> which their ancestors, painfully but not unhappily, gained
> their daily bread.[2]

The growth of agricultural organizations

The French peasants, through being mobilized in the First World
War, acquired a different outlook. They obtained new points of
comparison, they realized how unsatisfactory was their situation,
and, as Augé-Laribé observes, they learned how to complain.[3]
Improved education, communications and transport had their
inevitable effects on the mentality of the peasants and on their
ability to organize themselves.

The right-wing, aristocratic Société des Agriculteurs de France

---

[1] Introductory chapter to M. Cépède, *Agriculture et alimentation en France*
(Paris: Génin, 1961), p. 29.

[2] Ibid., pp. 29–30.

[3] Augé-Laribé, *La politique agricole*, op. cit.

in the rue d'Athènes[1] had already founded in 1886 its Union Centrale des Syndicats Agricoles, while its Republican and anti-clerical rival, the Société Nationale d'Encouragement à l'Agriculture (in the Boulevard Saint-Germain) had promoted the growth of 'co-operatives' (the co-operative involved greater collective responsibility and thus corresponded more to left-wing principles).

In 1919 there was an attempt to unify the different organizations in the Confédération Nationale des Associations Agricoles, but this was not successful. Augé-Laribé, who was Secretary-General of the Confédération for ten out of the twenty years of its existence, observed that it was handicapped by the unwillingness of the various associations to obey a central body and to give it adequate funds.

The creation of Chambres d'Agriculture was provided for in a law passed in 1924, but they came into existence only in 1927. These were public bodies, financed by an additional levy on the land tax. There was one Chamber for each Department, with its members elected by farmers, landowners and farm workers and one member in five nominated by the agricultural organizations. The task of the Chambers was essentially to provide a link between the central authority and the agricultural population. The Presidents of the various Chambers were grouped in a central body, the Assemblée Permanente des Presidents des Chambres d'Agriculture (rue Scribe).

Following the crisis of 1929 and 1930, several of the syndicates affiliated to the rue d'Athènes found themselves in financial difficulties, and the associated Caisse Centrale de Crédit Agricole collapsed in 1931; the rue d'Athènes was thereby seriously weakened. However a new type of right-wing syndicalism issued from the crisis, promoted by the larger farmers and the resulting Union Nationale des Syndicats Agricoles (rue des Pyramides) was a powerful body.

Specialist producer organizations – grouping producers of wheat, wine, sugar-beet, etc. – also grew in number and influence. They had the advantage of being able to concentrate their demands on precise action to assist individual commodities, and were perhaps the most effective agricultural pressure-groups.

[1] As the organizations multiplied and their titles grew increasingly complex, it proved easier to refer to them by their addresses.

General political movements also found expression in the countryside. The Communist Party was the first to develop a firm footing with its Confédération Générale des Paysans Travailleurs, instituted in 1929. The Socialists followed two years later with the Confédération Nationale Paysanne. A more spectacular development was the action of Henri Dorgères, who had avowedly Fascist views and advocated an illegal seizure of power: from 1931 onwards he campaigned on the theme of peasant misery, stressing that the peasantry should defend itself against the State, which was rotten and incapable, and should unite in a compact bloc to impose a strong government. Dorgères aimed to create this bloc in a Front Paysan, in which he combined his action with the Union Nationale des Syndicats Agricoles and another organization, the Parti Agraire et Paysan Français. There were violent scenes at meetings organized by the Front in 1934 and 1935. But the following year a scission between Fascist and democratic elements caused the Parti Agraire to break up, and with it the Front Paysan. Dorgères however continued his action with his 'green-shirts', a semi-military organization on Fascist lines, and he subsequently played a significant role in the agricultural policy of the Vichy Government.

A fair sample of current right-wing views can be found in the following passage from a book by one of the officers of the Parti Agraire:

> Will the tragic decline of French agriculture continue to the point of ruin and until our villages are finally abandoned? ... The future of our distressed agriculture depends on the rank given to it in the national economy and in public opinion. If society as a whole considers that the peasantry's task is to serve other sectors ... if the policy of the treaties of 1860, which still dominates [sic], is pursued, agriculture will never recover; it will moreover be condemned to death if the proletariat of the towns does not recognize that the price of agricultural products, in a country like France where small peasants predominate, is a wage which the consumer must pay, at a fair rate, in order to enable those who work the land to live with dignity.[1]

[1] M. Braibant, *L'agriculture française – son tragique déclin, son avenir* (Paris, 1936), pp. 164–5.

The proliferation of agricultural organizations, and the violence with which many of them expressed their views, ensured that the complaints of agriculture were kept well in the foreground. The political parties and the Governments of the time were bound to pay attention to the agricultural problem. However, the nature of the demands expressed, and the lack of co-ordination – the conflicts even – between the different agricultural organizations, did not favour the formulation of a coherent, long-term agricultural policy. It was easier to give satisfaction to agricultural producers by measures for supporting prices than to insist on the need for painful measures of adjustment. Few people were bold enough to suggest that if agriculture suffered from low incomes, the cause lay at least in part in the inefficiency of its structure and methods. Certainly none of the precarious and short-lived Governments of the time was in a position to carry through far-sighted reforms; the structure of holdings remained essentially what it had been and the problem of fragmentation was tackled only in a few regions.

It might have been hoped that the growth of farm organizations would at least lead to an increase in constructive co-operative action between agricultural producers themselves. In fact, little progress was made; by 1939 only about one producer in four belonged to a syndicate or co-operative and the French peasant remained essentially an individualist. In particular, there was no significant extension of co-operative marketing: the marketing system for most products remained unwieldy and unprofitable for the peasant, whose produce passed through a long chain of middlemen before it reached the consumer.

Consequences for agriculture and trade

The level of agricultural prices in France was initially affected to some extent by the crisis on world markets and the consequent increase in supplies entering the French market. Before long, however, the various measures of intervention insulated the French market for major agricultural products to such an extent that it was no longer subject to fluctuations in world prices. French market prices then became dependent primarily on domestic supplies and, in some cases, on the volume of imports from French North Africa.

The developments for wheat and wine have already been described. Unfortunately there seems to be no reliable price index for agricultural products as a whole. The available estimates indicate that there was only a moderate fall in prices in 1930 and 1931, and that a more serious decline did not occur till 1933, following the increases in domestic supply. On the whole, livestock products seem to have done better than crops, but even among the former there were cases where domestic production was in surplus or near-surplus and where import quotas failed to prevent a fall

Table 46

AGRICULTURAL AREA AND NUMBERS OF LIVESTOCK

(annual averages)

	1920–4	1925–9	1930–4	1935–8
AREA (million hectares)				
Arable land	22·6	22·2	21·4	20·6
of which wheat	(5·4)	(5·3)	(5·4)	(5·2)
Grassland	11·0	11·2	11·3	11·6
Vineyards	1·6	1·6	1·6	1·6
Other cultivations	1·1	1·1	·9	·9
Total	36·3	36·1	35·2	34·7
LIVESTOCK (millions)				
Cattle	13·6	14·9	15·6	15·7
Pigs	5·3	5·9	6·6	7·1
Sheep	9·8	10·6	9·8	9·8
Goats	1·4	1·5	1·5	1·3

Source: Statistique Agricole Annuelle.

in prices: thus the quotas for beef and beef cattle were progressively reduced after their introduction and became nil in the first quarter of 1933, but beef prices continued to fall during this period. In other cases there were temporary increases in the price level, resulting from unduly restrictive import quotas.

At any rate the crisis was not allowed to cause any drastic change in the pattern of French agricultural production. Table 46 shows that the distribution of the agricultural area as between arable land, grassland, etc., remained practically unchanged: the slight fall in the arable area does not appear significant. The numbers of cattle and pigs increased at a moderate rate, roughly in line with past trends; the number of sheep, already reduced to a low level, remained fairly stable.

On the other hand, agricultural imports were substantially reduced. The drastic fall in wheat imports has already been shown in Table 44: a more general picture is given by Table 47. The

Table 47

IMPORTS OF MAJOR FOODSTUFFS

(volume indices, 1925–8 average = 100)

	Grain and flour	Sugar, raw and refined	Live animals	Meat, fresh and frozen	Butter and cheese	Wine
1929	120	129	61	37	128	114
1930	101	104	205	84	165	128
1931	193	86	325	117	264	151
1932	190	104	134	52	166	134
1933	89	100	117	43	140	167
1934	76	108	85	31	95	122
1935	75	92	79	23	78	120
1936	85	82	108	22	78	123
1937	69	98	82	30	65	119
1938	62	80	72	26	69	155

Source: Statistique Agricole Annuelle.

sharp increase in imports of most foodstuffs at the beginning of the crisis is clearly shown; but from the time when import quotas were introduced (late 1931 for livestock, meat, butter and cheese, and 1933 for feed grains), imports of almost all products were reduced to levels well below those prevailing before the crisis. The major exception was wine, as a result mainly of increased imports from Algeria.

As Table 48 shows, the cut in imports took place at the expense of foreign countries. Imports of foodstuffs from the French overseas territories were maintained and even increased in value: wine and other foodstuffs from Algeria formed a large part of this trade.

Table 48

TOTAL IMPORTS OF FOODSTUFFS, BY ORIGIN

(billion francs, in current prices)

	All sources	Foreign countries	French territories[a]	of which Algeria
1925–8	11·8	8·0	3·8	2·0
1929	13·2	8·3	4·9	2·6
1930	11·8	7·1	4·7	2·9
1931	14·0	9·0	5·0	3·2
1932	11·0	5·6	5·4	3·1
1933	9·6	3·9	5·7	3·6
1934	7·5	2·8	4·7	2·6
1935	6·3	2·2	4·1	2·1
1936	7·8	2·3	5·5	2·6
1937	10·7	3·4	7·4	3·4
1938	12·5	3·2	9·3	4·4

[a] French colonies, protectorates and mandated territories, including Algeria.
[b] Annual average.
Source: *Tableaux Généraux du Commerce de la France*.

The reduction in imports was not an unmixed blessing, even for French agriculture: in several cases it led to retaliation by foreign countries against French exports, many of which were agricultural. Thus Switzerland retaliated against French restrictions on dairy products by prohibiting imports of French cheeses, and Denmark, badly hit by the measures taken in France, imposed quotas on almost all French products, wine and spirits in particular.

Chapter 9. Germany

A. The Weimar Republic

The First World War and the 1920s

At the outbreak of the First World War, Germany was dependent on imports not only for large quantities of foodstuffs, in particular bread grains from North America, but also for very considerable amounts of animal feeding-stuffs and fertilizers. Moreover, foreign labour was important to German agriculture at seasons of peak employment.

During the war, Germany's imports were cut off to a far greater extent than those of Great Britain, and as the war progressed the blockade of Germany was intensified. The food shortage was all the more serious because inadequate plans had been made before-hand and hardly any stocks had been built up, largely because the war was expected to be short. Further, in the first few months, the soldiers at the front were sent more food than was necessary and there was considerable wastage. It was only when it began to be realized that a long struggle lay ahead that measures to deal with the food shortage were introduced: by the end of 1916, food supplies in general were subject to control and rationing was in force.

But there were serious obstacles to an increase in production. The shortages of feeding-stuffs and fertilizers, and the severe lack of farm labour, led to a sharp fall in the yields of crops and live-stock. Price controls aimed mainly at preventing the cost of food from rising, and they were not counterbalanced by adequate measures to encourage production. By the end of the war the level of nutrition had fallen drastically.

For some time after the war, food remained short and price controls were maintained; they were gradually relaxed from 1920 on, and then food prices shot up, giving large temporary gains to farmers. However, after the currency reform in November 1923, the prices of farm products rose more slowly than costs of production – wages in particular. Demand for foodstuffs was restricted by growing industrial unemployment, and German agriculture was subject to the full force of international competition since tariffs on foodstuffs had been suspended at the outbreak of war and had not yet been restored. Farmers thus found themselves in serious difficulties, which reached a peak in 1925. Indebtedness was widespread and many farms had to be sold.

In 1925, however, Germany recovered its right (suspended by the Treaty of Versailles) to determine its own tariff. There was a vigorous controversy over the question whether protection should be restored to agriculture; arguments similar to those used before the war were revived. Thus some economists argued for free trade in grains, wanting Germany to develop a livestock industry in the way that Denmark and the Netherlands had done. In the Reichstag the left-wing groups, as well as the parties representing the small peasants, were against protection. Nevertheless, the conservative party and the big landowners obtained a majority for the new tariff, which came into force on September 1st, 1925. In general it re-established, at least nominally, the pre-war Bülow duties, but the rates were somewhat higher for livestock products and, initially, slightly lower for grains.

At the same time exports of agricultural produce were again permitted (they had been forbidden since the war), and the system of import certificates was revived in the same form as before the war: exports of grain gave entitlement to certificates which could be used to pay the duty on the import of a corresponding quantity of grain, which could be of a different type.

The reintroduction of tariffs helped to restrain the fall in prices; the import certificate system in particular, by encouraging exports of grain, relieved the pressure on the market. The prices of grains, which till then had generally been below the world price, now rose above it. Livestock prices fluctuated, but these on the whole were not so much affected by foreign competition at this period.

The crisis – tariffs and other measures

The situation around 1925 seemed bad enough at the time to be referred to as a 'crisis'. But the fall in prices which occurred after 1929, in Germany as elsewhere, was much more critical. It was particularly serious for the many German farmers who still bore a heavy burden of debt, resulting from expenditure during the relatively prosperous years of the early 1920s.

The agricultural organizations, united in the 'Green Front', demanded action to stabilize grain prices, reviving the Kanitz plan for a grain import monopoly.[1] The Government rejected this idea as both impracticable and contrary to existing commercial treaties. However, by a law of July 4th, 1929, it introduced a compulsory milling ratio, with the minimum proportion of domestic wheat in the flour fixed at 30 per cent; in July 1931 this was raised to 60 per cent and shortly afterwards to 97 per cent.

Further, in 1929 the Government received certain powers to adjust tariffs by decree, without passing through Parliament, and as the crisis deepened these powers were extended; by March 1931 the Government had acquired responsibility for the entire range of duties on agricultural products. The existing commercial treaties with Sweden and Finland were denounced because they involved commitments affecting duties on livestock products. The agricultural duties were then raised to high, often prohibitive levels, greatly exceeding the current world price: the duty on wheat rose to 25 marks in October 1930, by which time the German import price was only about 10 marks; for other grains the situation was similar. The duties on livestock products were also raised, though they generally remained at about half the world price.

Though the Government had rejected the demand for an import monopoly for wheat, in April 1930 it introduced a State monopoly for all trade in maize; since domestic production was

[1] After the war, the Bund der Landwirte was replaced by the Reichslandbund, which was similar in character and ideology to its predecessor; it too was led mainly by the Prussian landlords. The Green Front was a union of the Reichslandbund with the Catholic peasants and some other peasant associations which had grown up; the latter however played a subordinate role.

7

small, this was in practice an import monopoly only. The main reason for this step was that the import duty on maize was bound at a low level in a trade agreement with Yugoslavia, which the Government apparently did not want to denounce. This however did not prevent the new body from imposing a levy which was several times as high as the tariff.

Special measures had to be taken also for rye. The difficulties of 1925 had already caused the Government to support the price through purchases on the market; these were carried out by private bodies with Government assistance. In 1928 the Government bought up two trading businesses and in 1929, after a big harvest of rye, used them for large-scale market operations. This action proved expensive and not very effective. When the 1930 rye harvest turned out to be even bigger than that of 1929, it was difficult to dispose of the Government-owned stocks; it proved necessary to render part of the supplies unfit for human consumption and sell them at a low price for animal feeding. At first this action was financed by direct Government subsidies; later, purchasers of the 'denatured' rye were induced to pay a higher price by being allowed to import feeding barley at substantially reduced rates of duty.

The difficulties on the rye market led in July 1930 to the abolition of the import certificate system. As the German import duty – and hence the value of the import certificates – now exceeded world prices, there was a danger that German exporters would *pay* customers abroad to take their rye.

In contrast to France, import quotas did not play an important role. On a few occasions Germany granted certain countries an import quota at a reduced rate of duty: this was the case in 1930 for cattle from Sweden and butter and cheese from Finland. On these occasions Denmark received the same quotas as the other countries, though its previous trade with Germany had been much greater: though Denmark protested and demanded a distribution of these quotas in relation to past trade, Germany took no action till 1932, when it introduced a global quota for butter allocated in proportion to imports in 1929–31 (see also Chapter 10).

An interesting feature of many of the measures taken at this time was the inclusion of clauses designed to protect consumers; this was essentially a concession to the Social Democrats and other left-wing groups. Some of the provisions of the 1925 tariff reflected a concern with the interests of consumers. The sugar duty, introduced in 1928, was to be lowered if the price rose above a certain level. When the duties on wheat, rye and pigs were raised at the end of 1929 and beginning of 1930, it was laid down that the Government should attempt to maintain prices on the domestic market at certain levels by varying the duty within prescribed limits; in fact it proved impossible to keep prices up to the targets without raising the duties still further, and later the limits on the duties were abolished. The concern with the consumer interest found its most complete expression in the 'Index Law' of March 28th, 1931, which instructed the Government to eliminate the divergence between the price index of agricultural products and the other price indices, but also required it to keep the bread price below a specified level and to take appropriate action if the food price index should rise beyond a certain point. These provisions reflected a belief that conditions would soon return to normal; in fact, for several years to come the problem continued to be one of falling rather than rising prices.

Opinions on the agricultural crisis

The extent of concern with the agricultural crisis was reflected in a surge of literature on the subject from 1930 to 1933. In particular, two mammoth symposiums appeared in 1932, one edited by the eminent economist Max Sering, the other published by the Friedrich List-Gesellschaft, both dealing with the relation of German agriculture to the world economic crisis.[1] Sering, who by nature was a liberal economist, wrote in his foreword to the first of these works:

Is it possible for the food necessary for 65 million persons, tightly packed in a restricted area, to be obtained from our own soil? Is it possible for German farmers to withstand the competition of countries with extensive land resources without a degree of protection such that this nation, which since the war is poorer in raw materials than any other industrial country, becomes unable to compete on world markets? Is it possible for German farmers to keep pace even in livestock

[1] M. Sering and others, *Die deutsche Landwirtschaft* (Berlin, 1932); and Friedrich List-Gesellschaft, *Deutsche Agrarpolitik* (Berlin, 1932).

production with neighbouring countries, when capital is available in the latter at half its cost to the German farmer?[1]

There was no real conflict over points of principle between the various writers in these two works: it was generally accepted that the circumstances of the time made protection inevitable. Thus Baade, in the second work, laid stress on the instability of the world market and the increasing degree of intervention by both exporting and importing countries. A similar point of view was expressed in a book by Salin, who referred to Britain's departure from free trade and observed that:

> The logical correctness of the free trade doctrine is in no way upset by this development. But the conditions necessary for its application in practice have been removed to such an extent that it would be quite inappropriate and perhaps pointless to try to apply this historical ideal to the present situation.[2]

There was general agreement too that the orthodox processes of commercial treaties, 'most favoured nation' clauses and binding duties might have suited a situation where world trade was stable and relatively free, but that they had now become inappropriate. New methods were necessary, particularly since the increased degree of self-sufficiency in Germany was making tariffs less effective.

This question of self-sufficiency in food received an increasingly prominent role in the discussions. There was a widespread desire to raise the degree of self-sufficiency, but opinions varied as to what this degree should be. Responsible opinion pointed out that full autarky, in Germany's situation, was out of the question. Also, the more imports of food were reduced, the greater would be the difficulty in selling German manufactures abroad. In the symposium published by the Friedrich List-Gesellschaft, Landmann attempted to prove that restrictions on agricultural imports had not significantly affected industrial exports, because the latter consisted mainly of capital goods and high-value consumer goods, demand for which had fallen relatively little; he also claimed that increased food prices resulting from agricultural protection did not necessarily raise the level of wages and hence of industrial costs of

---

[1] Op. cit., p. III.   [2] E. Salin, *Wirtschaft und Staat* (Berlin, 1932), p. 88.

autarky: a policy of establishing a natl. economy that is completely self-sufficient & independent of imports from other countries.

production. These views were criticized by other writers in the same volume on the grounds that they did not take account of secondary effects – thus if Germany imported less wheat from Canada, Canada might import less manufactures from Britain, and Britain in turn might import less from Germany.

The debate among academic economists was thus rather inconclusive. In the field of practical politics, however, the issue was soon to be decided by the advent of National Socialism, with an aggressively autarkic policy.

German agriculture around 1933

The increased duties and the other measures taken from 1929 to 1933 succeeded in bringing about a drastic reduction in imports of foodstuffs, which by 1933 were only some 60 per cent of their level before the crisis (Table 49).

Table 49

IMPORTS OF FOODSTUFFS

(volume indices at 1928 prices, 1928 = 100)

	Crop products	Live animals	Livestock products	Other foodstuffs[a]	Total foodstuffs
1928	100	100	100	100	100
1929	92	104	104	100	96
1930	80	85	100	100	87
1931	69	49	83	87	74
1932	71	49	79	77	74
1933	61	47	62	80	62

[a] Including beverages and tobacco.

Source: Statistisches Jahrbuch für das Deutsche Reich.

As a result, prices on German markets were prevented from falling to anything like the same extent as world prices. The fall in price was nevertheless severe, as Table 50 indicates. The relatively large fall in prices of livestock products after 1928/9 is partly a reflection of the fact that the grain market had already come under pressure by this date, but it also suggests that the fall in consumer purchasing power resulting from the crisis was a factor

Table 50

AGRICULTURAL PRICE INDICES

(1928–9 = 100)

	Wheat	Rye	All crop products	Cattle	Pigs	Butter	All live- stock products	All agri- cultural products
1928/9	100	100	100	100	100	100	100	100
1929/30	115	82	87	105	102	89	89	95
1930/1	120	77	86	96	72	76	76	81
1931/2	108	92	85	62	57	66	65	67
1932/3	91	74	71	53	52	58	59	58

Source : As Table 49.

perhaps as important as foreign competition – and one against which import restrictions were useless.

The result was a serious fall in farm incomes : it was calculated that the net income of agriculture before the crisis amounted to about 2,195 million marks, but by 1932/3 it had dropped to

Table 51

RECEIPTS AND EXPENSES OF AGRICULTURE

(RM million)

	Receipts from farm sales			Farm expenses			
		of which			of which		Net farm income
	Total	Crop pro- ducts	Live- stock pro- ducts	Total	Feed- ing- stuffs	Wages	
1928/9	10,228	3,752	6,476	8,033	1,515	1,726	2,195
1929/30	9,808	3,564	6,244	7,881	1,314	1,815	1,927
1930/1	8,646	3,177	5,469	6,920	841	1,758	1,726
1931/2	7,350	2,985	4,365	6,127	844	1,511	1,223
1932/3	6,405	2,645	3,760	5,514	698	1,332	891

Source : As Table 49.

891 million marks (Table 51). The fall would have been even greater but for the reduced cost of feeding-stuffs.

Sering pointed out that the prices of manufactured consumer goods fell by about as much as those of agricultural products; at the same time, the output of agriculture rose while that of industry fell, so that agriculture had a larger share of a reduced national income.[1] This however was not much compensation for the many farmers who were ruined, and the distress in the countryside made it easy for Nazi propaganda to take root there as well as in other depressed sectors.

B. The Third Reich

The agricultural philosophy of National Socialism

The Governments of the Weimar Republic reacted to the problems of agriculture by a series of largely disconnected expedients. The National Socialists came to power with a clearly-defined policy for agriculture, forming an integral part of their overall aims.

The formulation of this policy was primarily the work of Walther Darré, who at an early stage had gained Hitler's confidence and had taken charge of agricultural matters. His programme for agriculture was published in 1930, and in various speeches and writings he elaborated on his theme.

The basis of Darré's thinking was set out in his work entitled 'The Yeomanry as the Life Source of the Nordic Race', which was first published in 1928 and ran into six editions.[2] The Germanic tribes, according to Darré, belonged to the settler as opposed to the nomadic types and were thus closely rooted to the soil. Moreover, the inheritance of farms and farming traditions from one generation to another ensured that the nobility of the blood and moral integrity were preserved. The slogan 'Blut und Boden' (Blood and Soil) neatly expressed these ideas.

It followed that the farmer was not just an economic factor and

[1] Sering, *Deutsche Agrarpolitik* (Leipzig, 1934).

[2] R. Walther Darré, *Das Bauerntum als Lebensquell der nordischen Rasse* (6th ed., Munich, 1937). Darré deliberately revived the archaic term 'Bauerntum' to describe the farming community. The translation 'yeomanry' is suggested by J. B. Holt in *German Agricultural Policy* (University of North Carolina, 1936), and it does seem to have roughly the right historical connotations.

should not be subjected to market forces: on the contrary, he should receive special care from the State and be assured of fair prices for his produce. The clearest expression of this idea appears in a speech by Darré on September 19th, 1933:

> We must be quite clear about this: the farmer is not an entrepreneur in the usual sense. The production of food cannot be subjected to the free play of market forces and exposed to the risks which that entails, for agriculture's duty to the nation is immensely important. We need the farmer as the blood source of the German people; we need him too as the source of our food supply. This is not so much a question of ensuring that the farmer gets as high a price as possible for his produce so that his holding produces the maximum rent, as of making certain that the farmer is firmly rooted to his land through a German law of land tenure and that he gets for his work a fair wage – in other words, adequate, equitable prices. The farmer must always see his activity as a duty towards his race and his people, never as a mere economic, money-spinning operation.[1]

Further implications for agriculture arose from the nationalistic urge of National Socialism: the nation's prestige and power could be ensured only if it was the master of its food supply. In the following passage, written in 1932, Darré clinches the long debate in Germany as to the role of agriculture in the economy and the desirable degree of self-sufficiency:

> If we except abnormal circumstances – such as military occupation by an enemy and commitments under treaty – the basis of foreign policy remains the following: the efficacy of every action undertaken by a nation in foreign affairs depends directly on the extent to which it is able to be and remain independent of other nations in its food supply.[2]

Darré considered, moreover, that if food had to be obtained from abroad, the least objectionable course was to get it from German colonies, but in this case the supply lines had to be safeguarded.

---

[1] Darré, *Um Blut und Boden* (a collection of articles and speeches republished in 1940, Munich), p. 359.
[2] Ibid., p. 332.

The point was made even clearer by another National Socialist writer:

The National Socialist leadership was in no doubt that the battle for honour and equality among nations could be won only on the firm basis of security in food supplies. So long as the food of the people was not assured against all circumstances, the policy of national liberation could not attempt any serious trial of strength. Together with the construction of a powerful navy and a highly productive industry, it was therefore essential to develop food production to the point where every individual in the nation could be sure of his daily bread.[1]

Darré swept aside the old objection that restrictions on imports of food would lead to reduced demand for German industrial exports. By controlling the import trade, it would be possible to ensure that purchases were made only from countries willing to take German goods in exchange. In 1935, in a speech to the Hamburg Senate (a body likely to be sensitive on this issue), Darré referred to past controversies and declared:

Today, however, the new German agricultural policy has shown the way out of this labyrinth and has built a bridge between the opposing interests ... The German farmer now has no advantage in campaigning for tariff protection and thus obstructing German trade policy.[2]

In a work published in 1958, Dr Haushofer draws a distinction between the policy of Darré and that of other Nazi leaders.[3] He considers that Darré, though he believed in the 'yeomanry as the life source of the Nordic race', did not subscribe to Hitler's 'Herrenvolk' theories; also that Darré, though his prime aim was to restore prosperity to the farming community, did not seek complete self-sufficiency for Germany in food supplies. Haushofer points out that the fulfilment of Darré's agricultural policy required peace, and refers to Darré's speech at the International Congress of Agriculture held in Dresden in 1939, in which he

---

[1] A. Schürmann, *Deutsche Agrarpolitik* (Neudamm, 1940), pp. 330–1.

[2] *Um Blut und Boden*, op. cit., p. 447.

[3] H. Haushofer, *Ideengeschichte der Agrarwirtschaft und Agrarpolitik*, vol. II (Munich: BLV, 1958).

wished for a removal of misunderstandings and the avoidance of war. Indeed, Darré offered his resignation early in the war and was finally dismissed in 1942. The fact remains that Darré's ideas on the racial importance of the yeomanry fitted conveniently into general Nazi thinking, and that the policy put into effect during his period as Minister of Agriculture served Hitler's aggressive purposes.

The philosophy in action

The tremendous expansion of the National Socialist Party, from twelve seats in the Reichstag in 1928 to 288 in 1933, was due at least in part to support from much of the agricultural population during the years of crisis. The party's campaign in rural areas began in 1930 on the basis of a programme offering relief from the burdens of debt, taxation and falling prices. The party workers stressed the failure of the Government to deal with the problems of agriculture. They took care not to alienate the farmers, suspicious of the 'socialistic' aspects of the new party: the programme was to strengthen the private ownership of the land, not to abolish it. The Nazis trod even more delicately in dealing with the Prussian landlords: the party programme deliberately laid down no systematic rule about the size of holdings and it was implied that, though the main aim was to have many viable small-to-medium holdings, large estates also had their place. This facilitated the formation, in October 1931, of the Harzburg Front, in which the Nazis joined forces with two groups dominated by the Junkers, the German Nationalists and the Reichslandbund.

One author has pointed out that on a number of points the views of the Junkers and those of the Nazis were similar, despite the gulf in class: the stress on raising domestic food production and on the importance of agriculture for military strength, the belief in an autocratic society (though they differed as to who should be the autocrats) and the opposition to Jewish traders and speculators were features in common.[1] The grain-importing monopoly proposed by the Junker Count Kanitz in 1894 was the forerunner of arrangements introduced by the Nazis, described below.

[1] Hope L. McBride, 'Note on the economic basis of the Junker class', in *The United States in a Multi-National Economy* (Council on Foreign Relations, New York, 1945).

When Hitler was appointed Chancellor in January 1933, most of the ministerial posts were occupied by German Nationalists, including the Minister for Economics and Agriculture, Hugenberg. Hugenberg pursued the previous policy of restricting agricultural imports, partly by raising duties still further but also by a significant new step: two State import boards (Reichsstellen) were set up, one for grains, feeding-stuffs and various agricultural products, the other for dairy products, oils and fats.

In June 1933 Hugenberg was forced to resign, and Hitler appointed National Socialists to take his post: Schmitt as Minister of Economics and Darré as Minister of Agriculture. Darré was now in a position to put all his ideas into practice. He moved swiftly, and within a few months a series of new measures had been taken. One of the most significant was the 'Reichserbhofsgesetz' (land inheritance law) of September 29th, 1933: this declared in particular that only persons of German origin could be farmers and that farms must be passed on undivided to the principal heir.

A far-reaching new organization of German agricultural markets was quickly set up. First, a law of July 15th, 1933, declared that the organization of agriculture, hitherto within the competence of the Länder, was now a matter for the Reich. Then a basic law of September 13th empowered the Minister to set up the Reichsnährstand (State Food Corporation).[1]

The Reichsnährstand was a comprehensive organization of all aspects of food production and distribution. All farmers and their families, all agricultural workers, all processors and traders dealing in agricultural produce and agricultural requisites, were legally obliged to belong to the Reichsnährstand. Existing agricultural organizations of a public character (such as the Chambers of Agriculture) were absorbed into it; private groups (such as breeders' or producers' organizations) were either associated with it or were wound up. Agricultural co-operatives were made subject to the supervision of the Reichsnährstand.

Its internal administration consisted of a chain of responsibility based on the Führer principle; at the head was Darré himself, and below were offices responsible firstly for each *Land*, then for areas within each *Land*, finally for localities within each area; at each level the leader was appointed by the head of the group

[1] 'Corporation' is the usual translation. The word 'Stand', however, means rather more than this, something like 'estate of the realm'.

immediately above. Instructions were passed down the chain and recommendations passed up. At each level there were three Verwaltungsämte (administrative offices) for each of the main aspects of policy, described as 'Mensch, Hof, Markt': i.e. the agricultural population, production and market regulation. The offices dealing with market regulation were further divided according to the commodities dealt with; they were responsible for the practical organization of the market, with the object of controlling supplies and ensuring producers the fair prices to which, under National Socialist philosophy, they were entitled.

> The main object of the market regulation is to bring about fair prices for the main products of agricultural labour. Sufficient and stable prices, bearing a correct relationship one to another, are to assure the farmer of an appropriate return for his crop and to eliminate the disturbing influences of the market. The law of supply and demand, which regulates prices and hence production in the capitalist economy, becomes inoperative: automatic price formation is replaced by the will of authority.[1]

In determining prices, the consumer interest was also to be taken into account: stable purchasing power was essential to National Socialist policy with regard to labour, for this would enable wages and hence the whole economy to be kept on an even keel.

For most of the major products – in particular bread grains, feed grains, flour, livestock, meat, butter, eggs, wool and potatoes – limits were prescribed between which market prices could vary, but in fact these limits were so close together that the price was practically fixed. Wider price margins were laid down for sugar-beet, hops and some other foodstuffs. In a few other cases – wine in particular – only minimum prices were prescribed. There was provision for variations in price according to quality and to region.

The Reichsnährstand became the instrument of the campaign for increased production. In autumn 1934 Hitler announced the beginning of the 'Battle of Production', the object being to raise German's self-sufficiency in food. Production targets were laid down in each subsequent year, and the Reichsnährstand issued many and detailed instructions as to how the land should be used and cultivated.

[1] B. Mehrens, *Die Marktordnung des Reichsnährstandes* (Berlin, 1938), p. 2.

Control over imports was vested in the Reichsstellen, or State Import Boards. These Boards were directly responsible to the Minister: they were not part of the Reichsnährstand, but they formed an indispensable complement to its action. Boards were set up for the following products:

1. Dairy products, oils and fats (April 1933).
2. Grain, feeding-stuffs and various agricultural products (May 1933).
3. Livestock and livestock products (April 1934).
4. Eggs (early 1934).
5. Fruit, vegetables and wine (November 1936).

All imports of these products had to be offered by the importer to the appropriate Board, which, if it decided that the necessary demand existed, authorized the importer to sell the produce on the domestic market after payment of a levy corresponding to the difference between the import price and the domestic price level which it was desired to maintain. The Boards could also take over the produce from the importer and resell it at a higher price, and they could import on their own account (this applied mainly to grains and feeding-stuffs). They could also buy and sell on the domestic market and keep stocks: this role gained increasing importance and the action of the Boards made it possible to even out fluctuations in supplies and prices, thus making an essential contribution to the work of the market regulation bodies of the Reichsnährstand.

The Boards not only enabled complete control to be exerted over the volume and prices of imports: they also made it possible to decide from which sources imports would be accepted, and thus served the aims of overall trade policy. The Neue Plan of 1934 stated that Germany should import only from countries prepared to buy German goods. The traditional system of commercial treaties with 'most favoured nation' clauses was abandoned and replaced by bilateral arrangements involving reciprocal guarantees of import quotas and preferential tariffs. Special Governmental committees were set up to supervise the development of trade between Germany and the countries concerned. Under the Neue Plan, Germany's trade was directed away from the democracies of Western Europe and North America, and towards Italy, South-East Europe and Latin America.

At the outbreak of war, all the necessary machinery existed for controlling food supplies and prices. There was some reorganization of the Reichsnährstand to provide even tighter control; by a decree of September 7th, 1939, all important foodstuffs were requisitioned and were to be sold only by order of the authorities; rationing was imposed.

In the countries which they occupied, the National Socialists imposed their corporative organization of agriculture (the measures taken in France are described in Chapter 13), and sought to make Continental Europe into a single, self-sufficing unit. Herbert Backe, who after being Secretary of State under Darré replaced him as Minister of Agriculture in 1942, wrote in that year that liberalism had led most of the European countries into a misguided dependence on colonial territories for their food supplies: the result had been to weaken their own agriculture. National Socialism was the first movement to restore strength to agriculture.

> The war of 1939–42 will demonstrate to the other nations of Europe the correctness of the German method, and will lead them to recognize that Europe's food supplies can only be assured by a community of Continental Europe within which the products of labour are freely shared.[1]

Results, 1933-1939

It is not easy to assess the results of Nazi agricultural policy, because of the lack of objective analysis within the regime. There is no doubt that agriculture gradually recovered from the crisis, but this was a feature common to all countries and cannot be entirely attributed to Nazi policy. Also, the recovery was no doubt due as much to the revival in purchasing power in the economy as a whole as to measures taken in the agricultural field.

The regulation of markets certainly stabilized prices and contributed to a gradual increase in the overall price level from 1932/3 to 1935/6, after which prices of almost all products were kept practically unchanged and the overall agricultural price index stood at 76–77 per cent of the pre-crisis level (Table 52).

The role played by import control in stabilizing prices is reflected in Table 53. The overall volume of imports was kept

[1] H. Backe, *Um die Nahrungsfreiheit Europas* (Leipzig, 1942), p. 261.

Table 52

AGRICULTURAL PRICE INDICES

(1928/9 = 100)

	Wheat	Rye	All crop products	Cattle	Pigs	Butter	All live-stock products	All agri-cultural products
1932/3	91	74	71	53	52	58	59	58
1933/4	85	72	71	59	56	70	69	64
1934/5	93	75	83	72	62	71	70	71
1935/6	93	77	85	90	67	72	72	77
1936/7	93	77	85	87	66	73	73	76
1937/8	93	87	88	87	67	73	74	77

Source : Statistisches Jahrbuch für das Deutsche Reich.

Table 53

IMPORTS OF MAJOR AGRICULTURAL PRODUCTS

	Wheat	Rye	Bar-ley	Sugar	Butter	Meat, bacon, saus-ages	Eggs	All foodstuffs[a]
	thousand tons							1928 = 100
1928	2,473	339	1,929	151	127	313	179	100
1929	2,141	144	1,766	58	135	343	168	96
1930	1,197	59	1,523	34	133	112	160	87
1931	798	102	757	14	100	63	143	74
1932	1,022	646	569	34	70	59	143	74
1933	770	238	235	29	59	49	84	62
1934	647	53	552	21	62	54	76	64
1935	159	220	158	30	71	64	65	55
1936	74	24	48[b]	11	75	112[c]	80[d]	55
1937	1,219	181	46[b]	10	87	111[c]	100[d]	71

[a] Volume index based on 1928 prices.
[b] Feeding barley only.
[c] All meat and meat products.
[d] Including egg whites and yolks.

Source : As Table 52.

well below the pre-crisis level, imports of barley in particular
being drastically cut, and sugar imports remained at the low level
to which they had already been reduced by the previous regime.
The effects of intervention are clearly seen in the wide fluctuations
of imports, especially as regards wheat and rye: this clearly was
the main factor in keeping the domestic price stable.

The official data on the net income of agriculture show a
considerable recovery, from 891 million marks in 1932/3 to
2,600 million marks in 1937/8. The increase in the value of sales,
particularly of livestock products, exceeded the rise in production
costs (Table 54). However, some sources critical of Nazi policy
declared that the problem of indebtedness among farmers had
not been solved, that costs had risen and that the move out of
agriculture had continued to such an extent that there was a
shortage of farm labour.

The 'Battle of Production' seems to have given partly dis-
appointing results (Table 55). Output of wheat was maintained
at a reasonable level but without any significant increase; on the
other hand, production of rye and oats declined, and there was
only a moderate increase in production of barley. Better results
were obtained with potatoes and sugar-beet, particularly the
latter. There was a smallish increase in the numbers of cattle and
pigs, and the sheep population revived for the first time in over a
century. The degree of self-sufficiency in food supplies rose, but
complete autarky was not attained: the percentage of domestic
production in total food supplies rose from 75 in 1932 to 83 in
1937.

Some observations on Nazi agricultural policy

Many of the basic ideas of Nazi agricultural policy were already
implicit in measures taken previously in Germany and in the
action of some other countries during the 1930s. The belief in the
social importance of the farm population, the desire to shield them
from market forces and give them fair prices, the aim for national
self-sufficiency in food – all these preoccupations were present to
varying degrees in the majority of countries. But only the National
Socialists in Germany combined these elements into a coherent
philosophy, forming an essential part of their overall policy; and
they alone systematically carried these ideas into practice.

Table 54

RECEIPTS AND EXPENSES OF AGRICULTURE

(RM million)

	Receipts from farm sales			Farm expenses			Net farm income
		of which			of which		
	Total	Crop products	Live-stock products	Total	Feeding-stuffs	Wages	
1932/3	6,405	2,645	3,760	5,514	698	1,332	891
1933/4	7,409	2,848	4,561	5,646	722	1,376	1,763
1934/5	8,302	3,145	5,157	5,670	610	1,443	2,632
1935/6	8,698	3,355	5,343	6,111	594	1,576	2,587
1936/7	8,910	3,375	5,535	6,369	597	1,687	2,541
1937/8	9,484	3,611	5,873	6,884	842	1,738	2,600

Source: As Table 52.

Table 55

PRODUCTION OF MAJOR COMMODITIES AND LIVESTOCK NUMBERS

	Wheat	Rye	Barley	Oats	Potatoes	Sugarbeet	Milk	Cattle	Pigs	Sheep
	million tons							millions		
1928	3·9	8·5	3·3	7·0	41·3	11·0	21·0	18·5	20·2	3·6
1929	3·3	8·2	3·2	7·4	40·1	11·1	..	18·1	20·0	3·5
1930	3·8	7·7	2·9	5·7	47·1	14·9	..	18·5	23·6	3·5
1931	4·2	6·7	3·0	6·2	43·9	11·0	22·9	19·2	23·9	3·5
1932	5·0	8·4	3·2	6·7	47·0	7·9	..	19·2	23·0	3·4
1933	5·6	8·7	3·5	7·0	44·1	8·6	..	19·8	24·0	3·4
1934	4·6	7·6	3·2	5·5	46·8	10·4	23·7	19·3	23·3	3·5
1935	4·7	7·5	3·4	5·4	41·0	10·6	..	18·9	22·8	3·9
1936	4·4	7·4	3·4	5·6	46·3	12·1	..	20·1	25·9	4·3
1937	4·5	6·9	3·6	5·9	55·3	15·7	25·4	20·5	23·8	4·7

.. Not available.

Source: As Table 52.

Their agricultural policy was thus an important event in the history of European agriculture, and if Germany had not lost the war this policy would have been extended to the greater part of Continental Europe. Moreover, although the career of the Nazis came to an abrupt end, much of their thinking on agricultural matters has persisted, both in Germany and elsewhere, and the methods they devised to carry out their policy were the predecessors of those which were widely adopted after the Second World War.

The inner logic of National Socialist thinking cannot be denied. Given the aim of ensuring, by force if necessary, the political and economic strength of a single nation, it was rational to seek to safeguard that nation's food supplies by encouraging domestic production through controlled markets and price supports, and to restrict imports by all possible means. These considerations were all the more compelling for a densely populated country, dependent on imported food and liable in war to be cut off from overseas supplies. The argument was also forceful at a time of severe agricultural depression, particularly when reinforced by an eloquent philosophy as to the role of the 'yeoman' in the nation. It must be granted that Walther Darré's writings and speeches made a remarkable impression: the ideas are clear and forceful, and are in sharp contrast with the anxious deliberations of Government and economist alike that preceded the advent of National Socialism.

Moreover, the ideas were put into practice rapidly and uncompromisingly. Darré was certain of what he wanted to do, and he lost no time; from the moment he took office his policy was consistently applied. In the Reichsnährstand and the Reichsstellen a remarkably efficient instrument was forged.

This policy could be objected to on grounds of economic liberalism: [extensive protection was likely to maintain inefficient branches of production and to lead to a maldistribution of resources. But it might be answered that the exercise of control according to a constructive plan permitted rapid economic growth, and that in a time of acute depression it was essential to preserve the nation's productive apparatus from destruction.]

There was also the objection that drastic protection must reduce the earnings of other countries and thus endanger exports. As has been seen above, Darré contested this, on the grounds that the planned direction of trade resolved the old conflict between agriculture and industry on this score, enabling export markets to be maintained. It was even suggested by Nazi writers that other countries benefited from the new policy, because the contracts they obtained gave them an assurance that did not exist under the free market. But on these points the argument seems vulnerable: the fact remained that the more food was produced at home, the less was imported from abroad, and hence the less other countries could afford to buy from Germany. The effects might not be significant so long as only one or a few industrial nations restricted their imports of food, but clearly all countries could not follow the same policy and still hope to export their manufactures.

Thus the National Socialist theory was weakest at its foundations. It made sense only in the context of a single nation aiming to reinforce its power; it was geared to the expectation of war if not the desire for it. Further, the pursuit of such autarkic aims was bound to contribute to international tension and to make the outbreak of war more likely. The National Socialist system was by its nature incompatible with long-run economic and political stability. In one of the few critical studies that have been made of Nazi agricultural policy, Bertrand pointed out:

If all countries imitated Germany and sought a solution to their agricultural problem in complete self-sufficiency in food supplies, there is no doubt that their standard of living would fall to a frightening extent. From an agricultural point of view, all countries have interests in common because their products are complementary. In the capitalist, liberal economy, their food supplies are only assured by international trade. If they set about organizing their own agriculture, that is all the more reason for needing additional supplies. Autarky therefore does not make sense except for those who subordinate everything to military requirements. The real solution to the problem of market organization can only be an international one.[1]

---

[1] R. Bertrand, *Le corporatisme agricole et l'organisation des marchés en Allemagne* (Paris, 1937), p. 340.

Chapter 10. Denmark

The crisis – the loss of export markets

During the First World War, Denmark remained neutral and was able to maintain her exports to both Germany and Great Britain. Her trade continued to expand after the war and was not seriously affected by the restoration of tariffs in Germany in 1925. In Britain, Denmark gained a larger share of the markets for eggs and bacon, but lost part of the butter market to increased supplies from New Zealand. The years 1928 and 1929 were reasonably prosperous, and even after the world grain price had begun to fall Danish agriculture at first did not feel the effects, since the prices of livestock products fell relatively little, and this fall was offset by increased production, making use of cheap imported grain and other feeding-stuffs. The maintenance of purchasing power in Danish agriculture sustained other sectors, and as a result unemployment did not increase significantly till the first half of 1931. In 1931 Denmark followed Great Britain off the gold standard, and devalued again in the autumn of 1932.

In 1931 Danish exports of livestock products were severely affected by the fall in purchasing power abroad and also by the increased tariffs and import restrictions applied in several countries, Germany in particular. On the British market, Danish butter continued to suffer from the competition of New Zealand and Australia, and in 1932 all Danish exports to Britain were subjected to import duties, while Empire produce continued to

Table 56

INDICES OF AGRICULTURAL PRICES

(1928 = 100)

	Crop products	Livestock products	All agricultural products
1928	100	100	100
1929	93	105	104
1930	68	87	85
1931	62	65	64
1932	66	56	57
1933	69	68	69
1934	94	79	79

Source : Danish Council of Agriculture, *Danemark – l'Agriculture* (Copenhagen, 1935).

enter free. As a result, in 1931 and 1932, the prices of livestock products in Denmark fell sharply (Table 56). The fall in agricultural receipts was not offset by a corresponding reduction in farm expenses, except for feeding-stuffs, and as a result farmers made little or no profit in 1930/31 and 1931/2 (Table 57). The distress

Table 57

RECEIPTS AND EXPENSES ON SAMPLE FARMS

(kroner per hectare)

	Gross receipts	Production costs[a]	Net income
1924/5–1928/9	902	798	104
1929/30	817	682	135
1930/1	651	637	14
1931/2	560	571	−11
1932/3	562	502	60
1933/4	530	460	70

[a] Including allowance for the labour of the farmer and his family.

Source : As Table 56.

of farmers was particularly severe since they had incurred a heavy burden of debt during the period of rising prices and land values early in the 1920s.

As in the depression of the 1880s, but now to an even greater extent, Danish agriculture's dependence on trade made import restrictions practically useless. Since Denmark's difficulties arose primarily from protectionist measures in other countries, her first reaction to the crisis was to seek better conditions for exports to the countries with the largest markets, Britain and Germany. This attempt was only partly successful. In 1932 exports of the main agricultural products were brought under the control of ministerial Export Boards, with the task of licensing exports and regulating prices by imposing and distributing export levies. Further, Denmark was gradually forced to adopt a series of measures affecting her domestic market and also to control some imports, in particular grain. This action represented a departure from the principles of laissez-faire to which the farmers themselves adhered and was adopted only reluctantly.

Efforts to improve trade relations

(a) With Britain

As other markets became increasingly restricted, Denmark sought to expand her sales to Britain. This gave rise to a vigorous campaign in some sections of the British press, where it was pointed out that the large British purchases from Denmark were not reflected in equally large Danish imports from Britain: on the contrary, Denmark's imports of manufactured goods still came mainly from Germany. The Danish agricultural organizations had some sympathy with this point of view and already at the end of 1929 had exhorted Danish traders and consumers to give preference to British goods. At first there were no great results, but in January 1932, following a further large increase in the German butter duty, the Danish Exchange Control Office was established: all imports had to be authorized by this Office, and it sought to restrict imports from Germany in favour of Britain and other countries.

However, the British Import Duties Act of February 1932 imposed duties of 10 per cent *ad valorem* on most Danish agricultural exports, and subsequently the Ottawa Agreements Act replaced most of these by specific duties which generally had a higher incidence. Free entry was maintained for bacon and hams, but – as has been seen in Chapter 7 – an import quota was imposed which halved Danish exports as compared with the peak figures of 1932; Canada, on the other hand, was granted a quota far in excess of her previous exports to Britain.

Negotiations for an Anglo-Danish commercial treaty began in December 1932, and an agreement was signed which came into force in June 1933; it was valid for three years. Britain undertook not to impose duties on bacon and ham, but reserved the right to limit the quantity of imports in connection with domestic marketing schemes, and Denmark was unable to obtain a guarantee for any specific quantity: the only concession was that Denmark could supply at least 62 per cent of all bacon imports from non-Commonwealth countries. For butter and eggs, Britain agreed to bind the duties at the existing levels; again, she reserved the right to impose import quotas, but in this case restrictions were not in fact applied.

On the whole, the treaty offered Denmark only the possibility of maintaining its exports at about the same level as before, with the disadvantage of a tariff giving preference to the British Empire. In the case of bacon, the import quota, though it reduced the volume of trade to about half that of 1932 (Table 58), led to prices more than double the previous level because of the inelastic demand by British consumers for Danish bacon. The outcome for butter was much less satisfactory, for New Zealand was helped by the preference to raise its exports considerably, capturing from Denmark the first place on the British market. In the case of eggs, however, Britain's trade war with the Irish Republic helped to increase the volume of imports from Denmark.

In negotiating with Britain, Denmark was in a weak bargaining position because of her dependence on the British market, and in the 1933 treaty she was forced to grant Britain substantial concessions, including the removal of certain import duties on manufactures and the reduction or binding of many others, together with an undertaking to purchase certain quantities of British goods such as coal, iron and steel. The treaty was renewed in 1936 and remained in force until the outbreak of war. The advantages it gave to Britain, together with the activities of the

Table 58

MAJOR AGRICULTURAL EXPORTS

	Cattle (000)		Pigs (000)		Bacon (000 tons)		Butter (000 tons)			Eggs (million score)		
	Total	of which to Germany	Total	of which to Germany	Total	of which to U.K.	Total	of which to		Total	of which to	
								U.K.	Germany		U.K.	Germany
1928	255	255	45	31	272	271	148	101	40	40	29	11
1929	270	261	51	45	249	248	159	108	43	39	31	9
1930	169	153	62	52	306	306	169	116	42	43	37	6
1931	124	91	34	30	376	372	172	123	30	49	42	7
1932	116	75	24	2	390	384	158	129	13	55	38	17
1933	48	17	73	32	294	284	151	126	16	54	38	12
1934	71	50	57	31	223	219	150	124	20	56	38	13
1935	97	81	53	44	200	197	138	109	25	59	39	13
1936	166	149	184	162	176	174	146	110	34	70	48	17
1937	172	141	167	157	182	178	153	116	35	81	60	18
1938	134	121	114	114	179	174	158	119	36	78	57	19

Source : Statistisk Aarbog.

Danish Exchange Control Office, caused Britain's exports to Denmark to double in value from 1932 to 1938, while the value of Danish exports to Britain recovered only slightly and failed to reach the level of 1929 (Table 59).

Table 59

VALUE OF TRADE WITH THE UNITED KINGDOM

(million kroner)

	Danish imports	Danish exports
1929	263	963
1932	255	728
1935	479	731
1937	638	824
1938	567	861

Source: H. P. Gøtrik, *Danish Economic Policy* (Copenhagen: Institute of Economics and History, 1939).

(b) With Germany

Until the crisis, Danish exports of livestock products to Germany benefited from relatively low rates of duty, largely as a result of concessions made by Germany to other countries and extended to Denmark through the 'most favoured nation' clause. At the end of 1929, however, Germany terminated its agreement with Sweden and in February 1930 raised the duty on cattle from 16 to 24·50 marks per 100 kg. Sweden however was allowed to export to Germany, at the old rate of duty, a certain number of cattle (5,000 for one year, 6,000 for a second year and 7,000 for a third): this amount was roughly equivalent to Sweden's previous exports to Germany. But whereas Denmark's exports of cattle to Germany were far greater (255,000 head in 1928), Germany interpreted the 'most favoured nation' clause in such a way as to allow Denmark only a tariff quota of the same absolute amount as Sweden. Denmark attempted to obtain a quota in proportion to past supplies, but without success, so from the beginning of 1930 most Danish cattle exports were subject to the higher rate of duty.

Similarly for butter, Denmark enjoyed the benefit of a reduction in the German duty granted in a treaty with Finland in 1926. In November 1930 Germany raised the duty from 27·50 to 50 marks per 100 kg. Finland was granted a quota of 5,000 tons at the previous, lower rate: this was a quantity nearly as large as her past exports. Denmark, whose exports had exceeded 40,000 tons, was given only the same absolute amount. In 1932 Germany raised the duty still further, to 100 marks, and introduced an 'exchange premium' of 36 marks on imports from countries which had devalued their currency (this included Denmark). The duty applied to Danish exports was then 86 marks for the quota of 5,000 tons and 136 marks for the remainder.

The Netherlands suffered in much the same way as Denmark from these measures by Germany, and both countries complained in the League of Nations against the German interpretation of the 'most favoured nation' clause. In June 1931 the League's Economic Committee produced a report that substantially agreed with the Danish case, to the effect that tariff quotas should be related to past trade. Germany however took no action till October 1932, when she introduced a complete quota system for butter and distributed the global quota of 55,000 tons among exporting countries in proportion to their share of exports in 1929–31.

When the National Socialists came to power in Germany, they denounced existing treaty commitments and – as has been seen in Chapter 9 – subjected almost all imports of agricultural products to the control of State import boards. A bilateral agreement of March 1st, 1934, between Denmark and Germany stated that the two countries would endeavour to promote trade between them and to settle difficulties by negotiation. Trade between Denmark and Germany then became subject to a considerable degree of intervention by both Governments. When German food requirements rose in 1935 and 1936, additional purchases were made in Denmark, but only on condition that Denmark should increase her imports from Germany by a corresponding amount. As there was difficulty in meeting this requirement the Danish Government was obliged, at the end of 1936, to take action to raise purchases from Germany. Starting in 1937, Germany subjected her imports from Denmark in each quarter to a maximum, determined by the total payments made by Denmark for German goods in the previous quarter.

The demands made by both Britain and Germany for a larger share of the Danish market aggravated Denmark's difficulties in finding enough foreign exchange to pay other foreign countries for the feed grains and other feeding-stuffs needed by Danish livestock farmers.

Intervention on the domestic market

The first intervention occurred in 1930, and consisted of subsidies to growers of sugar-beet to compensate them for low prices and to encourage production. In 1932 this scheme was replaced by arrangements under which licences for producing and refining sugar had to be obtained from the Minister of Commerce, and prices were fixed for both sugar-beet and sugar. Imports were prohibited except under licence. In 1933, arrangements for potatoes for industrial purposes were introduced along similar lines.

The import restrictions by Germany led to a sharp decline in meat prices, and measures of support were introduced in 1933. The details of the system underwent several changes: the final arrangement was that a slaughter-house tax was levied on all cattle sold for the home market, the revenue being used to buy up lower-quality cattle in order to raise market prices. From 1933 to 1938 some 600,000 cattle were bought in this way and slaughtered, many of them cattle infected by tuberculosis, and the market price was doubled. The effectiveness of the scheme was due to the relatively large proportion of the total output of beef and veal that was consumed in Denmark (about 75 per cent).

The low level to which butter prices fell also necessitated measures of support. In 1933 variable levies were imposed on butter sold for domestic consumption, in order to maintain a minimum price of 2·15 kroner per kg. The receipts from these levies were distributed to milk producers in proportion to their deliveries. A tax was also imposed on margarine to discourage any shift of consumption. In 1934, prices improved and the scheme was allowed to lapse, but it was reintroduced in 1937, levies being imposed on all sales of liquid milk as well as butter; the minimum butter price was fixed at 2·60 kroner and was raised to 3 kroner in 1939. The benefits of the scheme were rather limited since, in contrast to beef, only about a quarter of total milk output was consumed on the home market in the form of milk or butter: the amount which could be collected through the levies was thus limited.

In the case of bacon, the British import quota made it necessary to limit Danish production. A scheme was introduced in 1933 which constituted the most far-reaching innovation of the period. General authority was given to the Minister of Agriculture to regulate the production of pigs and the number slaughtered, and to order that each producer should be paid a preferential price for a certain number of pigs delivered, with a lower price for the remainder. 'Pig cards' or licences were distributed to producers, and pigs supplied to bacon factories received the preferential price only if they were accompanied by a card. The preferential price corresponded to the price that could be got on the British market; the price for excess deliveries was that available on other markets. The result of this scheme was a reduction in the number of pigs from 5·4 million in 1932 to 3 million in 1934; the bacon price rose from 0·75 to 1·55 kroner per kg.

This scheme, probably the first marketing quota system to be introduced for an agricultural product in any country, led to the inevitable difficulties in distributing licences. A compromise was finally reached with a complicated system in which the number of 'pig cards' allotted to each producer was calculated according to a number of criteria. To begin with, a small number of cards were allocated in an equal number to each farm regardless of its size (except for a reduction in the case of very small holdings); then a certain number were distributed on the basis of the land value of the farm, up to a specified maximum; a further quantity was distributed in proportion to the amount of skimmed milk which the farm used for feeding to pigs; and finally an allocation was made on the basis of past deliveries of pigs. This arrangement deliberately gave an advantage to the smaller producers, through the initial distribution of a fixed amount and through the maximum placed on the land value criterion.

The larger farmers, for whom grain was a more important product, were compensated by a system of guaranteed minimum prices for the various grains, implemented by means of a variable levy on imports. As a further step the proceeds of the levy were distributed to the small farmers who needed to buy feed grain for their livestock. In spite of this arrangement, and in spite of the

moderate price level that was guaranteed, many farmers felt this
levy on grain imports to be a serious departure from free trade
principles, and the scheme was decided upon only after long
deliberations among the agricultural organizations. The Government, however, was anxious to prevent an excessive increase in
grain imports which would have further endangered the balance
of payments.

In 1938, owing to a renewed fall in world grain prices, imports
of wheat and rye were suspended entirely. As an additional
measure to limit imports and maintain the price level, compulsory
milling ratios were introduced, the minimum quantity of domestic
grain in the flour being fixed at 50 per cent for wheat and 30 per
cent for rye.

Part III

Since the Second World War — State Involvement in Agriculture

Chapter 11. General

Rising production and low incomes in agriculture
By the end of the Second World War, food production in most of
the countries of Western Europe had fallen below the pre-war
level. The situation in Western Germany, now separated from the
grain-producing eastern regions, was critical. In most other
countries agriculture had suffered, if not from actual destruction,
from shortages of labour, machinery, fertilizers and so on. To
some extent Great Britain was an exception, for while food imports
had been drastically cut, the encouragements given to farmers had
borne fruit in an increased contribution by British agriculture to
the food supply.[1]

The immediate concern throughout Western Europe was
therefore to raise agricultural production as rapidly as possible.
Besides the problem of food shortages, there was a general need to
save foreign exchange by keeping imports as low as possible. The
recovery was rapid, and was greatly helped from 1948 on by
American aid under the Marshall Plan, administered through the
Organisation for European Economic Co-operation (OEEC). In

---

[1] Total output had fallen, but 'net output' – i.e. total output less imported
supplies of feeding-stuffs, seed and livestock (mainly store cattle) – had
increased: in other words British agriculture was producing slightly less but
importing considerably less. The distinction between total output and net
output is important for Britain but much less so for other countries. Figure 6
is in terms of total output.

8

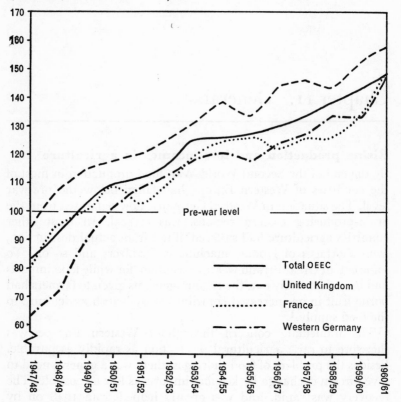

AGRICULTURAL PRODUCTION IN OEEC COUNTRIES
(INDICES, PRE-WAR = 100)

Pre-war level

Total OEEC
United Kingdom
France
Western Germany

Source: OEEC and OECD Statistics.

FIG. 6

the crop year 1949/50, agricultural production in the OEEC area exceeded the pre-war level (Figure 6); even in Western Germany, production was back to the pre-war level by 1950/1. Thereafter, the increase continued at a slower but still considerable rate, till by the end of the 1950s agricultural production in the OEEC area was some 50 per cent higher than before the war, for a total population which had increased by about 20 per cent.

This growth in production has taken place in spite of a large and steady fall in the numbers employed in agriculture. Output per man in agriculture has thus risen even more rapidly: in most countries labour productivity has risen faster in agriculture than in other sectors (Table 60). The outflow of farm labour has been offset by greatly increased efficiency in the use of the remaining labour force. Machinery of all kinds has multiplied on the farms: from 1947 to 1960, the number of tractors in OEEC countries rose from half a million to three million, and the amount of motor fuel used on farms almost doubled between 1952 and 1960. From 1947 to 1960, the consumption of fertilizers of all kinds more than doubled. Combined with rapidly spreading knowledge of new techniques, fostered by the activity of farm advisory services, all this progress has been reflected in greatly increased yields from crops and livestock.

Table 60

OUTPUT PER MAN IN AGRICULTURE AND IN ALL SECTORS IN 1959[a]

(1949 = 100)

	Agriculture	All sectors
Denmark	177	130
Germany	172	153
Italy	169	159
France	161	154
Austria	156	151
Belgium	156	132
United Kingdom	146	120
Netherlands	142	139
Norway	137	131
Ireland	127	129

[a] Based on changes in gross product (in constant prices) and in numbers employed.

Source: OEEC and OECD statistics.

The problem of food shortages has thus given way to one of overproduction of several commodities. With the growth in milk production, the markets of Western European countries are frequently oversupplied with dairy products, mainly in the form of butter: most countries have closed their markets to imports, and the only large remaining market, that of London, is liable to be swamped with excess supplies. There have been periodic surpluses of pigmeat, steadily growing more acute; and in various countries the markets for individual products, such as eggs, beef and wheat, are giving rise to concern. Since the middle of the 1950s, the United States has been grappling with surpluses of grains, dairy products and cotton, and other overseas exporting countries are faced with similar difficulties. As consumption of foodstuffs in the economically advanced countries seems unlikely to increase very rapidly, the outlook, by the early 1960s, is distinctly unpromising.

The progress accomplished by Western European agriculture in raising its efficiency and output has not been matched by a comparable advance in farm incomes. Though the product of agriculture rose in value, it rose considerably less fast than the national income. The period since the end of the Second World War has been, for most Western European countries, one of fast economic growth and of rapidly rising wages in the industrial sector in particular. However, once food consumption had recovered to a satisfactory level, it increased much less quickly than demand for other goods: as the output of other sectors rose, the share of agriculture in the national income diminished. With the outflow of labour, incomes per head in agriculture have been maintained or have even increased. But at the beginning of this period, farm incomes generally were well below the average of incomes in other sectors, and the subsequent improvement has generally been quite insufficient to close the gap.

In Figure 7, the trends in the gross product of agriculture and of the economy as a whole, together with the trends in the active population, are shown for four countries: these have been selected for convenience of presentation, but developments in most other countries were similar. It can be seen that in the course of the 1950s the gross product of agriculture, expressed as a percentage of the gross domestic product, declined in all these countries. Agriculture's share of the active population, at the beginning of

TRENDS IN GROSS PRODUCT AND IN ACTIVE POPULATION

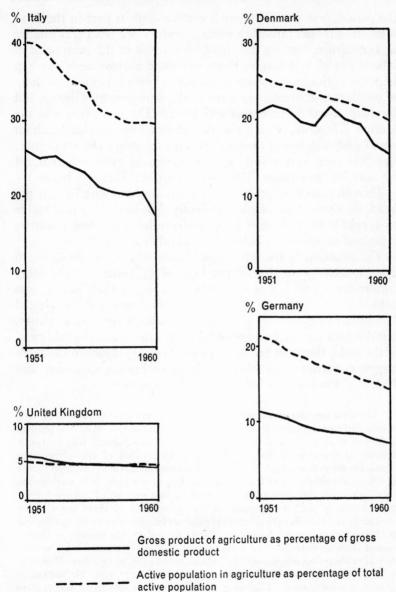

Gross product of agriculture as percentage of gross
domestic product

Active population in agriculture as percentage of total
active population

Source: OECD statistics.

FIG. 7

the period, was generally much greater than its part in the gross domestic product: in other words, product per head was smaller in agriculture. During the 1950s, as a result of the movement of labour out of agriculture, there was some narrowing of the gap between agriculture's share of the active population and its share of the domestic product in three of the four countries shown, but by 1960 the difference was still large. (The exception was the United Kingdom, where the two shares were originally about equal and afterwards declined at approximately the same rate: this, however, was mainly a consequence of extensive financial support for agriculture. This point is further discussed below.)

Though gross product per head is not identical with income per head, the correspondence is sufficiently close to make it reasonable to conclude that incomes in agriculture have in most countries remained substantially below those of other sectors.[1]

The situation in the late 1950s is indicated in Figure 8, which compares the gross product per head of agriculture and of other sectors for a number of countries. It appears that 'parity' was achieved, or nearly so, only in the Netherlands and the United Kingdom; Belgium and Denmark were also fairly close to parity, but the data for Belgium are of doubtful validity. At the other end of the scale, the gross product per head of agriculture in the three largest countries of Continental Europe – France, Germany and Italy – was only about half that of other sectors.[2]

---

[1] The gross product of a sector is the difference between the value of its total output and its total expenditure on current inputs; the gross domestic product is the sum of all sectors and represents the total income generated by economic activity in the country concerned. The gross product of agriculture thus represents the sum available for distribution between all those employed in the agricultural sector; out of it farmers have to pay not only their workers but also their rent, the interest on borrowed capital and an allowance for the depreciation of their equipment. As the importance of these items is not necessarily the same in agriculture as in other sectors, an inter-sector comparison in absolute terms cannot be precise. Nor do these data take account of income earned from activities off the farm: where part-time farming is important, they may therefore exaggerate the income problem in agriculture. However, these national accounts statistics are generally the only available indication of overall farm income. Moreover, an analysis of trends from one year to another in a given country should be reasonably accurate.

[2] This comparison, besides being subject to the difficulties attached to the use of national income data referred to in the previous footnote, is affected by inadequacies in the information on the active agricultural population, and in

At a time when preoccupation with rising standards of living is widespread, and when the farm population is kept fully aware of the rapid improvement in other sectors, this continuing disparity between farm incomes and other incomes has inevitably become a major concern of Governments. The problem is all the more difficult in that the most obvious ways of raising farm incomes are liable to encourage production and aggravate the problem of surpluses.

Price support

In the immediate post-war period of food shortages, the aim was to expand agricultural production by all possible means, and for this purpose financial guarantees were given to farmers in the form of price supports and other measures. In Britain the Agriculture Act of 1947 was of great historical importance: it stated the aim of raising net farm output to 50 per cent above pre-war, and committed the Government to providing financial assistance. For several years the wartime measures of fixed prices and Government purchase of foodstuffs were maintained. In France the Monnet Plan for 1947–50 involved a campaign to modernize French agriculture and raise its productivity, with the aim of raising output and exports of agricultural produce. In Western Germany, Dr Adenauer's Government in 1949 announced a policy to expand agricultural production, through the assurance of stable and adequate prices. Italy aimed to raise production of wheat in particular. Switzerland in 1947 inserted in its Constitution articles which provided a permanent legal basis for assistance to agriculture. Also in 1947 Norway laid down the general objectives of its agricultural policy, among which was the aim of assuring to the farm population a standard of living comparable to that of other sectors. A similar assurance was given in Sweden; here there was a special feature in that food production was intended to cover no more than 90 per cent of domestic requirements. Denmark was the only country during this period which dismantled its wartime apparatus of State control and returned to private trading.

From about 1953 there was a change in emphasis, as agricultural production caught up with demand. The aim was no longer to

particular by differences in the coverage from one country to another. The results are therefore to be regarded only as approximate.

GROSS PRODUCT PER HEAD IN AGRICULTURE AS A PER-
CENTAGE OF GROSS PRODUCT PER HEAD IN ALL SECTORS,
IN 1956–60

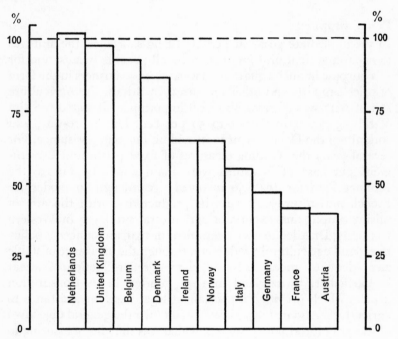

Source: OECD statistics.

FIG. 8

raise production at all costs, but to achieve selective expansion and to raise agricultural efficiency. At the same time, concern with the relatively low level of farm incomes was increasingly felt, and Governments were placed in a quandary as the price guarantees they offered farmers tended to stimulate excess production.

The shift in emphasis was particularly clear in BRITAIN. In 1951 the Labour Government was replaced by a Conservative one, which removed food controls. However, it maintained price guarantees to farmers, reviving for the purpose the pre-war instrument of deficiency payments which left markets free; it also restored the pre-war Marketing Boards, with the addition of some new ones. For a time, it pursued the policy of raising food production, but around 1956 the emphasis passed to 'selective expansion'. Successive annual price reviews altered the price guarantees according to the state of the market and attempted, through price reductions and other measures, to restrain output of certain products. At the same time, the Government was forced to give satisfaction to farmers in various ways, in particular by the 'long-term assurances' in 1956, which limited the extent to which prices could be changed annually and seriously restricted the Government's freedom of movement. As a result, it proved difficult to discourage output: in particular, production of milk came greatly to exceed the demand for liquid consumption, and the excess could only be sold at a loss for processing; egg production grew to the point where Britain became self-sufficient; output of pigmeat fluctuated but tended to rise unduly; the market for barley was oversupplied at certain periods. Market prices generally remained well below the guaranteed prices and were liable to be further depressed by increased imports, over which there was practically no control. The consequence has been a heavy increase in the volume of Exchequer payments to agriculture, and it seems likely that domestic production and imports will have to be more effectively controlled.

In FRANCE, when the Second Plan for Modernization and Equipment was being prepared in 1953, there was much discussion as to the advisability of further expanding farm production. Surpluses of wheat, wine and sugar-beet were already in evidence from about 1950. The Plan nevertheless provided for a further overall increase of 20 per cent, but indicated that the output of certain products should be reduced. At the same time, a variety of new measures were introduced for regulating markets and supporting prices, till by the mid-1950s the Government had a hand in regulating the markets for almost all major products, and imports of foodstuffs were subject to strict control. The Third Plan, from 1958, also aimed at a further 20 per cent increase in total production: the increase was to take place mainly in feed grains and livestock products, while production of wheat and sugar-beet was to level off and that of wine and potatoes to be reduced. In subsequent years, as new techniques made their impact on French agriculture, production rose faster than demand and surplus problems became increasingly acute for a series of products. The milk market had to be relieved by exporting butter, with the help of an expensive subsidy; the cattle market was in difficulties; various fruits and vegetables were in excess supply from time to time. Agitation by the peasants sometimes took violent forms, and their organizations exercised steady pressure on the Government and on public opinion. The Loi d'Orientation Agricole of 1960 proclaimed as its objective the attainment of 'parity' between agriculture and other sectors, and laid down a legal framework for further action in various fields. There was, however, increasing difficulty in using price support as a means of raising farm incomes. The Fourth Plan (for 1962–5) considers that increased production of most commodities is inevitable even though it will lead to surpluses in some cases; it is an important element in raising farm incomes. Consequently, a large increase is planned in agricultural exports. Faced with the limited growth in demand for foodstuffs at home, France has looked increasingly towards preferential access to the markets of Germany and Great Britain for a solution to her farm problem.

WESTERN GERMANY, as a net importer of foodstuffs, has not been particularly troubled by surpluses, and her main problem lies in the high costs of production resulting from a structure of small and often fragmented farms. Strict control of imports, carried out in particular by the Import Boards set up in 1950 and 1951, has enabled prices on the domestic market to be supported at levels well above those of the world market and of neighbouring countries. In 1955 an important Agricultural Act reinforced previous statements of policy, declaring that agriculture should share in the progressive development of the economy: the Government was required each year to submit a report on the agricultural situation and a plan for the measures envisaged (the 'Green Report' and the 'Green Plan'). Though a considerable effort has been made under the Green Plans to improve the structure of farms, German agriculture remains highly vulnerable to increased competition in the European Economic Community.

Numerous other countries have had to grapple with problems of surpluses, while trying to ensure adequate incomes to their farmers. In BELGIUM, the price of wheat was supported while feed grains were imported at world prices for the benefit of livestock producers: the result was an increasing price differential and an expansion of the wheat area at the expense of other grains, to the point where the extra wheat production (much of which was of poor quality) could not easily be disposed of. Moreover, the relative cheapness of feed grains encouraged an expansion of the livestock sector and here too difficulties were encountered: eggs and butter in particular had to be exported with the help of subsidies. Since 1957, imported feed grains have been subjected to a levy in order to encourage domestic production, but livestock producers have been compensated for the resulting rise in costs.

In ITALY, the system of control for wheat instituted before the war was revised in 1948, compulsory deliveries being limited to the quantities considered sufficient to stabilize the market. Production of soft wheat began to outrun demand in the mid-1950s, necessitating subsidized exports, and the price for State purchases was reduced. Rice also began to be in surplus in 1955 and 1956, and measures had to be taken to regulate the market. On the other hand, the output of products for which Italy's climate gives an advantage over most other European countries – in particular fruit and vegetables – has been able to rise unchecked.

In SWITZERLAND, the provisions added to the Constitution in 1947 concerning assistance to agriculture were implemented by the Agricultural Act of 1951, which aimed 'to maintain a large peasant population to facilitate the supplies of the country by ensuring agricultural production and encouraging agriculture, having regard to the interests of the national economy'. This Act provided the basis for subsequent legislation laying down detailed measures of support for various commodities, consisting primarily of intervention on the market and price guarantees handled by bodies responsible to the Government. Imports are strictly controlled, often by the system of *prise-en-charge* or 'conditional imports', under which imports are permitted only on condition that importers purchase home-produced goods of the same kind. As a result, prices are maintained well above the world market level: although Switzerland imports more food per head than almost any other country, its agriculture is one of the most highly-protected in the world. Special non-economic motives are largely responsible for this. Even Switzerland, however, cannot entirely resist economic trends: rising overproduction in the dairy sector has necessitated measures of restraint, and in addition it has become necessary to take into account both the cost of agricultural support and the problems which would arise if Swiss agriculture were exposed to greater competition in the context of European economic integration. A report by the Federal Council in 1959, while stressing the unfavourable natural conditions under which Swiss agriculture had to operate, made it clear that the number of holdings and the size of the farm population would have to be reduced.[1]

NORWAY, like Switzerland, has the problem of reconciling the social and strategic objective of a large agricultural population with difficult natural conditions. Under the Agricultural Production Programme of 1955, the aim has been to cover requirements of livestock products from domestic production mainly based on home-produced feeding-stuffs, and production of grain, fruit and vegetables was to be expanded; however, production is to be adjusted as far as possible to demand, and the general aim is to raise the production of commodities currently imported rather than to produce for the export market. Agricultural markets have been subjected to a far-reaching system of intervention, involving strict import controls.

In SWEDEN, after the war, the prices of the main agricultural products were maintained by a system of import monopolies and quantitative restrictions, and the difference between world prices and domestic prices was met by variable import levies. This arrangement fitted in badly with the principles applied in the rest of the economy: foreign trade played an important role and imports of manufactured goods were practically free from restrictions. An effort was therefore made to introduce a system by which changes in the world prices of agricultural products would be

---

[1] Conseil Fédéral, *Second rapport à l'Assemblée fédérale sur la situation de l'agriculture suisse et la politique agricole de la Confédération*, December 29th, 1959.

reflected on the domestic market, so that production would be guided along the right channels. Accordingly, in 1956 a system of 'fixed' import levies was introduced, subject to various safeguards for farm incomes. However, as these safeguards proved inadequate to maintain incomes at the desired level, the system was revised in 1959, with the result that the original aim of flexibility was to a large extent lost. (The import levy system has a number of interesting features and is further described in the following section.) At the same time, and despite a rapid movement of labour out of agriculture, difficulties have been encountered in bringing production down to the desired level of 90 per cent of domestic requirements: total production has remained approximately equal to requirements, and butter and other products have had to be exported, generally at a loss.

Importing countries generally have been able to maintain prices and support their farmers' income by restricting imports, up to the point where their own domestic supply begins to exceed demand. Agricultural exporting countries, however, do not have this possibility and moreover are harmed by the restrictions imposed by importing countries. DENMARK has been driven back into various forms of intervention, some of them resembling the measures adopted in the 1930s: domestic consumers are compelled to pay more for dairy products and pigmeat through the imposition of levies on domestic sales of these products, a milling ratio has been applied for bread grains and imports of feed grains are subjected to a system of minimum prices. A significant break with past traditions occurred when direct subsidies to agriculture were introduced in 1961. The NETHERLANDS, after the war, continued its pre-war and wartime arrangements: the Agriculture Act of 1957 co-ordinated past legislation and introduced new provisions; agricultural markets have remained subject to a large degree of intervention in various forms. In 1961 the IRISH REPUBLIC took steps to organize its export marketing on a more efficient basis.

Various attempts have been made to measure the degree of price support in various countries. The task is not easy, because of the variety of measures existing in different countries. Perhaps the most interesting estimates are those of McCrone, shown in Table 61. The calculation was made by valuing the output of agriculture in each country firstly at its own producer prices and secondly at a set of prices applicable to the same commodities if

Table 61

ESTIMATED LEVELS OF PRICE SUPPORT AROUND 1956

	Output		Price support			
	A	B			Per head active agri-cultural popula-tion	Per head total popula-tion
	At national prices	At Euro-pean import prices	Approx. value	As per cent of A		
	£ million		£ mln.	%	£	£
Finland	214	124	90	42	98	21·0
Switzerland	182	129	53	30	147	11·2
U.K.	1,298	990	308	24	251	6·3
Sweden	275	218	57	21	90	7·8
W. Germany	1,566	1,292	274	18	53	5·1
Norway	115	95	20	17	54	5·5
France	2,482	2,101	381	15	69	8·2
Italy	1,801	1,547	254	14	31	5·3
Belgium	320	303	17	5	41	1·9
Netherlands	440	419	21	5	28	1·9
Austria	206	197	8·9	4	9	1·3
Ireland	193	185	8·6	4	17	3·1
Denmark	368	359	9·7	3	19	2·2

Source: Gavin McCrone, *The Economics of Subsidising Agriculture* (London: Allen & Unwin, 1962).

imported: the difference between the two was taken to represent the amount of price support, which could then be expressed as a percentage of the value of output at national prices. It appears that Finland and Switzerland have the highest degree of price support, followed by the United Kingdom, Sweden and Western Germany. The main exporting countries – Denmark, Ireland and the Netherlands – not surprisingly, are at the bottom of the scale. The figures for Austria and Belgium are unexpectedly low: this seems to be a consequence of the importance of pigs and milk in their total output, these being products for which their producer prices are not much above the import prices used. France lies about the middle of the scale; the data however refer to the mid-

1950s, and after the devaluation of the franc in 1958 the degree of price support would have appeared somewhat lower.[1]

This table has other interesting features. The *benefit* of price support to farmers (the amount of support per head of the active agricultural population) is particularly big in the United Kingdom, though the *burden* of support (the amount per head of the total population) is not exceptionally large: this of course reflects the small proportion of the population which is employed in agriculture. In Switzerland the high degree of support also gives an important benefit to the farm population but constitutes a heavy burden on the population as a whole. Most countries with a large farm population cannot afford to be so generous.

Table 61 is concerned only with the effects of price support in one form or another. Much assistance is also given to agriculture by direct grants of various kinds, including subsidies on agricultural inputs and grants for structural improvement. The latter are of a different order from price support and are discussed in a later section; however, input subsidies may have an effect on farm incomes and production similar to price supports. In Britain direct grants are important, and a large part of these consists of subsidies on fertilizers and lime, besides other grants which cannot be classified as 'structural improvement'. If these items were included in the calculation, the degree of support would probably appear even higher in Britain in relation to other countries.

Some special devices: minimum prices and import levies

In various countries during the 1950s, there was an attempt to find new methods of price support. The British system of deficiency payments is discussed in Chapter 12. Several of the new schemes adopted in other countries can be described as 'minimum price systems'. These are of considerable interest, first because they demonstrate the degree of sophistication which was reached in supporting farm prices, secondly because they were to a large

[1] A more elaborate analysis of protective margins was made by the Economic Commission for Europe in the *Economic Survey of Europe* in 1960 (Chapter III). The results were given only on a commodity-by-commodity basis. On the whole they seem reasonably compatible with McCrone's analysis, though they suggest that his method underestimates the degree of protection in the dairy sector.

extent the forerunners of the system which afterwards became the main instrument of support in the European Economic Community.

One of the first of these systems was that applied by Western Germany after 1953 to imports of fruit and vegetables from Italy and a number of other countries (this scheme, like others affecting imports by members of the European Economic Community, is due to be replaced by measures laid down under the common agricultural policy of the EEC – see Chapter 16). This took the place of the previous system of bilateral quotas and seasonal prohibitions, under which imports were virtually excluded during periods of peak domestic production. Minimum prices were laid down for each product: if the average price on twelve important markets in Germany fell below the minimum for a specified period, the frontier was closed after five days' notice and remained closed until the market price again rose above the minimum. The minimum prices were determined annually by a joint commission of German and Italian representatives; Germany agreed to prices which were low in comparison with usual market prices, and as a result imports were rarely suspended for a long period. The system nevertheless provided a reasonable guarantee to German producers against a slump in prices. For the exporting country it represented a considerable improvement over the previous system, though it still caused difficulties in that when prices fell below the minimum, trade was completely stopped: some form of progressive suspension would have been preferable.

Similar systems were adopted by other countries: by France for various fruits and vegetables, pigmeat, lard, poultry and poultry-meat, and by Italy for butter, beef, veal and livestock. Norway has also introduced arrangements for fruit and vegetables which in effect constitute a minimum price system, but the price limits or minimum prices are well above the usual price level and as a result only small imports are allowed during the period of domestic production.

Minimum *export* prices were applied by the Netherlands to exports of fruit and vegetables to Western Germany. In 1950 Germany agreed not to restrict this trade (except by tariffs) provided that the Dutch exporters observed certain minimum prices. This system had the advantage lacking in the German-Italian scheme: trade was not suddenly and completely interrupted when prices fell: the prices of lower-grade produce were the first to fall below the minimum, while better-quality produce continued to fetch a higher price and to be exported. Trade was thus enabled to continue except on a few occasions when supplies were exceptionally heavy and prices correspondingly low. Similar arrangements were applied by the Netherlands and Denmark to exports of cheese to Germany.

In Benelux, minimum price systems played an important role for butter, fruit and vegetables. Already in 1935, minimum prices had been introduced for trade in agricultural products between Belgium and Luxemburg. The Benelux system had its origins in an agreement in 1947 between the Ministers of Agriculture of the three countries, to the effect that in the customs union each country should be free to restrict imports of agricultural produce as far as was necessary to guarantee to domestic producers a minimum price covering the cost of production plus a reasonable profit margin. The Netherlands often thought that the Belgian calculations put these costs too high, but its attempts to have the minimum prices reduced were not very successful, and provisions for arbitration proved ineffective. As a result the system enabled a significant degree of protection to be maintained for Belgian producers. Trade was frequently stopped, either because prices on the Belgian market lay below the minima or through deliberate action by the Belgian authorities; when trade took place, an export levy was collected on the Dutch side, making up the difference between the Dutch market price and the minimum prices, and as Dutch prices were usually relatively low, this levy was often substantial. (See also the section on Benelux in Chapter 16.)

The 'three-phase' system for fruit and vegetables, invented by Switzerland and later copied by Austria, is not unlike a minimum price system. Imports are allowed without restriction when domestic produce is not on the market, are admitted subject to restriction when domestic produce is on the market but in insufficient quantities, and are suspended when the market is fully supplied by domestic produce. In this case quantity of supply rather than price is the determining factor, and no precise criteria are laid down.

Minimum price systems, as well as the three-phase system, have been applied above all to fruit and vegetables because these products, particularly subject to wide seasonal fluctuations in supply and prices, are not easily protected by traditional devices. In Sweden, however, the system of import levies has become the main instrument of agricultural support. This system is perhaps the most complex of all those hitherto devised.

It has been pointed out in the previous section that Sweden wanted to abolish direct restrictions on agricultural imports and to introduce a more flexible arrangement which, while maintaining a degree of protection, would enable changes in world prices to be reflected on the domestic market. The basic feature of the new system, which began to operate in 1956, consists of levies on imports, corresponding in amount to the difference between world prices and certain 'middle prices' – these being the wholesale prices which are estimated to give the desired level of farm income. Since the levy is in principle fixed, a change in the world price should lead to a corresponding change in the domestic price.

Various safeguards were incorporated in the system from the start, but in the face of declining world prices for agricultural commodities, combined with inflation in Sweden and rising costs of agricultural production, these safeguards proved inadequate to maintain a satisfactory level of farm incomes. A new arrangement in 1959, therefore, fixed higher import levies and introduced new safeguards. There is now a '3 per cent rule', providing for an adjustment of import levies if an index of agricultural prices on the world market and an index of Swedish farm production costs deviate by more than three points for more than three months in succession: if world prices fall, import levies are raised to maintain the internal price level, or if production costs rise, levies are raised to compensate producers through higher prices; in principle, all levies are raised in equal proportion. There is also an 'income rule', under which import levies are adjusted whenever new agreements are reached on the general wage level: the adjustments are to bring about an increase in farm incomes equal to the increased incomes of industrial workers.[1]

The effect of the 3 per cent rule has been seriously to impair the original function of the supposedly 'fixed' levies in permitting

[1] The arrangements were more complex than the description given here. A fuller account can be found in the OEEC's *Fifth Report on Agricultural Policies* (chapter on Sweden).

variations in world prices to be reflected on the domestic market: this is particularly so because, on two occasions when the rule came into play mainly because of changes in the world prices for butter and pigmeat, the levies on these two products were changed more than those on other products. The 'income rule' is an interesting attempt to link farm incomes to developments in non-farm incomes; however, since a constant rise in industrial wages is to be expected, this arrangement could lead to a progressive tightening of restrictions on food imports, while domestic production is stimulated by higher prices. This might be effective up to a point, but once domestic production expands to meet all domestic requirements, further increases in the import levies are useless.

Reform of farm structures

The account given in the previous sections shows that it has become increasingly difficult to use price support as a means of raising farmers' incomes. Price guarantees are liable to stimulate unwanted production, and the resulting pressure on the market, while it tends to perpetuate the need for price support, makes this an even more costly procedure for the rest of the community. Further, all the measures of assistance that have so far been granted have failed – except perhaps in Britain and the Netherlands – to close the gap between farm and non-farm incomes.

It has therefore been gradually realized that the low level of farm incomes is due at least in part to deficiencies in the structure of agriculture itself, and that these will have to be remedied if in the long run farmers are to be assured of adequate incomes. Among the main obstacles to efficiency are the smallness of many farms, their fragmentation into numerous separate plots, low standards of farm management and unfavourable conditions in some regions resulting from climate, topography or other factors.

A rough comparison of the way in which the agricultural area is distributed between farms of different sizes is given by Figure 9. Holdings of less than 1 hectare, which are numerous in some countries (including Belgium, Germany and Switzerland), but which usually provide only part-time activity, are excluded. It appears that in the majority of countries, holdings of between 1 and 10 hectares cover nearly a third of the total area; they account usually for over half the total number of farms. It is only

PERCENTAGE OF AGRICULTURAL LAND OCCUPIED BY
HOLDINGS OF VARIOUS SIZES*

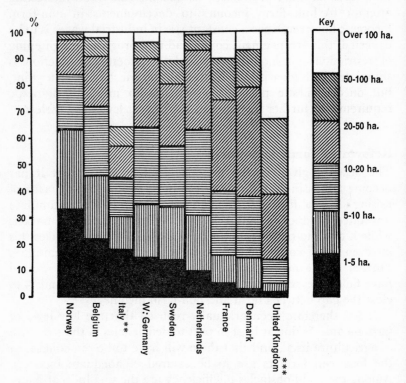

*Data refer to various years from 1949 to 1957, except for Italy
where the latest available data are for 1930.
**Includes forest.
***Excludes rough grazing.
Source: OEEC, *Agricultural Statistics* (Paris, 1959).

FIG. 9

in the United Kingdom, Denmark and France that these small holdings are comparatively unimportant in relation to the total area, though even in these cases they account for some 40 per cent of the number of farms. A special feature in the United Kingdom is the large proportion of the agricultural area accounted for by farms of more than 100 hectares. The data for Italy are unsatisfactory: the apparent importance of farms over 100 hectares results partly from the inclusion of forest, partly from the fact that the data refer to 1930, since when many large estates have been broken up into small holdings.

Lamartine Yates describes fragmentation as the worst affliction of the European farmer:

> It is found all over Europe except in the U.K., Ireland and Scandinavia. Perhaps the worst zone extends from the Netherlands, through Belgium and north-eastern France, down through south-western Germany, Austria, Switzerland and into Italy. It is also bad in Spain and Portugal. In these districts and countries a farm of 10 ha. may well be divided into 50 separate plots, a farm of 20 ha. into a hundred plots or more ... Plots will vary in size from 1 ha. or more down to one-twentieth of a hectare or less.[1]

Few exact statistics are available on the extent of fragmentation, but some data for Western Germany, the Netherlands and Belgium are given in Table 62. The situation in Germany is particularly

Table 62

FRAGMENTATION OF AGRICULTURAL HOLDINGS

	Average number of fragments per holding	Average area of each fragment (ha.)
W. Germany[a]	11·4	0·7
Netherlands	3·9	2·5
Belgium	6·4	1·1

[a] Data partly estimated.

Source: EEC, *Statistique Agricole*, 1961, No. 1.

[1] P. Lamartine Yates, *Food, Land and Manpower in Western Europe* (London: Macmillan, 1960), p. 174.

bad, with an average of over eleven fragments per holding, each fragment being on average only seven-tenths of a hectare in size. In Belgium too the situation is serious, and even in the Netherlands it is far from satisfactory. Unfortunately, no similar data have been published for France.

The shift in emphasis from price support to structural reform was particularly clear in FRANCE. The Loi d'Orientation Agricole of August 1960 provided for intensified action to improve farm structures, and the important complementary law passed in August 1962 set out a series of specific measures to this effect. The Fourth Plan (1962–5) declared that a reduction in the active agricultural population was essential if agricultural incomes were to be improved, and that the current low level of incomes resulted largely from the smallness and fragmentation of many holdings; it provides for a large increase in investment on land improvements of various kinds, as well as for increased expenditure on education and advisory services and on the improvement of marketing facilities. Special attention is given to certain depressed rural areas.

In WESTERN GERMANY a big effort has been made to improve farm structures under the 1955 Agricultural Act. The progress achieved and the further measures envisaged are the main object of the annual Green Report and Green Plan; 30–50 per cent of Green Plan funds are devoted to this purpose. The measures undertaken include consolidating fragmented holdings, combining two or more small holdings into a single unit and transferring farmsteads from villages to sites on their land.

Perhaps the most energetic and successful campaign is that carried out in SWEDEN. A useful distinction is made between 'internal' and 'external' rationalization. 'Internal rationalization' implies the improvement of existing farm land, buildings and equipment; subsidies are made available for this purpose. 'External rationalization' consists of measures to raise the average size of farms and to improve their layout. County Agricultural Boards control the sale and acquisition of land; they have priority in purchasing any land that comes on the market, and can resell such land to farmers able to use it to establish economically sound farms, or if necessary hold it in reserve until the opportunity arises for putting it to good use. Financial aid is available to help farmers enlarge their farms. Uneconomic holdings acquired by the

Agricultural Boards are afforested. This process of 'external rationalization' is assisted by encouraging farmers to move into other occupations: they can obtain training in other jobs and receive grants for the period of adaptation.

Though BRITAIN does not have the same structural problems as other countries, there has been increasing concern with what in Swedish terminology might be described as 'internal rationalization'. Grants are made to promote improvements in farm land, buildings and equipment. The Small Farmer Scheme of 1959 is aimed at holdings which give a barely adequate income, and provides for grants to assist in putting them on a sound economic footing.

In DENMARK too the reforms of an earlier period created a relatively efficient farming structure, but in modern conditions even the average Danish farm has begun to look rather too small. One authority has estimated that holdings of less than 10 hectares (which account for a quarter of the total number) are now too small, and that the minimum size should be 20–30 hectares if farm incomes are to equal those of industrial workers.[1] No overall programme has as yet been undertaken to enlarge existing farms, but the traditional policy of creating smallish holdings out of large estates has been affected: the average size of holdings thus established rose to about 12 hectares in the period 1954–9.

The NETHERLANDS also operates a programme of land consolidation; the Foundation for Land Administration can buy land as it becomes available and use it to enlarge other farms. Recently a scheme has been introduced whereby farmers can receive special payments if they give up their land. The rural population has facilities for training in non-farm occupations.

In ITALY the major problem is the backwardness of the South. Programmes of land improvement, pursuing Mussolini's *bonifica integrale*, have given special attention to depressed areas in the South and on the islands. The Cassa per il Mezzogiorno, formed in 1950, provides funds for irrigation, flood control, roads and many other schemes necessary for the development of the South. The programme of land reform concentrates on creating small peasant holdings (often too small for efficiency) out of large estates,

[1] K. Skovgaard, chapter on Denmark in Forschungsgesellschaft für Agrarpolitik, 'Agrarstrukturpolitik', *Berichte über Landwirtschaft*, 175. Sonderheft, 1962.

whose owners are compelled to sell against compensation. Land improvement and land reform account for nearly half the total funds of the 'Green Plan' for 1960–5, and the amounts involved represent an increase over those envisaged in the Vanoni Scheme for Italy's overall economic development in the years 1955–64.

It is difficult to evaluate the effects of these measures in different countries. It seems that to varying extents they have accelerated the trend towards amalgamation, consolidation and improvement of farms that was already taking place under the pressure of economic and technical change. This trend is reflected in the first place in the decline in the active agricultural population. Table 63 indicates that this decline, during the 1950s, was particularly

Table 63

ACTIVE AGRICULTURAL POPULATION IN 1960 AS A PER-
CENTAGE OF 1950

Sweden	64
Belgium	70[a]
W. Germany	72[a]
Norway	76
Netherlands	81[a]
Denmark	83
United Kingdom	84[a]

[a] Includes forestry, hunting and fishing.

Source: OEEC and OECD statistics.

rapid in Sweden, and here no doubt the energetic policy of rationalization has played its part. It has been relatively slow – though still not unimportant – in the United Kingdom, where already at the beginning of the decade the agricultural population was a bare twentieth of the total. Complete data are not available for France, but from 1954 to 1960 the decline is estimated to have taken place at about the same rate as in Western Germany.

Not much information is available on progress in consolidating fragmented holdings, but it seems that in most cases only a small proportion of the area needing consolidation has so far been dealt with. Moreover, some districts that have been consolidated need further attention because inheritance customs remain unchanged and farms continue to be split up on the death of their owners.

A better picture can be obtained of changes in the number of farms in various size groups (Table 64). In almost all countries a similar pattern emerges: the total number of farms has fallen, this being accounted for mainly by a reduction among holdings with under 10 hectares, while the number of medium-sized holdings has increased. The fact that this trend appears for

Table 64

PERCENTAGE CHANGE IN NUMBER OF HOLDINGS OF VARIOUS SIZES

	Size group (hectares)						All holdings
	1–5[a]	5–10	10–20	20–50	50–100	over 100	
W. Germany 1949–60	−26	−15	+12	+8	+8	−11	−17
Belgium 1950–9	−34	−10	+ 9	+8	+4		−21
Netherlands 1950–9	−40	− 6	+10	−1	−4		−12
Sweden[b] 1951–9	−11	−10	− 1 (10–15 ha.)	+4 (15–30 ha.)	0 (30–60 ha.)	− 7 (over 60 ha.)	− 7
Denmark 1946–56	−15	− 2	+ 3	0	−1	−10	− 4

[a] 0·5–5 ha. in Germany and Denmark, 2–5 ha. in Sweden.
[b] Data refer to area of arable land only.

Sources: W. Germany: *Grüner Bericht*, 1962. Belgium: EEC, *Conditions de production de l'agriculture*, No. 7, April 1962. Netherlands: Landbouw-Economisch Instituut, *Landbouwcijfers* (The Hague, 1961). Sweden: National Board of Agriculture, *The rationalization of Swedish agriculture* (1961). Denmark: K. Skovgaard, in *Berichte über Landwirtschaft*, 175. Sonderheft, 1962.

Belgium, where not much official action has so far been undertaken, as well as in other countries, suggests that economic forces are at least as much responsible as measures of policy. In some countries there has also been a reduction in the number of farms in the largest size groups. The statistics for France are unsatisfactory, but an analysis by Klatzmann indicates that between 1942 and 1955 there was a trend similar to that of other countries, with a reduction in the number of holdings with less than 20 hectares and with more than 50 hectares.[1] Though precise data are not available for Italy, it is known that many large estates have been divided up: as a result Italy is probably the only country where the number of small holdings has increased.

There is thus a tendency for Western European agriculture to consist increasingly of medium-sized farms. To some extent this is a contradiction of past policy, which in many countries concentrated on providing small holdings for landless labourers. It has now been realized that such small holdings generally do *not* provide a first step on the farming ladder, and are often incapable of providing an adequate income in present conditions. On the other hand, the Governments of Western European countries have set their face resolutely against any form of collective farm, regarding this as politically and socially unacceptable, whatever its technical advantages. In some cases, they are also doubtful about the desirability of an increasing number of industrial-type farming units – 'broiler' houses and so on. The family farm, sufficiently large to provide an adequate income, thus appears as the most desirable objective. In France the Loi d'Orientation Agricole provides for a study – not yet completed – of the area which would normally be required for a holding cultivated by two full-time labour units if it is to give a return on labour corresponding to that which could be obtained in other occupations, as well as a return on management and investment. In Germany an important study calculated that holdings of less than ten hectares could be economically maintained only on a part-time basis.[2] In Sweden the aim is now to promote farms with twenty-five to fifty hectares of arable land, providing employment for two full-time workers.

To transform the pattern of agriculture from one of small peasant holdings to one of efficient, medium-sized family farms is a task comparable with the great land reforms of the past. Lamartine Yates points out:

> Very few statesmen and agricultural leaders admit publicly that a vast reorganization of farming is needed. Europe's

---

[1] EEC, *Conditions de production de l'agriculture*, No. 11, September 1962.

[2] R. Plate, E. Woermann and D. Grupe, 'Landwirtschaft im Strukturwandel der Volkswirtschaft', *Agrarwirtschaft*, Sonderheft 14, 1962.

countryside is grossly over-populated. There is widespread unemployment and under-employment. Farmers cannot employ modern methods because they have not enough land and because as long as labour is in superabundance the old manual methods help to keep farm people occupied. But all this means low output per man and low incomes for farmers.[1]

The reorganization involves in the first place far-reaching measures within the agricultural sector itself – the consolidation of fragmented farms, the regrouping of small holdings into larger units, the modernization of buildings and equipment, the diffusion of new technology and improved methods of farm management. Such a programme needs time. Changes in the structure of farms generally cannot be forced upon their owuers: some countries now have legislation making consolidation schemes compulsory for all the farmers in a given district, but usually the work is one of slow persuasion, in which financial incentives are not the only factor.

In the second place, the reform of agriculture requires action to facilitate the inevitable movement of labour from the farms into other occupations (or into retirement). Till recently, most Governments refused to admit that this movement *was* inevitable; several even attempted to check it. Now, however, almost all Governments – if not their farming communities – recognize that the movement is an essential factor in maintaining the incomes of those who remain in farming, and a few have made a start in assisting the process. Sweden assists the retraining of farmers for other jobs; Germany and the Netherlands give additional pensions to retiring farmers; France intends to do both these things. Even Switzerland now admits the need for a reduction in the agricultural population. In some cases the decentralization of industry is seen as a means of assisting farm labour to find new work, as well as of providing an additional source of employment and income for families which hold to farming as their main activity.

Finally, efficiency in agriculture is inconceivable without an efficient marketing structure, reducing to a minimum the 'price spread' between farmer and consumer. This is a problem to which practically all countries are giving some attention.

[1] *Food, Land and Manpower*, op. cit., p. 160.

Chapter 12. The United Kingdom

The Second World War

In contrast to what happened in 1914, Britain entered the Second World War with a prepared plan for maintaining food supplies. Already in November 1936 the Government had set up a Food (Defence Plans) Department to prepare measures of food control and rationing. When the war broke out in September 1939, the prearranged plans were put into effect. The Ministry of Food was set up, replacing the Food Department, and became the sole buyer and importer of all major foodstuffs; existing stocks of the main foods were requisitioned; price control was imposed at one or more stages of distribution; rationing was introduced. The Marketing Boards were suspended, except those for milk and for hops – the former came under the supervision of the Ministry of Food. County War Executive Committees were formed, with authority to influence the cropping pattern, control the use of fertilizers and dispossess inefficient farmers.

These measures were useful and necessary, but they were not enough. It was soon found that shipping availabilities had been greatly overestimated. Food imports were cut much more than had been expected, and grain supplies in particular ran short. As the war went on, many ships were sunk by submarines, shipping continued to be required for other uses, and food imports steadily declined. The worst point was reached early in 1943, when a serious food shortage seemed imminent: it was averted only by success in the anti-submarine campaign and by the provision of more American ships. The volume of food imports, which had averaged 22 million tons a year before the war, was only 11–12 million tons a year from 1942 to 1944.

At first the Government was reluctant to encourage a large expansion in home food production, fearing difficult readaptations after the war: Churchill instructed his Minister of Agriculture to aim at a 'large but not excessive' increase in food production. However, the steady fall in imports made a greater effort un-avoidable. The basis of the policy adopted was the ploughing-up of grassland in order to grow more crops. Considerable success was achieved, for the arable area in Great Britain rose from 12 million acres in 1939 to 18 million in 1945, permitting a large increase in the output of wheat, potatoes, sugar-beet and other crops. The livestock situation, however, was difficult: imports of feeding-stuffs had to be cut almost to zero throughout the war, while the increased home production of feed grains and other items barely compensated for the reduced grazing area. Priority in livestock production was given to milk, output of which fell only slightly; but the numbers of pigs and poultry had to be drastically cut, and there was also some fall in meat production.

Overall, British agriculture managed to raise its contribution to the food supply: in terms of calories, the proportion coming from home production rose from 30 per cent at the beginning of the war to 40 per cent at the highest point in 1943/4. American supplies of cheese, dried egg, canned meat and fish and other items raised the availability of protein. Though the diet was often dull and unappetizing, the average civilian was held to be better fed than before the war; such indices of public health as infant and childbirth mortality rates showed a distinct improvement.

British farmers had to make a considerable effort to achieve this increase in output, and the Government was bound to help them by providing the funds necessary to restore productive capacity and give farmers the necessary incentive. From the first few months of the war, the system of purchase at fixed prices assured the farmers of a market and of satisfactory profits; special price incentives were given for certain products, in particular wheat, milk and potatoes. In November 1940, the Government undertook to maintain fixed prices and guaranteed markets for the duration of the war and at least one year thereafter. Later the

Ministry of Agriculture argued that if farmers were to raise their output still further they needed more security than this: the memory of the slump in prices and the 'betrayal' by the Government after the First World War was still in farmers' minds. As a result, the Government agreed in 1944 to give producers a guarantee, lasting up to 1948, of prices not lower than those then prevailing for milk, cattle and sheep; however, it would give no similar assurances for other products and warned farmers that the prices of grains and potatoes would probably have to be reduced. After discussions with farmers' representatives, a further agreement was reached in December 1944: in future years, the Government would review the level of farm prices in consultation with the National Farmers' Union; at this annual review, to take place in February each year, all factors relevant to price determination would be taken into account, including certain basic data derived from farm accounts.

Post-war policy – from shortages to surplus

These guarantees given during the war were put on a permanent basis by the Agriculture Act of 1947, which declared the objective of policy as being that of:

> ... promoting and maintaining, by the provision of guaranteed markets and assured prices ... such part of the nation's food and other agricultural produce as in the national interest it is desirable to produce in the United Kingdom, and of producing it at minimum prices consistent with proper remuneration and living conditions for farmers and workers in agriculture and an adequate return on capital invested in the industry.

This text left room for differences of interpretation, in particular on how much food it would be desirable to produce at home and on what would constitute 'proper' remuneration. Nevertheless, the Act of 1947 constituted a clear commitment by the Government to intervene on behalf of agriculture even in peacetime and was an assurance that there would be no repetition of the events of 1921.

The Government undertook to buy, at guaranteed prices, the

whole domestic output of grains, potatoes, sugar-beet and fatstock; wool was later added to the list. The annual review
procedure was to continue as the basis for determining prices.
Policy at this time was dictated by the world-wide food shortage
and by the need for Britain to conserve its depleted resources of
foreign exchange; farmers were therefore urged to raise net
output – i.e. gross agricultural output, less imports of feeding-
stuffs, seeds and livestock for use on farms – to 50 per cent above
pre-war by 1951/2, which represented an increase of 20 per cent
above the 1947 level.

The Labour Government which had taken office in 1945
maintained the wartime controls on food supplies: rationing was
continued and even had to be extended to some additional products. After the Conservatives took office in 1951, they proceeded
gradually to dismantle these controls: imports and distribution of
food were restored by stages to private traders, rationing was
ended and the Ministry of Food was merged with the Ministry of
Agriculture.

By the mid-1950s, food imports were practically free: some
restrictions were maintained on imports from the dollar area,
but otherwise only a few products were subject to quota. Import
duties were generally those established in the 1930s. The incidence
of specific duties had been greatly reduced by the rise in prices
(thus the duty of 15s. per cwt. on butter was now equivalent to
only about 5 per cent *ad valorem*). Wheat, maize, mutton and lamb
were among the products which were free from any duty; livestock
for food was also free, but animal health requirements practically
restricted imports to those from the Irish Republic. Fruit and
vegetables – which benefited from no price guarantee – were the
only products for which the pre-war specific duties were raised.
Commonwealth produce remained free of all but revenue duties,
while the reduced incidence of specific duties on foreign produce
meant a considerably smaller degree of preference for the
Commonwealth.

The Conservative Government, while restoring freedom to the
market, maintained the guarantees of the 1947 Act. This meant
that support for British farmers had once again to be given by the
system of deficiency payments. This system was applied in 1954
to grains, fatstock and milk. About the same time, the pre-war
Marketing Boards were revived and new ones were created:

by 1957 marketing schemes were in force for milk, pigs, eggs, wool, hops, tomatoes, cucumbers and potatoes; the British Sugar Corporation continued to function. In several cases the Marketing Boards were responsible for administering the Government subsidy or for maintaining fixed prices.

For a while the Conservative Government pursued the policy of agricultural expansion. By the time it took office, an increase in net output of 50 per cent over pre-war had almost been achieved, and it raised the target to 60 per cent. This was accomplished in 1956/7. The emphasis then passed to a policy of 'selective expansion' and to making agriculture more productive and more competitive; increasing use was made of price variations in an attempt to influence the pattern of production. The Government also tried to encourage farmers to save feed imports, by improved management of grassland and by better use of concentrated feeding-stuffs.

The Government's attempt to reduce the prices of some commodities worried the Farmers' Unions. However, the Unions succeeded in obtaining from the Government, in 1957, certain 'long-term assurances' under which the Government undertook not to reduce the guaranteed price for any commodity by more than 4 per cent in any year, nor to reduce the total value of the price guarantees by more than 2½ per cent. In spite of the Government's declarations to the contrary, these assurances severely limited its scope for influencing production. With the growth in output, the markets for several products encountered increasing difficulties. The supply of milk grew well beyond the capacity of the liquid milk market, and increased quantities had to be sold at a much lower price for manufacturing. At the annual review in 1961, the Government asked the Farmers' Unions to work out a scheme for limiting milk output which would have amounted to production quotas for individual producers, but after some months' consideration the Unions declared any such system unacceptable. Output of eggs also rose to the point where Britain ceased to require imports and in 1957 there were even some exports to the Continent, till this was stopped by the Government in response to complaints by other countries on the grounds that these exports were subsidized. The 1963 review introduced new arrangements whereby the amount of deficiency payments for eggs may be determined on the basis of an 'indicator' price, representing the price that might be expected if the market is not oversupplied. In 1961 provision was made for reducing the guaranteed price for pigs when deliveries rise above certain levels (and vice versa); in the 1963 review the penalty for excess production was increased. An increased area and rising yields of barley brought Britain close to self-sufficiency and led to reduced market prices; for a time imports were subjected to a minimum price system.

With the general change from shortages to surpluses on world markets, imports caused increasing trouble. The farmers frequently complained of dumping, sometimes with good cause, but the procedure for applying anti-dumping duties was generally cumbersome and ineffective. The most acute difficulties were experienced with butter. Many countries attempted to sell butter on the British market, and in 1958 prices fell to a low level. The next year there was a temporary recovery, but in the autumn of 1961 prices again fell to such an extent that the British Government requested exporting countries to observe specified export quotas for the next six months, backing this up with the threat of anti-dumping duties against countries which did not comply. All the exporters did in fact observe the quotas (the Irish Republic at first refused, but was soon compelled by prohibitive duties to change its mind). After April 1962, as there was little prospect of an improvement in the market, further steps were taken: total butter imports for the next year were limited to 390,000 tons (less than in any year since 1957), with quotas for individual exporting countries based on the traditional pattern of trade. The scheme now operates as a regular quota system, licences being required for all imports, including those from the Commonwealth. It is thus an important departure from past principles; however, as New Zealand stood to benefit from the arrangements, she agreed to the quota system, while stressing that it should not be regarded as a precedent.

A White Paper issued in December 1960, after talks between the Agricultural Departments and the Farmers' Unions, took stock of the situation.[1] It declared that British agriculture was making a valuable contribution to the balance of payments: the increase in net output over pre-war had reached 70 per cent and nearly half the nation's food was now being grown at home. Large

[1] *Agriculture*, Cmnd. 1249.

domestic food production was also a vital safeguard against the uncertainties of overseas supplies and played an important part in keeping down the cost of imported supplies, with a consequent beneficial effect on the nation's terms of trade. However, the situation was no longer the same as in 1947: the expansion in domestic output, combined with the increase in overseas supplies, meant more difficulty in finding profitable outlets. While for some commodities (beef and pigmeat were mentioned) there was clear scope for expansion, for others it would be in the national interest to expand output only if costs and guaranteed prices could be made more competitive with the true costs of imported produce.

The rise in domestic production and the absence of restrictions

Table 65

COST OF EXCHEQUER SUPPORT TO AGRICULTURE

	1955/6	1961/2	1962/3
	£ million		
IMPLEMENTATION OF PRICE GUARANTEES of which:	143	226	199
Cereals	36	73	64
Fatstock	52	113	107
Milk	35	12	–
Eggs	19	16	24
DIRECT GRANTS AND SUBSIDIES of which:	58	108	113
Fertilizer and lime subsidies	25	42	35
Ploughing grants	5	11	12
Calf subsidy	} 11	18	18
Hill farming subsidies		6	7
Grants for farm improvements	–	9	11
Grants to small farmers	–	7	8
OTHER ITEMS	5	10	10
Total	206	343	321

Source: Annual Review and Determination of Guarantees (H.M.S.O.), and OEEC *Fifth Report on Agricultural Policies* (Paris, 1961).

on most imports has meant that the cost of support under the deficiency payment system is liable to rise substantially and unpredictably. In 1961/2 the total subsidy bill reached the unprecedented height of over £340 million, and it remained high the following year (Table 65). There was therefore growing disquiet over the methods of agricultural support. Uncertainty over the future of British agricultural policy was accentuated by the prospect of membership of the European Economic Community (discussed in Chapter 17), but already in 1962 the Minister of Agriculture, Mr Christopher Soames, declared that the system of support would have to be changed whether or not Britain joined the EEC.

The deficiency payments system

It has been seen in Chapter 7 that deficiency payments originated in a proposal by the Milner Committee in 1915, implemented two years later. The system was abandoned in 1921 but was revived in 1932 by the Wheat Act and extended to oats and barley in 1937. During and after the Second World War it was replaced by Government purchase at fixed prices, till in 1954 the Conservative Government freed the market and adopted deficiency payments not only for grains but also for fatstock and milk. As a result, the system came to cover the greater part of British agriculture.

The essence of the deficiency payments system is that it allows prices to be determined by the free operation of the market, yet enables a minimum price to be guaranteed to producers. Compensation is paid for any amount by which the average realized market price falls short of the guarantee in a given period. The method of administration varies between products (for feed grains the payment is based on the farmer's acreage and not on his sales), but the principle is essentially the same. The system depends on reliable recording of the sales (or acreage) of individual farmers and on an accurate calculation of the average price obtained for all sales. All farmers receive the same rate of payment, regardless of differences in the market prices they obtain: thus every farmer has an incentive to maintain the quality of his produce and to get the best price he can.

Britain is unique in basing agricultural support on this method.

The reason why it has been found convenient is of course that it provides a means of reconciling support for farmers with free entry for food imports – the latter being desired because of trade links with Commonwealth and also to some extent with non-Commonwealth countries, as well as because of the traditional cheap food policy. Cheap food, by this method, is obtained only with a substantial charge on the Exchequer for financing the subsidy; however, there is a social advantage in that the taxation which provides the necessary funds is 'progressive', bearing most heavily on the higher income groups, whereas the high food prices which result from more conventional methods of protection are 'regressive', affecting above all the poorest consumers.

An advantage commonly claimed for the system is that it makes the cost of support clear, whereas import restriction by tariffs or quotas obscures the economic cost. For farmers, of course, this aspect appears as a disadvantage: they point out, with some justice, that the system puts support to agriculture in an unfavourable light, as compared with other industries which are protected by tariffs.

Another important advantage of deficiency payments, less often stated, is that they preserve the market as a guide to policy: market prices can be followed and compared with guaranteed prices, and too great a discrepancy between the two indicates that the guaranteed price should be revised. This in effect is what the Government has sought to do at the annual reviews, encouraging some products and discouraging others.

Perhaps the most serious drawback of the system from a domestic point of view is that the absence of controls on imports leaves the market open to external and largely unpredictable forces. A fall in market prices resulting from increased imports involves an increase in Exchequer payments. It is true that this is not a real cost to the economy but only a transfer of income from taxpayers to farmers: in principle, taxpayers, as consumers of food, should gain a corresponding benefit from lower prices. In practice, retail prices tend to fall much less than farm prices and a substantial benefit goes to middlemen for whom it is not intended.[1] This is perhaps an argument for a better marketing system rather than for abolishing the deficiency payments, but

[1] Cf. G. Houston, 'Meat marketing margins in Britain', *Journal of Agricultural Economics*, May 1962.

there are other objections. Farmers themselves have doubts about a system which may be unpopular with the general public, while the Government has become seriously disturbed at the 'open-ended' nature of its commitment: there is a constant danger of a fall in market prices causing a heavier subsidy bill than has been expected and upsetting the budget.

The system has an advantage for both domestic producers and exporting countries in that by keeping market prices relatively low it does not discourage consumption, as other methods of support are liable to do. Exporting countries may also derive some benefit from knowing that they can usually export to Britain, if at uncertain prices, whereas exports to other countries are liable to be interrupted with little or no notice. Mainly for these reasons, the 'Haberler Report' was inclined to prefer deficiency payments to other methods of support.[1] The effects of the system on international trade, however, depend mainly on how it is used. In principle, it could be used simply to provide a safeguard against exceptionally low prices. In fact, the guaranteed prices in Britain are set at levels well above world prices and stimulate increased production. As a result, the effects on imports are necessarily unfavourable: where domestic production expands faster than demand, the prices of both home and imported produce have to fall and the volume of imports is reduced. This is in fact what has happened, notably for eggs and barley.

The question arises whether the deficiency payments system could be applied by other countries. The standard objection is that where domestic agricultural production forms a large part of the total supply, the burden of payments would be too high: Britain can operate the system because domestic production is relatively small. In strict economics, this argument is faulty: the cost of supporting a large domestic agriculture is heavy whether this is done by direct payments, leaving market prices low, or by restrictions on imports, raising prices to consumers. The difference in method simply alters the incidence of the burden. The real objection, no doubt, is of a political order: since the burden of support would become evident and since it would be very large, it would probably be unacceptable to public opinion and it would be difficult to raise taxation by the necessary amount.

[1] GATT, *Trends in International Trade* (Geneva, 1958).

Assistance for farm improvements

In addition to the measures of price support so far described, British farmers benefit from large subsidies designed to reduce the cost of certain farming operations. These include in particular subsidies on fertilizers and grants for ploughing; their effect on farm incomes is similar to that of price support measures, and they also tend to encourage increased output. To some extent they have the advantage of giving farmers an incentive to adopt improved farming practices. Grants are also paid to assist farmers in regions where farming is subject to particular difficulties: the most important are the subsidies for the typical products of hill farms.

In line with the growing stress on improved agricultural efficiency, the Government in 1957 introduced grants to assist certain long-term improvements to agricultural land, including the construction or improvement of farm buildings, roads and bridges, the supply of electricity and the reclamation of land. One-third of the cost of such improvements can be covered by the grant. The sum originally provided was £50 million for ten years; as the scheme proved successful, the amount was later raised.

In 1959 the Small Farmer Scheme was introduced. This is designed to improve farms which are providing a bare living but which can be made more economic. To be eligible, farms must have not less than 20 and not more than 100 acres of land; further, they must be capable of reaching a 'standard labour requirement' of at least 275 'man-days' a year after improvement, and they must not have more than 450 'man-days' at the outset. (It was calculated that 275 'man-days' constituted, on the average, a minimum corresponding to full-time employment for one man: the second criterion thus reinforces the first in excluding from the scheme holdings which are too small to provide a living on a full-time basis.) Farmers who participate in the scheme are required to carry out an improvement plan over three to five years. They are entitled to 'farm business grants', paid at a standard rate per acre and intended as a contribution towards the cost of additional equipment, livestock and so on. In addition, 'field husbandry grants' are available to defray the cost of specific operations involved in the improvement plan, such as ploughing, ditching and land reclamation.

A supplementary scheme was introduced at the same time, to help small farmers who for the time being were not in a position to carry out an improvement plan. This scheme provided mainly for grants to supplement the existing subsidies on ploughing, fertilizing and other operations.

Since 1960 a Horticultural Improvement Scheme has provided grants at the rate of one-third of the cost for various improvements to horticultural equipment and buildings.

As Table 65 has indicated, expenditure on the various improvement schemes has risen, but it remains small in relation to the cost of price support.

Agriculture in the economy – post-war controversies

In the early stages after the war, there could be little question as to the need to encourage a high level of agricultural output. However, once the immediate problem of food shortages had been overcome, there was intense debate as to the desirability of permanently maintaining, through subsidy, a large domestic agriculture. The case for doing so was based largely on the balance of payments problem; the arguments in question continued to be advanced even after Britain had recovered from the critical post-war shortage of foreign exchange. Professor E. A. G. Robinson, as an eminent economist with an influential position in Whitehall, was the most powerful exponent of this view. His arguments appeared in numerous articles from 1950 onwards: an attempt is made here to bring together the essential points.[1]

The basis of Professor Robinson's argument was his pessimism as to Britain's capacity to finance increased imports of foodstuffs. In the first place, he was doubtful as to the prospects for world trade in manufactures and for Britain's share in this trade: he stressed the consequences of industrialization in primary producing countries and of increasing competition for British exports (from Germany and Japan in particular). In the second place, he feared that the price of food would rise in relation to that of manufactured goods, as a result of the demand for food in the less

[1] Articles in the *Three Banks Review* of March 1953, June 1958 and December 1958; paper read at I.C.I. Conference in 1956; and joint article with R. Marris in the *Economic Journal* of March 1950 (see also article by C. H. Blagburn in the same issue of the *Economic Journal*).

developed countries with large and rapidly growing populations and rising standards of living.

Professor Robinson's calculations of Britain's probable receipts from exports provided an estimate of the total amount of imports which could be financed. Out of this total, a certain quantity of raw materials and fuels would be indispensable, and as a result the amount of food that could be imported was limited. In articles in 1953 and 1954, Professor Robinson declared that Britain would have to live on a volume of imports not much more than four-fifths that of 1938; later he became more hopeful, but in 1958 he still calculated that food imports could not be raised enough to meet the expected rise in demand in coming years. It followed that domestic food production would have to be expanded still further.

To objections that increased food output meant an uneconomic use of resources, Professor Robinson replied by a detailed analysis of what would be involved in raising export earnings sufficiently to finance extra imports of food. He showed that the elasticity of demand for exports was almost certainly too low – i.e. too large a reduction in price would be needed to sell an increased volume of exports – for it to be profitable to transfer resources from agriculture to export industries. He thus calculated in 1958 that, since before the war, extra agricultural output to the value of £100 had been obtained with the expenditure of some £150 in resources: but to purchase additional food imports worth £100 it would be necessary to use some £340 worth of domestic resources in the export industries.[1]

---

[1] The argument was somewhat involved, and illustrates the degree of sophistication that was reached. Professor Robinson worked out that artificially-induced import-saving by agriculture amounted to £300 million, that by industry (through duties on manufactures) to £200 million. He therefore inquired what would be involved in raising British export earnings by £500 million, an increase of 15 per cent over the current level. With an assumed elasticity of demand for exports of 2·5, an increase of 50 per cent in the volume of exports would involve a 20 per cent fall in export prices; total export earnings would rise by only 20 per cent $\left(\dfrac{150}{100} \times \dfrac{80}{100}\right)$. The increase in exports would involve a proportionate increase in imports of raw materials, etc.: estimating the average import-content of exports at 15 per cent, the net increase in earnings would be from 100 − 15 to 120 − 22·5, or from 85 to 97·5, i.e. 14·7 per cent, or approximately the figure of 15 per cent required. However, 50 per cent more resources would have been used in export industries:

Further, Professor Robinson pointed out that a devaluation of the pound sufficient to reduce export prices by the necessary amount would make most of British agriculture appear competitive at world prices. He therefore concluded one of his articles as follows:

> I do not myself believe that we are using our resources uneconomically, if by that we mean that by a different disposal of our resources we could appreciably add to the real income of the United Kingdom. I would rather argue that we are on the whole using our resources economically, but achieving that result by somewhat unorthodox and roundabout methods.[1]

This point of view, though it carried much weight and influenced many of the Government's pronouncements, was far from being accepted by other economists.[2] To begin with, they disagreed about Britain's export prospects. Indeed, the experience of the 1950s hardly bore out Professor Robinson's gloomy forecasts: there was a continued rise in world trade in manufactures, in which Britain shared; Professor Robinson himself later admitted that Britain's performance had been much better than he expected. Moreover, other experts criticized the whole method of Professor Robinson's analysis, pointing out both the difficulty of calculating the elasticity of demand for British exports and the limitations of such elasticities, which could be valid only for a short period of time. They also observed that Professor Robinson treated exports and imports as independent of each other, and that this ignored the possibility of retaliation by countries wanting to export food to Britain. It was further pointed out that there was a chain of causation from food prices, through the cost of

the financing of every £100 of additional imports therefore required the use of resources worth $£\dfrac{100}{14\cdot7} \times 50$, i.e. £340. Similar reckoning showed that to reduce this figure to about £150 (the value of the resources calculated to produce an extra £100 worth of output in agriculture), the elasticity of demand for exports would have to be as high as 5 – a figure which Professor Robinson thought unlikely.

[1] *Three Banks Review*, December 1958, p. 13.
[2] In particular, Graham Hallett, Gavin McCrone, Professor Nash, Dr Raeburn and Professor Tress (see Bibliography for details).

living and wages, to export prices and export sales. Moreover, any further expansion of British food production could only take place at costs still further above the prices at which imports could be obtained.

Some economists have cast doubt on the contribution actually made by the expansion of agriculture to the balance of payments, on the grounds that imports of feeding-stuffs have risen along with the increase in production, and that a large proportion of these come from dollar sources (North America); meanwhile, the expansion of livestock products has displaced mainly non-dollar imports (from Oceania and South America). The net savings of dollar expenditure therefore appear small. Thus Gavin McCrone declares:

> The payment of dollars for imported feed to be used for the production of milk, which was surplus to liquid requirements and had therefore to be sold at a loss, was a complete waste of money. And in so far as these dollar imports were used to enable home production to be substituted for goods from Australia and New Zealand, it would seem that the burden imposed on the balance of payments was heavier than that which was lifted.[1]

Many people have found it difficult to swallow the idea that producing goods at home at a cost greater than that at which they could be had from abroad could be sound economics. The *Economist* has consistently attacked the whole system of agricultural support. Vigorous criticism has also come from Professor Nash, who in 1955 calculated that the produce of British agriculture was receiving prices averaging 24 per cent above those of imports; he also pointed out that the various price-raising and cost-reducing measures enjoyed by farmers provided roughly the whole of net farm income.[2] A joint work by Professor Nash and E. A. Attwood, comparing agricultural policies in Britain and Denmark, found little in favour of Britain. An adaptation of British agriculture to make it competitive with that of Denmark would be technically possible; however:

---

[1] Gavin McCrone, *The Economics of Subsidising Agriculture* (London: Allen and Unwin, 1962), p. 81.

[2] E. F. Nash, 'The competitive position of British agriculture', *Journal of Agricultural Economics*, June 1955.

The major obstacle to the changes required in order to transform British agriculture into this new and revitalized industry is the protective system itself ... We maintain the protective system in the interests of those sections of the agricultural community who would find difficulty in adapting themselves to its withdrawal, who would be unable or reluctant to move to alternative employment or who would lack the resources, the ability or the ambition to attempt more economic methods of farming. But in doing so we inevitably encourage the industry to resist the very changes it needs in order to free itself from its dependence on protection and subsidies.[1]

The authors therefore favoured a system of payments to individual farmers suffering hardship during transitional adjustments: such payments should not be such as to influence decisions concerning how much to produce, nor should they affect the choice whether to stay in agriculture or to move to other occupations.

A comprehensive study of British agricultural policy published in 1960 tried to discover what principles of policy could be drawn from various basic criteria such as agricultural history, science, sociology, strategy and economics. It concluded that the strategic argument provided the main reason for maintaining British agriculture at a level higher than that which would be economically justifiable (it avoided the question as to what level *would* be economically justifiable). It nevertheless thought that a high degree of self-sufficiency in peacetime was not essential: the potential for expansion was more important than the actual level of output.[2]

In general the strategic argument has been pushed into the background of discussion. In the nuclear age, a war seems likely to be short; also, most of the land and agricultural produce of a small island would probably be contaminated by fall-out. The traditional argument concerning the social role of the farm population has also lost its weight: the numbers engaged in agriculture have fallen to a mere one-twentieth of the population, and the advantages of country life cannot easily be proclaimed in the

[1] E. F. Nash and E. A. Attwood, *The Agricultural Policies of Britain and Denmark* (London: Land Books, 1961), pp. 87–88.

[2] *Principles for British Agricultural Policy*, edited by H. T. Williams (London: O.U.P., 1960).

face of such striking evidence that many country people themselves prefer to live in the towns.

In popular discussion the rising cost of agricultural support has given rise to much criticism. Many farmers have become fairly prosperous through subsidies, and the charge of 'feather-bedding' has been launched. Since the greater part of subsidy is paid in the form of price support, most of it goes to the farmers with the biggest output who probably need it least.

The National Farmers' Union

The Farmers' Unions have exerted themselves vigorously to win over public opinion and have succeeded in exerting considerable influence on official policy. Before the Second World War, farm organizations in Britain played only a limited role; during the war the Government needed their assistance in converting agriculture to a wartime basis, and the habit of close consultation was formed. The annual price review system, at which the Government recognizes the Farmers' Unions as the official farmers' representatives, has put them in a strong position.[1] The Government has come under pressure to attune its policies to the wishes of the Unions: though it has insisted that the reviews are to be regarded as 'consultations' and not 'negotiations', it has often been willing to pay a substantial price to avoid open disagreement. After the early period of the production drive, the attitude of the Government and the Unions began to diverge, but it was only in 1956 that the first complete break occurred. Subsequently, with the attempts by the Government to reduce guaranteed prices on some commodities, there has been increasing difficulty in reaching an agreed settlement: in 1958, 1960, 1962 and 1963 the Unions refused to endorse the results of the price review.

The strength of the National Farmers' Union for England and Wales has been reinforced by intelligent tactics. By refraining from making agricultural policy a party issue, the NFU has contrived to gain the support of both political parties. It has also

[1] The National Farmers' Union of England and Wales, the NFU of Scotland and the Ulster Farmers' Union take part in the Annual Review. An independent Farmers' Union of Wales, formed in 1955, is not recognized by the Government. The NFU of England and Wales is by far the most influential and acts as spokesman for farmers throughout the United Kingdom.

managed to convince politicians that the agricultural vote is an important political force: in this belief, Labour spokesmen have sometimes outdone the NFU in their demands for favourable treatment for agriculture, and they have carefully avoided the topic of land nationalization. In fact, it has been queried whether the farm vote is really so important: in 1956 there were only six constituencies where agriculture provided over 40 per cent of regular male employment, and rural constituencies tend to remain firmly Conservative even when farmers are not happy with Conservative policies.[1]

The NFU's position rests on a large membership, which reached a peak of 210,000 in 1953 and amounted to 194,000 in 1959; this may be compared with the total of about 220,000 full-time farmers in England and Wales. It has been prepared to pay high salaries to obtain expert staff; its publications are of a high quality, comparing very favourably with those of farm organizations in other countries. In its chief economist, Asher Winegarten, it has an advocate able to meet the criticisms of economists on their own ground, making the most of the balance of payments and other arguments.[2]

During the 1950s the NFU became one of the most powerful farm organizations that have existed in any country. However, membership by Britain of the European Economic Community would mean that the NFU would lose the special relationship which it had established, through the price reviews, with the British Government. Probably this, as much as any real likelihood of adverse effects on British farmers, accounted for the NFU's distaste for the prospect. The objections which it raised are further described in Chapter 17.

The outlook

Since the Second World War, British agriculture as a whole has achieved a high standard of technical efficiency and has regained a large measure of prosperity. This prosperity, however, is

[1] Cf. P. Self and H. J. Storing, *The State and the Farmer* (London: Allen and Unwin, 1962).

[2] Cf. in particular his paper 'Some reflections on the basis of international competition for the British market', read to the Agricultural Economics Society in July 1960, published in the *Journal of Agricultural Economics*, December 1960.

dependent on subsidies, which form a large part of farm income. There are many efficient farmers, with holdings which are well situated and permit a sufficiently large scale of operations, who obtain good incomes and could probably do with much less subsidy than they now receive. Others are less fortunate, being handicapped by the poor soil, the smallness or other shortcomings of their holdings, as well as in many cases by their own low standard of management: these farmers may be heavily dependent on support, and even with the subsidy their income is often unsatisfactory.

It might have been expected that the events of the past would have eliminated uneconomic production and created an efficient agriculture. As a result of Britain's early start in industrialization, the decline in the relative importance of agriculture also began early, and the movement of labour into other sectors has continued almost without interruption to the present time, being accelerated by the unmitigated effects of the Great Depression and probably also by the adverse developments of the 1920s. Agriculture in Britain now provides a smaller share of the national income and occupies a smaller part of the population than is the case in any other country.

However, the adaptation forced on British agriculture did not necessarily have favourable results even in the long run. Gavin McCrone rightly criticizes the basic principles of Free Traders who believed that through laissez-faire agriculture would reach a new equilibrium. He points out that agriculture's ability to compete depends on its general standard of efficiency as well as on natural resources, and that the depression caused by the contraction in British agriculture damaged its efficiency: the more enterprising farmers left, and those who remained ran down their capital equipment.

> The idea of forcing the inefficient producers out of production sounds plausible in theory; but in agriculture they often stay until they have ruined the other factors of production and until the job of repair and reclamation is too expensive to be worth undertaking.[1]

In fact the number of farmers in Britain, after falling during the Great Depression, subsequently revived and is now approximately

[1] Op. cit., p. 45.

what it was a hundred years ago; the decline in the total agricultural population has been mainly accounted for by farm workers. On the other hand, the statistics show a fairly big fall in the number of farms, mainly in the smaller size groups, but it seems that in the past many of the holdings counted were not genuine independent farms.

However this may be, there remain many farms which for one reason or another do not provide a reasonable income, and the need now seems to be to concentrate assistance on these farms. In the first instance, an effort may be made to improve their efficiency in various ways, as is being attempted through the Small Farmer Scheme in particular. But there are probably many holdings which cannot be made viable, and these may eventually have to be amalgamated with other farms, or possibly be run on a part-time basis only; the occupiers of such holdings may require assistance to enable them to move into other occupations or into retirement. The need for such developments was stressed, with surprisingly little opposition, by Professor D. K. Britton at the 1963 Oxford Farming Conference.

Action along these lines may gradually reduce the need for price support, but some degree of support will no doubt have to be maintained in the foreseeable future. If Britain eventually enters the EEC, her system of support will presumably have to be brought into line with that of the common agricultural policy. The breakdown of negotiations in Brussels, however, leaves the Government free for the time being to make its own decisions. The rising cost of deficiency payments, due to pressures on the market for which both domestic production and imports are responsible, has put this system of support in question. The price review announced in March 1963 makes no drastic changes, but indicates the direction of Government thinking: some limitation on the output of certain commodities and some regulation of imports appear necessary. The intention is, in the first instance, to persuade exporting countries to regulate their supplies, but it seems likely that measures of import control by Britain will prove necessary.

This need not mean the end of deficiency payments. It has been pointed out above that the system has definite economic advantages. It would be perfectly compatible with measures to restrain domestic production, and with a flexible system of import control (which might consist of liberal import quotas or of minimum import price systems with the minima fixed at low levels). Deficiency payments could then continue to assist British producers by making up the difference between the market price and a higher guaranteed price, but the amount of payment would no longer be subject to large and unforeseen variations.

Chapter 13. France

The agricultural policy of the Vichy Government
The philosophy of the 'retour à la terre' received its consecration in France during the Second World War. The aim of restoring French agriculture was in line with a strong current of French thinking from Méline down; it also fitted in with Hitler's strategy of turning France (and other occupied nations) into food suppliers for industrial Germany. Pétain himself came to be known as 'Le Maréchal paysan': shortly after taking office in 1940 he invited the country to follow a new path, calling a halt to excessive industrialization and declaring that 'France shall become once more what she should never have ceased to be, an essentially agricultural nation'.[1]

In December 1940 a Corporation Paysanne was instituted, modelled on the German Reichsnährstand. All existing farm organizations were forcibly united in the Corporation, which had the object of defending 'the moral, social and economic interests of the great peasant family'. Various measures were taken to reform aspects of legislation affecting the peasantry, to improve the standard of rural education and so on. The prices of agricultural products were officially fixed, and these fixed prices were progressively raised in the course of the war. The movement of labour out of agriculture practically ceased.

The peasantry, however, subjected to increasingly burdensome

[1] Quoted by M. Braibant, *La France, Nation Agricole* (Paris, 1943).

exactions for the benefit of the occupying power, were hardly in a mood to appreciate Vichy's action in their favour. Even the prosperity which they gained from high official prices and from still higher earnings on the black market was largely illusory: they were running down their capital for lack of replacements, and after the war their savings were depleted by the need to restore the productive capacity of their farms, as well as by inflation. Agricultural production by 1945 had fallen to two-thirds of its pre-war level.[1]

Post-war policy – from shortages to surplus

The first of the post-war Plans, for the years 1947–50, aimed at reconstructing the French economy. An increase in agricultural production was essential both to meet food shortages and to relieve the balance of payments. The Plan aimed therefore to encourage land improvement, mechanization, road-building, the provision of electricity, the construction of processing plants and other measures to assist agriculture.

In 1948 the Organisation for European Economic Co-operation, which had the task of administering the Marshall Plan, asked France to submit its economic programme. In their reply the French authorities stated that in general the objectives of the Plan remained unchanged, but that there was an important new factor concerning agriculture: whereas the original aim had been only that France should achieve self-sufficiency in food, it was now intended to develop exports of basic agricultural products.

This new aim was an outcome of studies which indicated that when the Marshall Plan came to an end, France would still have a large deficit on its balance of payments, and that only an increase in agricultural exports could fill the gap. It also appeared that the products which could find a market abroad were not France's traditional exports – they included wheat, meat and dairy products. In the Agricultural Plan for 1948–52, the production objectives were revised accordingly. Already in 1948 France exported substantial amounts of wheat, as part of a deliberate policy to gain a footing on world markets.

By around 1949 agricultural production had revived to the

[1] A full account of wartime developments appears in M. Cépède, *Agriculture et Alimentation en France durant la IIe guerre mondiale* (Paris: Génin, 1961).

pre-war level, and from 1950 onwards problems of surpluses made their appearance. Exports of wheat and sugar soon had to be promoted by means of subsidies, and steps similar to those adopted before the war became necessary to absorb the surplus of wine – distillation, blocking on the vineyards and uprooting of vines.

The First Plan was extended for three years, to 1953. The draft of the Second Plan provided for a further increase in agricultural production. This caused much concern among agricultural circles, and the Agricultural Commissions reported as follows:

> There is anxiety, felt particularly by the representatives of the profession, at the risk of overproduction leading to a crisis similar to that which overtook agriculture from 1930 to 1936. In endorsing the expansionist policy desired by the Commissariat, the Commissions wish to stress that they have done so only on the express condition that the realization of the Plan should be intimately linked with concurrent and effective steps to guarantee prices to producers and with the opening of permanent and remunerative export markets.[1]

The objective that was adopted for the Second Plan, from 1954 to 1957, was a 20 per cent increase in agricultural production. It was agreed, however, that output of some products, in particular wine, alcohol and oats, should be reduced. In accordance with the condition laid down by the Agricultural Commissions, measures were taken to give firmer price guarantees to producers. A decree of September 30th, 1953, provided for the institution of a Fonds de Soutien et de Garantie Mutuelle, which was to support agricultural markets: it was financed in part by the State and in part by producers, as well as by levies on imports; it came into being in 1955. The markets of almost all important products were subjected to intervention in one form or another, and the price support mechanism became increasingly complex. Frequently the guaranteed price was 'indexed' so as to rise in company with increases in retail prices, in the cost of farm requisites and in farm wages. In July 1960 the various Funds for supporting

[1] Covering letter to: Commissions de la Production Agricole et de l'Équipement Rural, *Rapport Général au Commissariat Général du Plan* (October 1953).

the markets of different commodities were merged in the Fonds d'Orientation et de Régularisation des Marchés Agricoles (FORMA). Domestic markets were virtually insulated from outside influences by strict controls over imports, exercised for most products through import licensing but for grains and dairy products through State-controlled import monopolies. There was also an increasing degree of assistance to exports of products in surplus, through direct export subsidies and other means.[1]

In the case of wheat, a means of restraining production existed in principle in the quantum: the guaranteed price was applicable only to a standard quantity, any additional output receiving only the price realized on the export market. When the total output was expected to exceed the standard quantity, a deduction from the guaranteed price was made in the payments to each producer, those with the largest deliveries being penalized more heavily than the small producers. In fact this arrangement was not very effective in discouraging excess output. The standard quantity was usually fixed at an amount well above the needs for domestic consumption; also, many of the larger farmers could make a profit even at the world price, while the small producers were not much discouraged by the comparatively light penalties on small deliveries.

The Third Plan (1958–61) pursued a policy of selective expansion. There was to be a further overall increase of 20 per cent in agricultural output: in line with prospects on export markets, feed grains and livestock products were to expand most, while production of wheat and sugar-beet was to level off and that of wine and potatoes to be reduced. In fact it proved extremely difficult to restrain the production even of commodities in surplus. Not only was it politically almost impossible to reduce prices in order to discourage output, but the rapid spread of new technology throughout French agriculture enabled greatly increased productivity. In 1961 the agricultural correspondent of *Le Monde* wrote:

> Too much wheat, too much barley, maize, meat, milk, sugar, too many artichokes, apples and very soon also too many cauliflowers.... The peasants, having been encouraged by

---

[1] For a fuller account of the various measures of intervention, see OEEC, *Reports on Agricultural Policies* (Paris, 1956 to 1961).

optimistic planners to raise production, are now finding
that they don't know what to do with their output – this
even when, in many cases, they have not even reached the
planned targets.[1]

At the same time, and in spite of the increasing complexity
of the price-support apparatus, farm incomes remained low in
relation to those of other sectors: it was calculated that, between
1949 and 1958, the average income per head of the active agricultural population (in constant prices) rose by about 23 per
cent, while that of the non-farm population rose some 46 per cent.[2]
The discontent of the peasants found expression in more or less
violent demonstrations, of which the more common consisted of
strewing unsold produce on the roads and erecting road-blocks
to hold up city-dwellers on their holidays.

The Loi d'Orientation Agricole of August 6th, 1960, sought
to assuage this dissatisfaction. In its opening Article it declared:

The Law on Agricultural Guidance has as its objective,
within the framework of overall economic and social policy,
the achievement of parity between agriculture and the other
economic sectors.

The objective was to be attained by various means, which the
Law indicated only in vague and general terms: they included
the raising of productivity, further efforts to improve the structure
of agricultural holdings, improved marketing and processing
facilities and a reduced margin between producer and retail
prices. A study would be made of the size which a holding should
normally have if worked by two 'labour units', and financial aid
would be given in priority to realize the optimum conditions indicated by this study. The FORMA would continue to ensure a
satisfactory organization of agricultural markets, and prices
would be fixed which would give producers a purchasing-power
at least equivalent to that of 1958. A long-standing demand of
the agricultural organizations was satisfied by the provision that
the Government would present each year to Parliament a report

[1] F.-H. de Virieu, 'Vers des surplus permanents dans l'agriculture?', *Le
Monde*, January 27th, 1961.
[2] M. J. Klatzmann, 'Revenus agricoles et non-agricoles', *Études statistiques*
(Institut National de la Statistique et des Études Économiques), October–
December 1959.

on the agricultural situation, in which it would indicate the measures envisaged to establish 'parity' of incomes.

These provisions were not enough to satisfy the peasants, and in July 1961, after a further series of demonstrations, a number of specific measures were taken to relieve the market for certain products, the prices of grains and of wine were raised, the FORMA was given increased power to support agricultural markets, and producers were authorized to combine in selling their produce.

The Loi Complémentaire and the Fourth Plan, 1962

A year later, a further step was taken with the Loi Complémentaire d'Orientation Agricole. To intensify the effort at putting together separate holdings in larger units, the Sociétés d'Aménagement Foncier et d'Etablissement Rural (SAFER) – created by the 1960 Law – were given priority in purchasing holdings that came on the market. A new Fund – the Fonds d'Action Sociale pour l'Aménagement des Structures Agricoles (FASASA) – was set up with several new tasks, designed above all to facilitate structural adjustments by relieving the social problems involved in abolishing small and uneconomic holdings. It is to provide additional pensions to elderly peasants who, by giving up their farm, facilitate a scheme of structural improvement; to give loans to peasants who leave overpopulated areas to install themselves in less crowded regions; to make grants and loans to peasants who leave holdings that are too small to be viable and begin again elsewhere; and to give financial assistance to peasants (or their sons) who want to learn a new trade before going to the towns. The Law includes provisions to restrain the accumulation of holdings in the hands of a single individual, to prevent persons whose major occupation is outside farming from building up a farming activity linked to their other occupation, and to control the development of industrial-type livestock units (such as broiler houses); these provisions correspond to grievances expressed by the farm organizations.

The Loi Complémentaire also carries further the possibility given by the 1960 Law for producers to combine their activities: groups of producers of a given commodity can receive official recognition and be given priority in the allocation of State financial assistance; various local groups can join up and apply

common regulations concerning production, prices and marketing; and eventually such regulations can be made compulsory
for all producers of the commodity in the region. The effect
should be to strengthen the position of producers in the market,
in a manner similar to the British Marketing Boards.

The Loi Complémentaire is thus more important in several
respects than the Law of 1960. Its success depends on the energy
with which it is applied and on the funds made available, but it
provides the legal basis for a far-reaching reorganization of
agricultural production and marketing, and establishes as an
immediate priority the need for such action if agricultural incomes
are to be improved.

This significant shift of emphasis is also reflected in the Fourth
Plan for 1962–5. The aim of the Plan as regards agriculture is
stated to be that of 'improving the incomes of the agricultural
population and accomplishing a first step in the movement towards parity'. For the first time in an official French document
the need for a further reduction in the agricultural population
is openly recognized:

> The improvement of agricultural incomes ... implies a re-
> duction in the active agricultural population which, if it is
> not to take place in the most unsatisfactory way, must be
> foreseen, accepted, humanized.

The Plan stresses the need for structural reform, pointing out
that the small size of many holdings and the seriousness of fragmentation are important causes of low incomes. The work of
regrouping fragmented holdings should accelerate from 500,000
to over 600,000 hectares a year; the volume of investment envisaged for this purpose is much increased and constitutes by
far the largest item of expenditure on agriculture under the Plan
(Table 66). Large increases in investment are also foreseen for
agricultural education and research, and for improvements in
marketing and processing. The Plan provides for intensified
action in backward rural areas.

On the other hand, the Plan states that the system of target
prices can no longer be applied, in particular because prices
now have to be determined in accordance with the common
agricultural policy of the European Economic Community. The
relative prices of different products will nevertheless continue to

Table 66

INVESTMENT IN AGRICULTURE AUTHORIZED BY THE THIRD
AND FOURTH PLANS
(NF millions)

	Third Plan (at current prices)	Fourth Plan (at 1961 prices)
Structural improvement	1,549	2,693
Equipment of individual holdings	236	356
Education, advisory services, research	210	680
Regional development programmes	360	526
Afforestation	44	96
Storing, processing and distribution facilities	456	1,133
Equipment of services	11	16
Total	2,867	5,500

Source: IVe Plan de Développement Économique et Social Projet de loi No. 1573,
Assemblée Nationale.

guide production: the aim is to encourage the livestock sector,
beef in particular.

An increase in production appears inevitable and is expected
to take place at the rate of about 4·5 per cent a year, even though
this will give rise to permanent surpluses in some commodities –
wheat and dairy products in particular.

> The expansion of agricultural output constitutes one of the
> long-term opportunities before our country. It is an im-
> portant element in raising agricultural incomes, since a
> general rise in prices would lead to even larger surpluses
> and would moreover be liable to endanger the overall eco-
> nomic balance. There can therefore be no question of
> restraining the effort of our farmers; the aim must rather be
> that of guiding it towards the commodities which are the most
> in demand (beef, fruit, vegetables), and of supplementing
> this effort with financial assistance by the State combined
> with a reasonable contribution by the agricultural sector
> itself.[1]

[1] Ibid., pp. 19–20.

The Plan accordingly envisages that from 1959 to 1965 agricultural exports to countries outside the franc area will more than double (while agricultural imports will rise by only 25 per cent). It does not indicate in detail where export markets can be found, but considers that the best prospects are offered by the market of the EEC.

Economics, politics and the peasant

It has been seen in the previous chapter that in Britain after the war the economic case for agricultural expansion and the justification of support were the subjects of long and detailed arguments. In France there was hardly any such debate. One of the few independent writers was Pierre Fromont, who stressed the importance of reducing the costs of production and marketing and the need to move people out of agriculture.[1] Another is Denis Bergmann, who in 1957 analysed the principles of agricultural policy in the light of economic criteria; he criticized excessive reliance on price support, declaring that markets should be allowed to operate as freely as possible (he pointed out the advantages of a deficiency payments system along British lines), and wrote that:

> The only real way of reducing the income gap is to increase the mobility of manpower ... Any measure which arbitrarily, through direct payments, raises prices and incomes would in the long run have results opposite to those which are sought for. In other words, a policy whereby prices and incomes are systematically increased would be self-defeating.[2]

In general, however, agriculture in France has seemed hardly to be a subject for economics: its importance is generally recognized almost without question, and the rest of the community seems to accept an obligation to preserve a large and reasonably prosperous agriculture. This attitude can be attributed to developments over a long period, during both the Great Depression of the late nineteenth century and the crisis of the 1930s; it was

[1] P. Fromont, 'Les problèmes actuels de l'agriculture française', *Problèmes économiques*, August 7th, 1956.

[2] D. Bergmann, 'Les principes directeurs d'une politique agricole française', *Économie rurale*, October 1957, p. 20.

well expressed in the passage by Augé-Laribé already quoted in Chapter 8.[1] There has been an extreme reluctance to admit that the agricultural population has to fall. Even a senior official of the Finance Ministry, writing in 1959, pointed out that a more rapid reduction would enable incomes per head to rise more rapidly, but declared:

> We are well aware of the conditions in which the rural exodus takes place. We know that it leaves a surplus of manpower in some regions, a shortage in others, and that it brings about a dramatic increase in the average age of the rural population as well as a general economic decline in the areas concerned.[2]

In an important study of the agricultural income problem, Marc Latil points out that, in regions of general economic progress, agriculture can usually contrive to adapt itself to new conditions; in backward areas, either agriculture fails to progress or, if a movement of labour does take place, the land is abandoned for lack of initiative and of capital. 'In the first case, the emigrant from agriculture leaves behind him a modern and mechanized agriculture: in the second, he leaves a decaying hovel and land going to waste.'[3] The same point is made by the International Labour Office:

> ... The effects of the rural exodus in France have long been a subject of controversy. The push factors – contracting employment and a downward trend in agricultural incomes – were strong because aggregate demand for food in the internal market did not increase. The pull factors – higher earnings and growing employment in industry – were weak, until the industrial expansion of recent years.[4]

The farm organizations have increased greatly in strength. The most powerful group to emerge after the war was the Fédération Nationale des Syndicats des Exploitants Agricoles (FNSEA), in the rue Scribe. This descended from the right-wing syndicalist

---

[1] Cf. pp. 183–4.

[2] P. Grimanelli, in Société Française d'Économie Rurale, 'L'économie agricole française 1938–58', *Bulletin* No. 39–40, January–June 1959, p. 14.

[3] Marc Latil, *L'évolution du revenu agricole* (Paris: Colin, 1956), p. 168.

[4] International Labour Office, *Why Labour Leaves the Land* (Geneva, 1960), p. 54.

movement that was active in the 1930s. It is closely linked with the specialist producer associations (for wheat, sugar-beet, wine, etc.) which, as before the war, constitute effective pressure-groups.

The radical tendencies of the Boulevard Saint-Germain have been pursued in the Fédération Nationale de la Mutualité, de la Coopération et du Crédit Agricole. In a useful study of French farm organizations, H. Mendras observes that it is difficult to find any doctrinal basis for the differences between the rival groups. Nevertheless:

> Our villages are almost always divided between two clans: the red and the white, the republicans and the reactionaries, the faction of the schoolmaster and that of the *curé*. The history of the agricultural organizations, indeed, is that of a long struggle between the village squire and the radical-socialist deputy.[1]

The Assemblée Permanente des Présidents des Chambres d'Agriculture (APPCA), as a public organization, is officially neutral in political matters. In fact it also constitutes a strong pressure-group, expressing views generally similar to those of the FNSEA, with which it shares the same address in the rue Scribe (one president of the FNSEA, M. Blondelle, passed in easy transition to the presidency of the APPCA).

For a time the various farm organizations were officially united in the Confédération Générale de l'Agriculture, set up at the end of the war. This body, however, incurred mounting criticism from the FNSEA for being too closely associated with official policy, and in 1953 it ceased to be an effective force.

The demands of the farm organizations have generally concentrated on higher prices and better markets. Mendras describes their programme as follows:

> The first requirement is that the family holdings must be preserved, the rural exodus restrained; here everyone is in agreement. But the measures envisaged are generally negative; positive steps on the other hand are usually expressed in

[1] H. Mendras, 'Les organisations agricoles', in Association française de science politique, *Les Paysans et la Politique dans la France contemporaine* (Paris: Colin, 1958), p. 232.

vague and general terms, and they are always difficult to implement. The vital demand is of course for price support: this necessitates increased outlets, hence assistance for exports and the elimination of imports, as well as a reduction in the price of industrial products used by agriculture in order to reduce the costs of agricultural production. To allow small holdings to survive, demands are made also for additional credits to promote equipment and modernization, and for action to disseminate the latest agricultural techniques ... Behind these demands there lies a deep concern felt by the agricultural population: the fear of overproduction and falling prices. The general agreement on this programme is in striking contrast with the rivalries between the organizations, and shows clearly that the quarrels are between different headquarters which are contending for the same body of troops.[1]

Besides demanding more effective intervention on the domestic market, the farm organizations frequently insist on an even stricter control of imports; it is implied that France should not import any agricultural produce that could be grown at home, regardless of differences in costs. At the same time the farm organizations have given increasing attention to the prospect of improved outlets in the European Economic Community, and are always ready to denounce the slowness of France's partners – especially Germany – to admit French exports on preferential terms.

The nature of the agitation has not been such as to favour a coherent and constructive agricultural policy. Most of the farm organizations are reluctant to admit that a long-term improvement in the agricultural situation can be achieved only by a thorough reform of farm structures, involving a further large reduction in the agricultural population. It is even suggested by Professor Michel Cépède that the larger and more efficient farmers who tend to dominate the agricultural organizations do not find it in their interest to promote improvements among the more backward sectors:

The fact is that the constant policy of this group has been to use the high costs of production which technical backwardness imposed on the greater part of French agriculture as an

[1] Ibid., p. 250.

argument in order to obtain prices from which the most efficient farms derive a large profit. This profit being largely attributable to the difference in technical standards, the question arises whether the dominant group has an interest, in the short term at least, in reducing the difference.[1]

Cépède further points out that the leaders of the FNSEA, who to a large extent belong to this group of advanced farmers, have been entrusted by the Government with the task of administering funds for promoting agricultural progress: this, he thinks, is why relatively small amounts have been spent on diffusing technical information.

The representation of agriculture in Parliament seems to have been weak in quality, if not in quantity. In a study of this question, Mattei Dogan criticizes severely the standard of debate and the value of legislation on agriculture:

> An examination of the parliamentary debates leaves the impression, which is confirmed by many witnesses, that the majority of deputies from rural areas are short-sighted conservatives, incapable of seeing the problems from a national point of view ... Parliamentary initiative in agricultural matters is abundant but ineffective.[2]

Progressive thinking seems to have been even rarer in the Senate, where rural districts are over-represented, than in the National Assembly.

A new tendency has recently appeared among the farm organizations with the growing influence of the Centre National des Jeunes Agriculteurs. The CNJA grew out of a Commission des Jeunes, included in 1947 in the Confédération Générale de l'Agriculture; in 1954 it became a separate body, which subsequently established close links with the FNSEA while maintaining its independent point of view. The leaders of the CNJA, as representatives of the young farming generation, are naturally more progressive than their elders and not so much influenced by traditional habits of thought: their policy is determined not by a vested interest in the established order but by a concern with the future prosperity of French agriculture. Their programme thus

---

[1] Op. cit., pp. 491–2.

[2] Mattei Dogan, 'La représentation parlementaire du monde rural', in Association française de science politique, op. cit., pp. 217 and 223.

tends to stress action that would rejuvenate French farming, doing away with the inherited pattern of uneconomic small and fragmented holdings and giving increased opportunity for young and dynamic farmers to make their way. The leaders of the CNJA are exerting an influence even within the FNSEA, which in consequence is becoming increasingly divided between the progressive and the conservative tendencies.

The outlook

There has thus been growing awareness in France that in the long run the peasants can receive an adequate income only if the structure of agriculture and of agricultural marketing is drastically overhauled. The instability of the Governments that succeeded each other up to 1958 did not make it easy to take controversial action, and the installation under the Fifth Republic of a strong Government was the first step towards a more constructive agricultural policy. The Minister of Agriculture appointed in August 1961, M. Edgard Pisani, is young and dynamic, and the ideas of the young farming generation correspond to his own. Building upon the programme of the Centre National des Jeunes Agriculteurs, he was able to put through Parliament – not without substantial amendment, which nevertheless left the essential points more or less intact – the Loi Complémentaire of 1962. The success with which this law can be applied remains to be seen, but there is reason to hope that this and the Fourth Plan for 1962–5 represent an overdue turning-point in French agricultural policy.

However, a situation which has resulted from almost a century of inaction cannot quickly be transformed. Technical progress is tapping the vast potential of French agriculture, and the flow of increased production, which is the French peasant's main hope of a better income, can hardly be stemmed. Since only a part of the increased output can be absorbed at home, access to markets abroad is essential; and since for many products France can make a profit only from prices well above those of the established exporters, this access has to be on preferential terms. The arrangements for agriculture in the European Economic Community, and the terms on which Britain can be admitted into the Community, are thus of vital importance for French agriculture.

Chapter 14. Western Germany

Post-war developments – the Agricultural Act, 1955

Immediately after the Second World War, food distribution in Western Germany was controlled by the occupying powers. When the Federal Republic was constituted in September 1949, shortages were still the major problem: Dr Adenauer, on taking office as Chancellor, declared that the agriculture of Western Germany must be made more efficient and food production raised. The necessary condition for this was the assurance to producers of stable and well-balanced conditions of production and marketing, at prices which would cover the costs of well-managed average farms and at the same time permit the poorer sections of the community to meet their needs.

In 1949 imports of food were still being subsidized in order to reduce prices to consumers. Between November 1950 and April 1951, Einfuhr- und Vorratsstellen (Import and Storage Boards) were instituted for the main agricultural products, with the object of stabilizing prices and maintaining them at levels consistent with the aims of agricultural policy: these Boards controlled imports in a manner similar to the Nazi Reichsstellen, and could intervene on the domestic market by purchasing, selling and stockpiling.

As the food situation eased and world prices declined, the Import and Storage Boards, together with other measures of import control, were used to maintain German prices at levels well above those of the world market. There was increasing concern with the problem of agricultural incomes, and the Deutsches Bauernverband (German Farmers' Union), formed in 1948, began to demand 'parity' with other sectors. The Agricultural Act of July 8th, 1955, laid a firm statutory basis for measures to assist agriculture. Its objects were:

- to ensure a reasonable standard of living for the agricultural population on well-managed farms;
- to raise agricultural productivity;
- to stabilize agricultural prices;
- to ensure a regular food supply at prices enabling the lower income groups to buy sufficient quantities.

The Act did not commit the Government to maintaining any clearly-defined level of prices or incomes for agriculture; however, the Government was required to submit an annual report to Parliament, showing in particular the development in farm incomes, and on this basis to put forward an annual plan for achieving the objectives of the Act. The annual Green Reports subsequently provided a detailed analysis of the agricultural situation, based in part on a regular study of the accounts of a sample of farms of different types and sizes. Under the Green Plans various steps were taken to support farm incomes: several measures already being applied by the Federal Government were transferred to the Green Plan budget, and other action was initiated.

Price support and import control

Since Western Germany remains a net importer of most agricultural products, it has proved possible, up to the introduction of the common agricultural policy of the European Economic Community, to support prices on the domestic market mainly by restricting imports in a variety of ways, the chief instrument for this purpose being the Import and Storage Boards. Four such Boards were set up in 1950 and 1951, covering (a) grains, (b) milk products and fats (including margarine), (c) meat and live-stock, (d) sugar. The Board for sugar was an Import Board only; the others also had power to intervene on the domestic market and to build up stocks.

The Boards did not themselves purchase abroad, but imports of any of these commodities had to be offered to the appropriate Board, which could then act in one of the following ways:

1. It could buy the produce and then pass it back to the importer at a price corresponding to the level which it was desired to maintain on the domestic market. For grains and sugar, this level was prescribed annually by Parliament; for livestock products, the Minister of Agriculture instructed the Boards as to the price level which should be aimed at. In theory, the domestic price level might occasionally be below the import price, in which case the transaction involved a subsidy from the Board to the importer. But usually the opposite was the case, so that the Board in effect imposed a levy on imports corresponding to the difference between the world and the domestic price.

2. The Board could pass the produce back to the importer with instructions as to when and where it should be marketed. It could thus prevent temporary oversupply of the market and ensure regular supplies to a given area (such as West Berlin). The Board could also require that the produce should be used for processing, in order to relieve the market. Such arrangements were frequent for meat and dairy products.

3. The Board could buy the produce and store it for a while before resale in order to prevent the market being oversupplied. This happened sometimes when imports had to be made in fulfilment of trade agreements with other countries. The Board for sugar could insist that the produce should be stocked by the importer for a prescribed period.

4. The Boards also had the right to refuse the produce, thus preventing the import from taking place: this might happen because necessary formalities had not been observed or because the price quoted by the importer was considered too high.

The extent to which the domestic price could be influenced by import control depended largely on the proportion of domestic production to total supply. In the 1950s, this proportion was fairly low for wheat, feed grains and sugar, but for rye, beef and veal, pigmeat and butter Western Germany approached self-sufficiency.

In so far as the volume of imports permitted effective action, the Import and Storage Boards were a powerful instrument of

10

protection. While leaving the actual business of importing in private hands (thus retaining a certain element of competition and encouraging importers to buy on the cheapest market), the system enabled absolute control over the volume and timing of imports, the price at which they entered the domestic market, and even when, where and for what purpose they were sold.

The efficiency of the system was perhaps its major drawback in the long run. By enabling domestic prices to be supported at a high level, it encouraged production, and the more production rose, the less effective was import control in maintaining prices. An almost complete ban on imports of butter and pigmeat became necessary to maintain the price level, and price fluctuations resulting from changes in domestic supply could not be avoided.

The action on imports was reinforced by intervention on the domestic market. This occurred regularly for grains, which are relatively easy to store: the Board stood ready to purchase at the prescribed minimum price and to resell at the maximum. The market for wheat was also supported by a milling ratio. Butter was purchased and stored in an attempt to even out seasonal fluctuations, but the difficulty and expense of storage limited the effectiveness of this action. The same was true for meat.

Like other systems of protection at the frontier, the import control exercised by the Boards practically eliminated the price mechanism as a regulator of supply and demand, causing distortions such as an excessive price for rye as compared with other grains. Also, the cost of agricultural support by this method was not apparent, being represented by the relatively high prices of foodstuffs and not, as with a deficiency payments system, by direct subsidies. In a critical analysis of the Import Board system, Boerckel estimated that the burden on German consumers (arising from the difference between import and domestic prices) was of the order of 3 billion marks in 1956. He considered that deficiency payments along British lines might be less costly.[1] However, so radical a change in the method of support was never seriously considered.

From the point of view of agricultural exporting countries, the Import Board system had almost all possible disadvantages. Trade

[1] W. Boerckel, *Einfuhr- und Vorratsstellen als Mittel der Agrarpolitik* (Mainz-am-Rhein: Diemler, 1959). Much of the present account of the Import Boards is indebted to this study.

could be reduced or cut off entirely with little or no warning; there was not even the guarantee of an annual quota. In the longer run, the stimulus given by the system to production in the importing country was liable to cause former markets to be reduced or even to disappear.

In addition to the control exercised by the Import Boards, all imports into the Federal Republic were subject to the Aussenhandelsstelle (Board of Foreign Trade), which was set up originally to control imports for balance of payments reasons but later operated primarily as a means of protection. Imports of all non-liberalized commodities required a licence from the Board of Foreign Trade: commodities subject to the Import Boards were included in this arrangement, and there were cases of conflict when for example the Board of Trade, for reasons of general commercial policy, authorized agricultural imports at a time when the competent Import Board judged the market oversupplied.

Import duties were applicable to most agricultural products and were generally high; however, the duties on products subject to the Import Boards were generally either reduced or suspended.

Imports of fruit and vegetables were regulated in a special way. For some years, a system of *Sperrfristen* (lock-out periods) was applied, under which imports were prohibited during periods of peak domestic production. This arrangement was replaced from about 1953 by the more flexible minimum price system: imports were suspended only so long as the German market price remained below certain levels. This system was applied first to imports from Italy, then extended to other exporting countries. Similar arrangements were made with the Netherlands, but in this case the system was operated by the Netherlands at the export stage. These minimum price systems are more fully described in Chapter 11.

Reform of farm structures

In spite of the large degree of price support provided by the various methods of import control, in spite of direct subsidies granted in particular for milk, and in spite also of subsidies reducing the cost of fertilizers and other agricultural inputs, incomes in German agriculture have remained well below those obtained in other sectors. The official data for recent years are reproduced in Table 67: from 1954/5 to 1960/1 there was a fairly large increase in income per head in agriculture, but an almost equally large rise in non-agricultural earnings (the comparison is with smallish communities where the cost of living is similar to that of farm families): the gap between the two narrowed slightly. In 1961/2, however, agricultural incomes fell and averaged less than two-thirds of the figure for the other occupations.

Table 67

AVERAGE INCOMES PER UNIT OF LABOUR

	Agriculture	Comparable non-agricultural activities	Agriculture as per cent of other activities
	DM	DM	%
1954/5	2,318	3,500	66
1955/6	2,507	3,822	66
1956/7	2,684	4,168	64
1957/8	3,278	4,418	74
1958/9	3,538	4,656	76
1959/60	3,621	4,948	73
1960/1	4,009	5,441	74
1961/2	3,701	5,975	62
1961/2 as % of 1954/5	160	171	.

Source: Grüner Bericht, 1962 and 1963.

It was recognized early in the 1950s that the main factor limiting progress in agriculture was the highly unsatisfactory structure of agricultural holdings. The great estates of Prussia had passed into other hands; Western Germany was predominantly a country of small holdings, made even more unfit for modern conditions by an appalling degree of fragmentation. Farm equipment was frequently obsolete and farming methods left much to be desired.

Two lost wars, inflation and deflation, the depletion of capital, have had the result that most farm buildings are too old and are unsuitable for a modern, rationally-organized holding.

Machinery is generally inadequate, the fertility of the soil, the quality and the yields of livestock are well below those of other countries. Farm structure (holdings that are too small and, above all, are split into too many separate plots) are further obstacles to a modern, low-cost farming enterprise.[1]

Increased capital was all the more necessary for German farms because mechanization had to compensate for the loss of agricultural labour, attracted by an expanding industry. Above all, the realization that for most agricultural products the average costs of production were well above those of Germany's future competitors in the European Economic Community gave rise to growing concern.

The annual Green Plans have therefore concentrated attention on measures to raise the efficiency of German agriculture, in particular by structural reform. As the Green Report for 1962 pointed out:

> Agriculture is in a process of rapid change and adaptation, which requires an improvement in agricultural structures, in part through the consolidation of holdings, through re-settlement and through an increase in the average size of farm. This adaptation to economic conditions determined above all by modern techniques cannot take place without social and economic strains, which agriculture cannot overcome from its own resources alone. Extensive State assistance is necessary to temper the hardships and to facilitate the process of adaptation. This assistance, however, can be successful only if it is based on the determination of agriculture to help itself.[2]

A general picture of expenditure under the Green Plans is given by Table 68. The data are not easy to interpret, because there is considerable overlapping between the Green Plan, regular expenditure from the Federal Budget and contributions by the Governments of the Länder: thus the increase in Green Plan expenditure to some extent corresponds to a transfer of

[1] H. v.d. Decken, 'Paritätssystem und Agrarstruktur', *Wirtschaftsdienst*, July 1954, p. 382.

[2] Bundesministerium für Ernährung, Landwirtschaft und Forsten, *Grüner Bericht*, 1962, p. 42.

Table 68

EXPENDITURE ON AGRICULTURE UNDER THE GREEN PLANS
AND THE FEDERAL BUDGET

	1956	1961	1962
I. GREEN PLANS	(DM million)		
STRUCTURAL IMPROVEMENTS, ETC.	250	700	860
of which:			
Consolidation		165	195
Enlargement of farms, transfer of farmsteads	} 80	190	315
Regional programmes	–	70	80
Old age assistance	–	70	100
INCOME SUPPORT	366	850	1,312
of which:			
Fertilizer subsidy	226	185	185
Promotion of quality and marketing	59	498	684
Reduction of interest charges	46	54	224
TOTAL GREEN PLANS	616	1,550	2,172
II. OTHER FEDERAL EXPENDITURE	1,483	981	751
of which:			
Storage for stabilization purposes	182	515	386
TOTAL FEDERAL EXPENDITURE	2,099	2,531	2,923

Source: Grüner Plan, 1963.

activities from the Federal budget. However, rising amounts have
been devoted to consolidating fragmented holdings, to enlarging
farms by the reclamation of land or by putting two or more
holdings together, and to the transfer of farm buildings from
villages to more convenient sites on their land. The Green Plans
have also incurred expenditure for assisting agriculture in certain
difficult regions, particularly mountain areas. Of particular
interest is the provision, under legislation introduced in 1957,
of pensions for elderly farmers who agree to give up their
farms.

The Green Plans have also incurred large expenditure for a
programme designed to encourage the production of high-quality,
tuberculin-free milk (this is the main item under 'promotion of

quality'). In 1962 a greatly increased sum was provided to make credit more easily available by subsidizing the interest paid by farmers.

For the sake of comparison, Table 68 also indicates the amount of expenditure from the Federal budget. The main item in this is now the cost of storage for price stabilization purposes by the Import and Storage Boards: most of the action related to improving agricultural efficiency has been transferred to the Green Plan.

The task of improving the agricultural structure is inevitably a slow one. By force of circumstance as well as through the action undertaken, the number of holdings of less than 10 hectares fell during the 1950s, while there was an increase in the numbers between 10 and 100 hectares. From 1945 to 1960, 2·3 million hectares were consolidated; by the end of 1960, as Table 69 shows, consolidation or reconsolidation was still regarded as urgent for 22 per cent of the agricultural area and thought desirable for a further 57 per cent; only 20 per cent of the land could be considered satisfactorily dealt with. The process of consolidation, moreover, became increasingly difficult as it progressed, for it was generally the easiest cases that were dealt with first.

Table 69

STATE OF LAND CONSOLIDATION BY THE END OF 1960

	thousand hectares	per cent
Consolidated – further consolidation essential	655	4
Consolidated – further consolidation not so essential	2,816	19
Consolidated – further consolidation not essential	3,037	20
Not consolidated – Consolidation essential	2,743	18
Not consolidated – Consolidation not so essential	5,738	38
Total agricultural area	14,989	100

Source: Grüner Bericht, 1962.

The outlook

The prospects for German agriculture are examined in an important study by Drs Plate, Woerman and Grupe in 1962. They analyse the economic trends of the 1950s and the probable future development of agricultural production, demand for foodstuffs, prices and incomes. They point out that, in a highly-developed economy where economic growth is continuing rapidly, demand for agricultural products rises relatively slowly since it has already reached a high level. This makes it difficult for farm incomes to rise in line with those in other sectors:

> In the process of economic growth, which remains the current preoccupation and which is expected to continue, incomes in the economy as a whole follow a rising trend. This provides a basis of comparison for those who are employed in agriculture. Their claims can be satisfied only if the productivity of labour in agriculture grows as fast as the national average, or if the real prices of agricultural products rise at a corresponding rate.
>
> Since demand for agricultural products, taken as a whole, is not very elastic in response to income, it rises at a rate substantially less than that of the average income per head. As a result – and to some extent also because of technical and other factors affecting agricultural holdings – German agriculture can raise the volume of its production only at a relatively slow rate. Consequently, an increase in labour productivity in agriculture corresponding to the national average is possible only if the numbers employed in agriculture are reduced. This however presupposes far-reaching changes in the agricultural structure, as well as disturbances in occupational and social relationships which frequently involve hardships for those concerned.[1]

The authors observe that it is no longer possible to raise farm incomes through price support. Already it has been found that import restrictions are effective only so long as there is scope for imports. Above all, the possibilities for supporting German farm prices will be still more limited in the European Economic

[1] R. Plate, E. Woerman and D. Grupe, 'Landwirtschaft im Strukturwandel der Volkswirtschaft', *Agrarwirtschaft*, Sonderheft 14, 1962, p. 74.

Community, where the agricultural price level will have to be lower than the current German level.

Further structural adjustments will therefore be essential. The authors examine the prospects for farms of different sizes, and come to the conclusion that those with less than 5 hectares can, in general, be economic only on a part-time basis. Those with between 5 and 10 hectares can be profitable only if operated by one full-time worker; the same applies to many holdings with rather more than 10 hectares, though these have more scope for raising their productivity and output. Holdings of around 50 hectares have a better chance of becoming profitable family farms; the best opportunities lie with the largest holdings, which can increase or decrease their intensity of cultivation according to circumstances.

> A substantial number of holdings – above all the smaller holdings working in unfavourable natural and economic conditions – lack the scope necessary for adaptation. These holdings must therefore disappear as full-time enterprises; they can remain only on a spare-time or part-time basis; otherwise they will have to be absorbed into other holdings. Even in regions near a centre of industry, this structural adjustment takes time, for it is difficult for members of the older generation to change their jobs. In regions which are less advanced economically, the pre-conditions necessary for the structural adjustment will first have to be created by a programme of regional assistance.[1]

To facilitate the adjustment, the authors suggest, among other measures, improved rural education and facilities for training in other jobs, better transport and communications to encourage industrial development in rural areas, and measures of assistance (e.g. additional pensions) to farmers who cannot easily change to another job. In addition, the programme of structural improvement, the measures to assist investment in agriculture, the provision of advisory services, should be pursued in order to help those farms which can be made economic. The authors consider that direct support to incomes might be given during the period of adjustment: it should be in a form that does not hinder the adaptation and should gradually taper off. Finally, they observe

[1] Ibid., p. 73.

that it is essential to keep the agricultural population informed about inevitable future trends: this, they say, is 'a thankless task, but it is the only way in which those concerned can be guarded against disappointments and hardships'.

Prospects for German agriculture in the European Economic Community are further examined in a study carried out at the request of the EEC Commission by a group of experts composed of six Germans, one Dutchman and one Italian. Among the German experts were Drs Plate and Woerman, so the analysis contained in this study corresponds in several respects to that which has just been outlined. It concentrates, however, on the

Table 70

PROSPECTS FOR GERMAN AGRICULTURE IN 1970

	Unit	1958/9	1970 Slow economic growth	1970 Rapid economic growth
		With unchanged prices		
Value of output	DM billion	22·0[a]	27·3[a]	27·7[a]
Cost of inputs	,,	9·7[b]	13·1[b]	13·3[b]
Value added	,,	12·3	14·2	14·4
Income expectation	DM per head	4,730	6,650	7,200
Persons working full-time	millions	2·6	2·15	2·0
		With reduced prices		
Value of output	DM billion	22·0[a]	25·4	25·8
Cost of inputs	,,	9·7[b]	13·2	13·4
Value added	,,	12·3	12·3	12·5
Income expectation	DM per head	4,730	6,650	7,200
Persons working full-time	millions	2·6	1·85	1·75

[a] Including subsidies on milk, eggs and rape-seed.
[b] After deduction of the subsidy on fertilizers.

Source : EEC, 'Wirkungen einer Senkung der Agrarpreise', *Studien*, Reihe Landwirtschaft, No. 11, 1962.

probable effects of a reduction in German farm prices in the EEC. The starting-point in constructing the 'model' is the assumption that by 1970 the price of wheat will be 14 per cent below the 1958/9 level, that of feeding barley 12 per cent lower; corresponding price reductions are assumed for other crops and for some livestock products. It is also supposed that the existing subsidies on certain products and on fertilizers will disappear. The resulting trends are shown in Table 70: it appears that – depending on the rate of general economic growth, which determines in particular the demand for foodstuffs – there will be little or no increase in the 'value added' by agriculture (representing agriculture's net income). On the unlikely assumption that prices remain at the 1958/9 level, there would be a moderate increase in value added by agriculture.

It is further assumed in the EEC study that those employed in agriculture expect their incomes to rise at the same rate as average incomes in other sectors (this would still leave the same percentage gap between agricultural and other incomes as in 1958/9). For this increase in incomes per head to be achieved, it would be necessary for the number of persons employed full-time in agriculture to fall at an accelerated rate: from 2·6 millions in 1958/9 to 1·85 or even 1·75 millions in 1970. With unchanged prices the reduction need only be to 2·15 or 2·0 million.

An adaptation in German agriculture thus appears inevitable if the agricultural population is to share adequately in the general improvement in living standards: this is the case whether or not German farm prices have to be reduced in the EEC. The fact that reduced prices necessitate a particularly drastic adaptation accounts for the stand taken by the German Government in the negotiations with its EEC partners.

Chapter 15. Denmark

Post-war decontrol

With the Second World War the problems of excess supplies and falling prices in Denmark gave way to the opposite problems of shortages and inflation. This necessitated various measures to control prices and maintain supplies, particularly in the case of bread grains and feed grains, since the German occupation cut Denmark off from its usual sources of supply. The minimum price for butter on the home market, instituted in 1933, operated during the war as a fixed price, keeping down the cost of butter to consumers. Maximum retail prices were also fixed for beef, bacon and other products.

In the period of food shortages immediately after the war, these controls were maintained, but in 1948 and 1949 they were almost all removed. Only the pre-war arrangements for sugarbeet and for potatoes for industrial use remained in force.

In 1950 the ministerial Export Boards, set up in 1932 to control exports and regulate prices, were replaced by independent Export Boards formed by the co-operative marketing organizations and commercial exporting firms. These Boards were set up for all the important export commodities. They can negotiate with both the Danish authorities and foreign countries in order to obtain better terms, and can fix minimum prices, impose export levies and operate stabilization funds to smooth out returns to producers.

Imports of the major agricultural products are subject to licence, but in most cases the low price level makes the Danish market unattractive to other exporters: the main object of the licensing is to act as a safeguard against abnormal dumping and it hardly constitutes a regular measure of protection, except perhaps in the case of certain fruits and vegetables.

Difficulties on export markets

Until about 1956, long-term contracts with Britain ensured outlets, at moderate prices, for specified quantities of bacon, butter and eggs. After these contracts came to an end, increasing difficulties were encountered in Britain and on other export markets as well, as a result of the general rise in food production and the intensified competition for markets. In 1957 an increase in supplies of bacon to the British market caused a sharp fall in prices. The associations of pig producers and bacon curers in Denmark, Britain and the Netherlands (later joined by Ireland and Sweden) formed a Bacon Consultative Council, which held regular meetings to exchange information on expected supplies to the British market and sought thereby to maintain prices at a satisfactory level. This effort had some success, until in 1961 the British market was again glutted by higher domestic production and increased exports by other countries (including Poland and Yugoslavia).

Worse difficulties were encountered with butter. Prices fell

Table 71

EXPORT PRICE INDICES

(1955 = 100)

	Bacon	Butter	Eggs	All agricultural exports
1956	111	99	97	105
1957	101	84	92	97
1958	106	65	90	94
1959	99	96	79	100
1960	100	82	84	96

Source: Statistisk Aarbog.

sharply in 1958 (Table 71), and the Butter Export Board had to build up stocks and reduce the price paid to producers. In subsequent years the problem became acute, as the rapid growth of milk production throughout Western Europe led to reduced imports and increased exports of butter. By 1961 Britain was almost the only market left open and was the arena of competition between not only the traditional butter exporters but also newcomers such as France. The London price was well below the level maintained on the markets of most of the exporting countries, and large export subsidies were being applied. The quotas introduced by Britain at the end of 1961 have enabled prices to recover, but the outlook remains uncertain.

Danish eggs have suffered even more on the British market, for the rise in Britain's own production reduced her imports to a negligible quantity from 1956 onwards (Table 72).

Table 72

MAJOR AGRICULTURAL EXPORTS

	Cattle (000)		Pigs (000)	Bacon and Pork (000 tons)		Butter (000 tons)		Eggs (000 tons)		
	Total	of which to W. Germany	To W. Germany[a]	Total	of which to U.K.	Total	of which to U.K.	Total	of which to	
									U.K.	W. Germany
1936/8	167	137	144[a]	179[b]	175[b]	156	115	86[c]	62[c]	20[c]
1950/5	256	208	69	208	196	137	103	93	60	25
1956	284	245	194	233	222	120	89	99	10	58
1957	231	207	136	250	229	118	87	102	4	65
1958	321	291	138	246	222	115	96	106	6	68
1959	349	306	189	274	252	118	96	106	2	83
1960	353	321	190	311	291	118	101	83	7	62

[a] Equivalent to total exports, except in 1936–8 when the total was 155.
[b] Data apparently referring to bacon only.
[c] Estimates based on numbers of eggs.

Sources : Statistisk Aarbog, and Danemarks Vareindførsel og Udførsel.

Denmark's trade with Western Germany in live cattle and pigs expanded during the 1950s, and there was also a growth in exports of eggs which largely compensated for the decline in trade with Britain. Exports of butter to Germany, however, became unimportant.

Denmark attempted to overcome these difficulties by diversifying its exports, and some increase was achieved in sales of products which formerly were of comparatively small importance: thus there were increased exports of cheese, beef and veal, and canned meat.

Table 73

RECEIPTS AND EXPENSES OF AGRICULTURE

(kroner per hectare)

	Gross profit		Operating costs			
	Total	of which from live-stock	Total	of which		Net profit
				Labour	Raw materials	
1945/6–1949/50	1,496	1,144	1,328	628	403	168
1950/1–1954/5	2,328	1,905	2,028	833	703	300
1955/6–1959/60	2,681	2,241	2,470	959	897	211

Source: Landbrugsstatistik.

However, the persistently low level of prices on export markets, at a time when the costs of agricultural production were rising, caused a decline in the net income of Danish agriculture in the course of the 1950s (Table 73). Coming at a time when incomes in other sectors were progressing fairly rapidly, this was all the more unacceptable to Danish farmers. The result has been to drive Denmark back into various forms of intervention, some of them resembling measures taken in the 1930s.

The return to intervention

After the fall in the butter price, an Act passed in June 1959 authorized a levy on all dairy products sold on the home market, in order to maintain a minimum price level corresponding to a 'butter settlement price' (i.e. the price paid by the Export Board to dairies) of 6 kroner per kg. The proceeds of this levy were to be distributed to the dairies in proportion to their deliveries, and ultimately to be passed on to producers. Throughout most of 1959 the butter price lay slightly above 6 kroner, and the system scarcely came into play; in 1960 however the 'settlement price' fell to 5 kroner and levies were applied. In January 1961 this system was replaced by new arrangements, introduced by the producers' associations with the consent of the Monopolies Commission: a minimum price of 7 kroner was set for sales by dairies for the domestic market. This soon came into effect, as the price fell again in the summer of 1961. In February 1962 the domestic price was raised to 7.50 kroner: this represented some increase over the average of previous years.

In June 1958 a Grain Marketing Act provided for guaranteed producer prices for bread grains, to be ensured primarily by a milling ratio. The existence of this scheme, even though the guaranteed prices were low by comparison with those of other countries, induced a big increase in the area of bread grains and a corresponding increase in production. In 1960 the milling ratio was raised to 100 per cent for both wheat and rye, thus cutting out imports. Even so, it was not possible to sell the whole domestic crop for milling at the guaranteed price and part of it had to be used for animal fodder, the loss being borne by the Government.

The same Act of 1958 provided for minimum import prices for feed grains, to be maintained by import levies. Grain producers were thus protected against dumping and excessive price fluctuations. At the same time, to reduce the adverse effects of higher prices to pig producers, who were the main users of feed grains, a provision was included to the effect that the import levies would be reduced if the price of pigs fell. Further, the proceeds of the levies were to be distributed in various ways to help small farmers.

An import levy was also introduced in June 1959 for skimmed

milk powder, to ensure a minimum price to Danish producers of about 1.40 kroner. The proceeds of the levy were to be used to subsidize the price of home-produced milk powder used as live-stock fodder.

The most drastic break with Danish traditions of non-interven-tion in agriculture occurred with the Agricultural Products Marketing Act of 1961. This established a 'Rationalization Fund', for which 250 million kroner are to be appropriated each year from the Treasury; the use of the Fund was left open (in its first year of operation direct payments were made to farmers on the basis mainly of land values and numbers of cows). Secondly, the Act introduced a subsidy on fertilizers, to the amount of 50 million kroner each year. Thirdly, it provided for steps to raise the home market price of pigmeat over the average export price by 50 kroner per 100 kg. Finally, the Act authorized the expenditure, over the following two years, of 150 million kroner for measures to assist the marketing of agricultural produce through the promotion of exports, research into methods for improving quality and so on.

Danish agriculture thus can no longer be said to depend entirely on its own unaided efforts. It now receives a not insig-nificant degree of support in the form of direct Exchequer pay-ments, higher prices imposed on domestic consumers for dairy products and pigmeat, and protection against imports of bread grains, feed grains and milk powder.

The outlook

These developments confirm the vulnerability of Danish agri-culture, already evident in the crisis of the 1930s. Its efficiency in livestock production is hardly an advantage when other countries support their producers, restrict imports and subsidize exports. For a country whose past prosperity has been so much bound up with the expansion of its agricultural exports, the outlook is gloomy. Denmark's obvious interest lies in obtaining access on favourable terms for her agricultural exports to both the major markets – Britain and Western Germany. The best prospect therefore would be offered by membership of the European Economic Community, provided that Britain is also a member; the decision by Britain in the summer of 1961 to apply for entry to the EEC made it inevitable that Denmark would follow suit. Britain's failure to gain admittance puts Denmark in a difficult position. There is limited scope for obtaining favourable treatment for her exports to Germany, and Denmark can only attempt to secure from her partners in the European Free Trade Association more far-reaching concessions in agriculture than those which they have so far been willing to grant (see Chapter 17).

Part IV

International Aspects

Chapter 16. European Economic Integration

The Belgium-Luxemburg Economic Union

Already in 1922, Belgium and Luxemburg had formed an Economic Union. All trade between the two countries was freed from import duties and other restrictions, and a common tariff (corresponding generally to the previous Belgian one) was adopted for imports from third countries. The Belgian franc circulated freely in Luxemburg.

The Union was generally successful, but agriculture was its greatest problem. Farming in Luxemburg suffers from unfavourable natural conditions: the land is broken by steep hills and valleys and much of it is of poor quality; the majority of holdings are small and seriously fragmented. Moreover, since 1842 Luxemburg had been within the German tariff system and its agriculture had therefore been sheltered behind the high duties imposed during and after the Great Depression. Belgium at this stage had relatively little protection for its agriculture: many products, including bread grains, were free of duty and the rates of duty on other products were fairly low. It thus appeared necessary to give special assistance to agriculture in Luxemburg, and the treaty establishing the Economic Union provided that payments would be made to Luxemburg farmers, out of the customs receipts of the Union, in the amounts necessary to make up the difference between the market price of bread grains and the higher price prevailing on the protected French market (which

309

Luxemburg farmers would have received if their country had joined France instead of Belgium). Luxemburg wine was given advantages on the Belgian market, in part-compensation for the loss of free entry to the much larger German market.

During the crisis of the 1930s, Belgium – as has been seen above – was forced to intervene in agricultural markets in various ways. This action was apparently not sufficient for Luxemburg and further measures were introduced: a Convention of 1935 entitled Luxemburg to exercise control, by means of import licences or minimum prices, over imports of grains, meat and livestock, butter, eggs and other products. Under this arrangement, imports were authorized only in the amounts needed to complement domestic supplies.

After the Second World War, when preparations were made for the wider union of Benelux, Luxemburg agriculture was still benefiting from special treatment and seemed no nearer to standing on its own feet than in 1922 when BLEU had been constituted.

Benelux

In Benelux, Belgian agriculture was faced by problems similar to those of Luxemburg agriculture in BLEU, with the difference that the Belgian market was too important to the Dutch for them to let their partners off lightly.

Benelux brought about an economic union between a country which had established itself as an exporter of livestock products, fruit and vegetables, where agriculture as a whole was extensively organized and where individual holdings were efficiently managed, with another country which was predominantly industrial and regularly imported most agricultural products, where no constructive agricultural policy had been developed, where the peasants had been slow to organize themselves, and where many of the farms were too small and too fragmented to be efficient. The situation of Luxemburg agriculture in Benelux was of course even more precarious than it had been in BLEU.

The customs union between the three countries came into force on January 1st, 1948: restrictions on internal trade were removed and a common external tariff was applied without any transitional period. The basic principles concerning agriculture were laid down in a Protocol resulting from a meeting of Ministers of

Agriculture in May 1947: it was agreed that each country should be free to adopt an agricultural policy which would guarantee to its producers a minimum price covering their costs of production plus a reasonable profit margin. The calculation of costs of production would be carried out by each country in consultation with its partners, but each would have the right to impose its own minimum prices. Imports of agricultural products from other Benelux countries, as well as from outside countries, could be restricted so far as necessary to maintain these minimum prices; however, preference should be given to supplies from other members of Benelux over imports from other countries.

The Dutch soon found that the Protocol of 1947 was not operating as they had hoped: it was being used to justify permanent measures of protection for Belgian agriculture. At a further meeting of Ministers of Agriculture in October 1950, the Dutch attempted to revise the existing provisions. The outcome was the Luxemburg Protocol. Restrictions on intra-Benelux trade could henceforth be applied only to products indicated in a certain 'List A': this included most types of meat and livestock, most dairy products, eggs and the principal fruits and vegetables. In addition, special regulations could be applied to products appearing in 'List B': these were, in particular, grains and sugar. Shortly afterwards 'List C' was added: this concerned products for which Luxemburg was entitled to control imports and exports; it included almost all major products.

At this meeting the Dutch also obtained an agreement that the minimum prices would be fixed by independent arbitration. However, the Belgian Parliament refused to endorse this.

Further progress awaited another ministerial meeting in May 1955, at which the Dutch appeared to obtain some satisfaction. It was agreed that within a year the determination of minimum prices should be subjected to independent arbitration. Further, national agricultural policies were to be 'harmonized' by 1962, so that by then free movement of agricultural produce could be permitted (still with the exception of Luxemburg). It was also agreed that an agricultural fund should be set up in Belgium and Luxemburg to assist the process of adaptation (an 'Equalization Fund' already existed in the Netherlands).

Meanwhile, negotiations between the partners continued with

the object of establishing the full Economic Union, involving the
co-ordination of economic, financial and social policies and the
free movement of labour and capital. Progress was held up by
various difficulties, including the problem of agriculture, but in
February 1958 the Treaty of Economic Union was signed.

Agricultural organizations in the Netherlands, however, were
still acutely dissatisfied, and the provisions of the Treaty did not
make them any happier. Besides a provision (Article 66) allowing
a country to take measures of an emergency nature if its agriculture
should be threatened by a crisis, and another provision (Article
67) confirming Luxemburg's right to give special treatment to
its agriculture, the Treaty of Economic Union was accompanied
by a Transitional Convention devoted mainly to agricultural
problems. This Convention authorized the maintenance of Lists
A, B and C and the special arrangements connected with them:
in particular, minimum prices continued to be determined on the
basis of the cost of production plus an appropriate profit margin.
Experience had already shown the Dutch that this was not a
satisfactory basis: it was difficult to agree on how to calculate
costs of production and the arrangement tended to frustrate
desirable changes involving greater specialization and improved
efficiency; moreover, the Dutch feared that this provision might
form a precedent for the European Economic Community. The
transitional arrangements were to be progressively abolished as
agricultural policies were harmonized, and harmonization was to
be achieved within five years; the Dutch however were afraid of
this being interpreted to mean that no restrictions need be
removed in the meantime, and they were sceptical about the chances
of harmonization being achieved in this time.

The Dutch agricultural organizations therefore opposed the
Treaty and succeeded in having its ratification postponed. In
February 1960 their Government obtained some concessions from
Belgium: Dutch agricultural produce would be given preference
over that of other countries of the European Economic Community
and the effort to harmonize agricultural policies would be
intensified. With these assurances, the Dutch Second Chamber
finally ratified the Treaty on March 16th, 1960. But at the same
time it unanimously passed a motion declaring that the system
of minimum prices set out in the transitional Agreement was
unsatisfactory and urging the Government to ensure that the

same criteria should not be adopted in the European Economic Community.

The experience of Benelux in agriculture was thus discouraging. While in other sectors a common market was achieved, trade in agriculture continued to be subject to various restrictions. The minimum price system proved much too effective in maintaining protection for Belgian agriculture; behind this barrier Belgian farmers were able to expand their production even at the expense of imports from the Netherlands. Output of butter in particular grew to such an extent that imports practically ceased, and Belgium even had net exports (heavily subsidized) at some periods; imports of fruit and vegetables from the Netherlands were frequently stopped.

The 'Green Pool' proposals

In 1950 the Consultative Assembly of the Council of Europe decided to initiate a study on how the countries of Europe could organize their agricultural markets in common. In the Special Committee set up for this purpose, the initiative was taken by France: this for the double reason that in France at that time 'European' feeling was strong – it had already found expression in the Schuman Plan for coal and steel (the 'Black Pool') – and that France had a strong interest in widening the market for her agricultural exports. A plan drawn up by the French delegate, M. René Charpentier, proposed the creation of a High Authority for agriculture with extensive supranational powers: it would control production, fix prices and aim at eliminating all restrictions on agricultural trade between the participating countries. The exports of these countries would be given preference over supplies from other sources, even if the latter were cheaper. 'European' prices would be determined in relation to costs of production and should be independent of supply and demand. The costs of production in different member countries would be harmonized. In a transitional period, there would be 'compensatory taxes', representing the difference between the European price and the domestic price of each member country; these would act to protect countries with high costs of production.

The supranational aspects of the Charpentier Plan gave rise to vigorous debate. A counter-proposal submitted for Britain by

Mr (now Lord) David Eccles ostensibly accepted the idea of an 'Authority' but stressed that it should only be intergovernmental and should be allowed merely to make recommendations to Governments. Under the Eccles Plan, the 'Authority' would examine national policies for agricultural production and trade, and suggest how they could be reconciled; it would also study how participating countries could co-operate in trading with outside countries.

In spite of this opposition by Britain (supported by Denmark), the Special Committee on Agriculture adopted the Charpentier Plan, and the Consultative Assembly in December 1951 decided by a two-thirds majority to go ahead with the preparation of a draft treaty along the lines indicated in the Plan.[1]

But meanwhile the French Government was seeking more rapid action. In March 1951 it sent a memorandum to other Western European countries, proposing immediate negotiations with the object of setting up a European Agricultural Community. This French proposal – known as the Pflimlin Plan after its author, then Minister of Agriculture – was based on essentially the same principles as the Charpentier Plan. Unification of European agriculture would provide a wider market and thus give greater stability, while healthy competition would lead to more efficient production. The three main elements of the organization of markets would be:

1. Pooling of production resources; all countries would act together to solve difficulties in the marketing and supply of foodstuffs.

2. Measures to adapt production to demand and to stabilize the market. The pattern and volume of production would be guided as appropriate, imports and exports would be co-ordinated, measures of stockpiling would be taken when necessary.

3. Establishment of a common market. The aim was to eliminate all restrictions on agricultural trade between the member countries.

The institutional arrangements would be modelled on those of the Coal and Steel Community (then in draft form).

About the same time, the Dutch Government issued another

---

[1] It was afterwards discovered that the vote had been wrongly counted and that the necessary majority in fact had not been obtained, but the result was nevertheless upheld.

set of proposals in the name of its Minister of Agriculture, Dr Sicco Mansholt. This Mansholt Plan, while it had features in common with the French proposals, stressed the points of greatest interest to Dutch agriculture: it advocated a common market for agricultural products throughout Europe, in order to achieve the maximum efficiency of production through specialization. An upper limit should be set to the permissible degree of protection, and this limit should be gradually reduced until a common price level was achieved. There would be a High Authority for agriculture, with supranational powers.

The outcome of these proposals was a Preparatory Conference on the Organization of European Agricultural Markets, held in Paris in March 1952. (This was held independently of the Council of Europe, which subsequently ceased to play an effective role in European agriculture.) Fifteen Western European countries were represented at the Conference, and M. Pflimlin was elected chairman.

The Preparatory Conference decided to call a full Conference the following year, and set up a Working Party to prepare the ground. The first European Conference on the Organization of Agricultural Markets was accordingly held, again in Paris, in March 1953. Not surprisingly in view of the attitude already taken by Britain, it proved impossible to reach agreement on the basis of the Pflimlin Plan. It was decided to set up an Interim Committee to work on a product-by-product basis. The report of this Committee was considered at a second Conference in July 1954, also in Paris.

The Interim Committee was able to reach agreement only on vague statements of aims and on certain points of minor importance. On the basic question of arrangements for trade, there was an open conflict between those countries which insisted that in an organized agricultural market the member countries should give preference to one anothers' exports, and those which declared this inconsistent with existing trade policies. The same conflict appeared in the analysis of individual commodities: thus for grains the majority favoured a preferential arrangement involving regulation of prices and of quantities traded, but this whole concept was disputed by the remaining countries.

The Committee was also forced to admit that there were marked differences of opinion about the institutional framework, in particular as to whether the proposed agricultural organization should be attached to the Organisation for European Economic Co-operation or should be an independent and specialized body; there was growing doubt as to the desirability of the sector-by-sector approach which characterized the Black and the Green Pools. The Committee stated moreover that there was no longer any question of a supranational body: indeed the French Government then in power had moved away from the original intentions of the Pflimlin Plan. The Dutch Government, on the other hand, was discouraged by the prospect of inadequate supranational control, which it regarded as essential if protectionist influences were to be overcome.

It was therefore clear to participants in the 1954 Conference that no significant agreement could be reached. On a British initiative it was decided to examine whether the work could be continued in the OEEC; in January 1955 the Council of the OEEC decided to set up a Ministerial Committee for Agriculture and Food.

Seen as an attempt to set up an agricultural organization covering all Western Europe, the Green Pool was probably doomed from the start. As a step in the gradual move towards European integration, it served a useful purpose. It represented the first serious attempt to work out the problems involved in unifying agricultural markets; the various studies that were carried out showed clearly what were the difficulties and threw light on the positions of the various countries. France's efforts received support in particular from Western Germany, where the desire for closer integration was shared, as well as from Belgium and other countries. Britain, on the other hand, was shown to be deeply suspicious of any arrangement tainted with supra-nationalism and determined to maintain its preferential arrangements with the Commonwealth. Somewhere between the two extremes was Denmark, anxious above all to preserve the outlets for its agricultural exports and thus seeing advantages both in its trade relationships with Britain and in a unified agricultural market; the Netherlands, with similar preoccupations but a firm belief in supranational principles; and Italy, who too was already allied with France and Germany in the Coal and Steel Community but who was generally willing to make compromises for the sake of a wider agreement.

These various attitudes persisted and influenced the developments which were to follow. While the limited approach favoured by the British found expression in the OEEC's work on agriculture, the attempts to create a preferential European market for agriculture were absorbed in the general movement towards closer economic integration between the six countries of the Coal and Steel Community.

The Organisation for European Economic Co-operation

The activity of the OEEC in agriculture before 1955 was related to its general aims of promoting post-war recovery and freeing intra-European trade. The Sixth Report of the Organisation, in March 1955, was able to record that a substantial increase had taken place in agricultural production. The trade situation was much less satisfactory. The encouragements given to member countries to remove restrictions on trade, with the help of a multilateral clearing system (the European Payments Union, operated by OEEC), had been reasonably successful in sectors other than agriculture. In agriculture, though a fair degree of liberalization from quantitative restrictions had been attained, a large proportion of trade remained subject to State control.[1] Import duties were outside OEEC's competence (in principle they were a problem for the General Agreement on Tariffs on Trade, but GATT did not have much success so far as agriculture was concerned – see Chapter 18).

OEEC's work in agriculture took a new turn with the institution of the Ministerial Committee for Agriculture and Food in January 1955. Its objectives were:

1. The 'confrontation' of national policies for agriculture and their co-ordination.
2. The search for new methods of freeing trade, adapted to the characteristics of the market for individual products.
3. Intensified action to raise productivity in agriculture.

As the inheritor of the moderate approach favoured by Britain in the Green Pool discussions, the Ministerial Committee had

[1] The official calculation was that, at the end of 1954, 79 per cent of the 'private' trade of member countries in food and feeding-stuffs had been liberalized from quantitative restrictions, as compared with 78 per cent for manufactures and 92 per cent for raw materials. But these 'liberalization percentages' raise several statistical difficulties and are of doubtful significance.

strictly limited functions. It had no powers to coerce Governments and it was understood that its decisions, like those of other organs of the OEEC, would only be taken unanimously: any member could thus veto a proposal.

The basis of its work was the principle of 'confrontation', a process of examination and questioning designed to bring into evidence those aspects of a country's policy which were likely to harm others. It was hoped that offending countries might be induced by polite persuasion to mend their ways. This was a method which could hardly be expected to resolve the serious problems which arose after about 1955, as production of various commodities began to outrun demand. The work of the Ministerial Committee nevertheless built up a certain standard for agricultural policies, emphasizing the extent to which measures taken in one country could affect another, and some of its recommendations concealed hard punches behind diplomatic wording. Though it is difficult to point to any changes in policies which can be directly ascribed to the work of OEEC, the necessity imposed on Governments of accounting for their actions probably ensured that they took greater account of the interests of other countries than they would otherwise have done. Moreover, the five bulky reports which appeared from 1956 to 1961 were the most thorough documentation ever published on European agricultural policies, and served to make clear the basic problems of Western European agriculture at this time.

The European Economic Community

(a) The Treaty of Rome

Preparatory work for a wider economic union between the six members of the Coal and Steel Community – France, Germany, Italy and the three Benelux countries – began in June 1955. In April 1956 the Spaak Report, containing a plan for the establishment of a common market, was published: the following month it was accepted by the Foreign Ministers of the Six as a basis for negotiation.

On March 25th, 1957, the Treaty of Rome was signed. The European Economic Community which it set up is in the first place a common market or customs union, in which restrictions on trade between members are to be removed and a common external tariff established over a transitional period of twelve to fifteen years. It is also an economic union, in which the movement of labour and capital will eventually be freed. It possesses common institutions: a Council of Ministers, responsible for final decisions on matters of policy; an Economic and Social Committee, to advise the Council; a Commission, entrusted with planning and administration; and a Parliamentary Assembly, whose functions initially are limited, but which was conceived as the embryo of a genuinely European Parliament. There is a supranational element in that decisions by the Council of Ministers can in certain cases be taken by majority vote – this element is to be reinforced at each successive stage in the realization of the Community.

Agriculture is subject to the same general provisions as other sectors: the aim is the institution of a common market, with free internal trade and common measures concerning trade with the rest of the world. However, it was realized from the start that agriculture would require special treatment. The Treaty therefore provided for various measures to soften the impact of competition during the transitional period. Minimum import price systems could be applied; the minima were to be fixed on the basis of 'objective criteria' to be determined by the Commission, taking account both of 'average national costs of production' and the need to promote adjustment and specialization within the Community (Article 44). Also, 'countervailing duties' (*taxes compensatoires*) might be levied on imports from a member country in cases where internal regulations in that country gave it a competitive advantage (Article 46). Long-term contracts could be concluded, pending the creation of common market organizations, between exporting and importing member countries (Article 45).

By the end of the transitional period, agricultural markets in the Community will still be organized – but by joint measures in the context of a common agricultural policy (Article 40). The Rome Treaty did not set out the nature of this common policy except in the most general terms, and the task of formulating it occupied the following years. A conference held at Stresa in July 1958 discussed the problems involved and drew up recommendations for the work of the Commission: these however were too vague to be of any great significance.

(b) The common agricultural policy

The Commission's proposals for the common agricultural policy were first issued in November 1959. The document in question was long, containing a detailed examination of the agricultural situation, a statement of general principles and a description of the measures proposed; these measures concerned both structural reform and market organization.

All the main organs of the Community were involved in examining these proposals. In June 1960 the Commission, taking account of discussions in the Economic and Social Committee and in the Parliamentary Assembly, submitted slightly revised proposals to the Council. From September 1960 these were examined by a Special Committee on Agriculture set up by the Council. In December, following a number of interim reports by the Special Committee, the Council reached its first major decision of principle: a system of levies was to be adopted as the principal instrument for regulating agricultural trade during the transitional period. The levies on trade between members of the Community would diminish and finally disappear, while those on imports from other countries would remain, thus creating a preference for intra-Community trade.

In the course of 1961, the Commission submitted to the Council specific proposals for applying the levy system to a number of products. Discussions were pursued in the various bodies. In the Council, on November 30th, the German Minister of Agriculture stressed his Government's legal obligation to raise the living standards of its farm population and stated its wish to continue giving subsidies of various kinds; he also objected to the Commission's proposal for using part of the proceeds of the levies to subsidize agricultural exports by the members of EEC. Successive meetings of the Council failed to bring agreement and a critical stage was reached: the second stage of the transitional period, involving further freeing of trade within the Community and additional steps towards the common external tariff, was due to begin on January 1st, 1962, but the Council had first to declare unanimously that the objectives laid down for the first stage had been achieved. France refused to give its approval unless satisfactory progress was made in agriculture. By December 30th the Council was still divided: the clock was formally stopped, negotiations were resumed on January 4th and finally (after an all-night session) an agreement was reached on January 14th, 1962.

This agreement concerned the arrangements which are to replace national measures of agricultural support for a number of major products, both during and after the transitional period. The system is inevitably complex and need not be fully described here. The key to the whole structure is the system of import levies, designed to maintain prices in the EEC at certain levels. During the transitional period, while price levels in different member countries are being 'harmonized', levies are to be applied both to intra-EEC trade and to imports from third countries; once the common market is established, only imports from outside the EEC will be subject to levies. The transitional period for the establishment of a common market and common policy in agriculture is fixed at $7\frac{1}{2}$ years – i.e. from July 1st, 1962, to December 31st, 1969.[1]

For grain, the agreement provided for 'target prices' (*prix indicatifs*) to be fixed each year. These serve as a basis for determining 'intervention prices' (*prix d'intervention*), some 5 to 10 per cent below target prices: at the intervention prices, the responsible market organizations are obliged to buy all grain offered to them by producers. In addition, 'threshold prices' (*prix de seuil*) are determined at levels corresponding to the minimum price at which imports may be admitted if the target price is to be maintained (the threshold prices would be lower than the target prices by approximately the amount of transport costs from the frontier to the main consuming centre). Finally, to implement the threshold prices, import levies are applied, equal to the difference between the lowest price at which imports can be obtained and the threshold price: the amount of the levy varies with changes in world prices, a fall in price being offset by an increase in the levy, so that the internal market is fully insulated.

At the beginning of the transitional period, the price levels in the various member countries were different: consequently, a high-price country is allowed to impose levies on imports from a

---

[1] The decisions taken on January 14th concerned grains, pigmeat, poultry, eggs, fruit and vegetables, and wine; they came into force, after one month's postponement, on July 30th, 1962, replacing or complementing existing national regulations. The Commission's proposals concerning dairy products, beef and rice were submitted in May 1962; by April 1963 these proposals had still not been adopted, and no proposals had yet been made for sugar.

low-price member country in an amount corresponding to the difference between the price at which the produce is offered and its own threshold price, reduced however by a lump sum (*montant forfaitaire*) so that intra-EEC trade has a preference over imports from outside.[1] As prices are harmonized, levies on internal trade will gradually disappear: by 1970 there should be one target price for the whole Community, so that there will be no need for levies on trade between members.

For most other commodities the arrangements decided upon or under consideration are similar in principle, though the details vary according to the particular situation of each product. The system envisaged for rice is similar to that for grains, except that there are no target prices. More complicated arrangements have been proposed for dairy products: target prices for milk, serving as a basis for determining threshold prices for dairy products other than butter; for butter and possibly other products too, intervention prices at which the domestic market would be supported and threshold prices at which imports would be admitted.

For beef the intention is to have 'guidance prices' (*prix d'orientation*), serving as a basis for determining 'sluice-gate prices' (*prix d'écluse*) at which imports would be admitted. Import duties would be applied: those on imports from outside the EEC would gradually be aligned on the common external tariff, those on imports from other members being gradually removed. If the import price plus duty falls below the sluice-gate price, an appropriate levy would be imposed.

For those livestock products which depend largely on the use of feed grains – pigmeat, poultry and eggs – there are no stipulations concerning prices, but protection is given by import levies. These levies are determined by a complicated procedure, involving the calculation of several different elements and taking account in particular of differences in the cost of feeding-stuffs in the export-

---

[1] Exporting member countries also benefit from the fact that they no longer need to reduce their export prices to the level of the world market in order to compete with other exporters. The levy corresponds, in the case of imports from a member country, to the difference between that country's export price and the threshold price: in the case of imports from outside, to the difference between the world price and the threshold price. Importers no longer have any advantage in obtaining supplies from cheaper outside sources: the deduction from the levy of the *montant forfaitaire*, in the case of imports from a member country, means on the contrary that these can be had more cheaply.

ing and importing countries. Levies are applied to trade between member countries during the transitional period but will gradually be abolished; the levies applied to imports from outside the community include certain additional elements, and are to be permanently maintained, thus ensuring preference for intra-Community trade. In addition, there are sluice-gate prices based on the world market prices of feed grains together with an appropriate measure of the rate at which grains are converted into the livestock products in question (the purpose is apparently to indicate a price below which imports can reasonably be regarded as 'dumped'). If offers are made by third countries at prices below the sluice-gate prices, the import levy is increased correspondingly.

Different arrangements were decided upon for fruit and vegetables. For some years past an effort had been made throughout Europe to establish uniform quality standards: it appeared that if these were rigorously applied and preference given to the best-quality produce, it would be possible to keep the market reasonably stable. During the transitional period, tariffs on intra-EEC trade are to be gradually reduced, while quantitative restrictions and similar measures are removed by stages: produce of the quality 'extra' is the first to be liberalized and the other grades follow. At the end of the transitional period, all standardized produce will move freely within the Community. Restrictions on imports from third countries will gradually be co-ordinated and by the end of the transitional period a common external tariff will be applied. These imports may also be suspended or made subject to a 'compensatory duty' (*taxe compensatoire*) in cases where the markets of the Community are being seriously disturbed by imports from third countries at prices below certain 'reference prices' (*prix de référence*).

The system in force for the major products, being designed to maintain prices within the EEC above world market levels, could make it impossible for member countries to export profitably to markets outside the EEC. Provision is therefore made for a system of 'export refunds' (*restitutions à l'exportation*), which in effect are import levies in reverse: they are intended to compensate for the extent to which the domestic price is higher than the export prices or – in the case of pigmeat, poultry and eggs – for the extent to which feed grain prices are higher.

The minimum price systems provided for in Article 44 of the Rome Treaty are not applicable to products for which a common market organization has been instituted. The 'objective criteria' for these systems laid down by the Council in January 1962 further limited their use and subjected them to various safeguards.

In addition, the Council laid down financial regulations related to the common agricultural policy. On this point the interests of France and Germany were directly opposed. France wanted revenue from import levies on agricultural products to be used for financing expenditure for agricultural purposes – in particular for the necessary refunds on exports to countries outside the Community. This meant that Germany, as the biggest food importer, would bear most of the cost of subsidizing French agricultural exports. For the French, this was a logical consequence of the Community principle; the Germans were by no means ready to endorse this view. The result was a complicated set of regulations which left some vital points unsettled. It was agreed to set up a European Agricultural Guidance and Guarantee Fund (Fonds Européen d'Orientation et de Garantie Agricole). This Fund, once the common market is established, will finance export refunds, intervention on the internal market and other measures (including structural reform); during the transitional period, it will finance export refunds, but the eligibility of other expenditure is subject to decisions by the Council, taken initially by unanimous vote but by a qualified majority after the end of the second stage in the formation of the Community (thus making it more difficult for a single country to block expenditure for purposes of which it disapproves). The proportion of finance for these items coming from the Fund, as opposed to existing national sources, rises progressively until, by the end of the transitional period, expenditure is wholly financed by the Fund. The question then arises as to how the Fund itself is to be financed. The regulations declared that the proceeds of import levies, once the common market is established, would be the property of the Community; they did not say that they would go to the Agricultural Fund, nor did they indicate what would be done with them during the transitional period (which presumably means that they remain the property of the country which applies the levy). However, it was laid down that initially the Fund's revenue should come from national budgets according to the usual scale of contributions in the EEC (by which Germany pays the same amount as France); but in the second and third years a part of each national contribution is to be determined in proportion to the country's net agricultural imports from third countries. By the end of the third year, the Council has to take a further decision. In doing so it must observe a provision of the Treaty (Article 200, paragraph 3) which allows the Council to change the usual scale of contributions only by unanimous vote: this seems to give Germany the possibility of insisting that her contribution to the Agricultural Fund should not exceed that of France.

It was recognized that measures affecting agricultural prices and markets could only be one element in the common agricultural policy: a major cause of low farm incomes was the inadequacy of farm structures, and intensified competition would cause additional hardships to high-cost producers unless steps were taken to promote basic improvements in the conditions of production. The Commission accordingly submitted proposals for structural policy in February 1962, and on December 4th, 1962, the Council took a number of decisions which aimed essentially at reinforcing and co-ordinating the action undertaken by the individual member countries, with provision for additional financing out of Community funds in approved cases.

(c) Problems and opportunities ahead

The agreements concerning the common organization of agricultural markets represent an important achievement. They provide the tools with which the common agricultural policy can work. The apparent complexity of the measures adopted results largely from the strangeness of concepts such as 'threshold prices' (especially when translated into English); in fact, most of these measures were already in force in one or more countries of the Community, their kinship with minimum price systems being particularly evident. There is indeed a certain simplicity in that a single measure – the import levy – becomes the major instrument of control, in place of a multitude of different devices such as tariffs, quantitative restrictions, State trading, minimum prices and so on; this instrument serves to iron out differences in price levels, both between the EEC and the outside world and (in the transitional period) between different member countries.

It was above all an outstanding achievement to agree that by 1970 the six countries of the Community will constitute a single agricultural market, free from restrictions on internal trade. As the President of the Commission wrote:

> These decisions, which confirm the success of what has without doubt been the most arduous task of all, namely to create conditions for a Common Market in agriculture, which is traditionally the least liberalized sector, have made a deep impression on public opinion and have strengthened confidence in the future Europe.[1]

The effects of free competition within the EEC could be striking, for each of the member countries has branches of agriculture which have hitherto been protected and the variations in production costs are wide. Table 74 provides a comparison of price levels in 1960/1 for some major commodities at current exchange rates. The national prices are expressed as a percentage of the average for the EEC: this average is unweighted, but it does not take account of the relatively high prices in Luxemburg. On the assumption that prices are harmonized around this average, France would be competitive in grains and even to some extent in livestock products. The Netherlands also has low prices for most products; one would have expected a bigger differential between the Dutch and the Belgian prices than the figures show. German agriculture appears vulnerable in almost all its branches, except possibly in cattle. Italy too has a high price level for wheat and some other products; on the other hand, the Italian climate enables fruit and vegetables to be produced more cheaply than elsewhere in the EEC.

What in fact happens depends above all on the level at which the common price level is fixed. A high level could maintain in existence even the inefficient farms, and stimulate an increase in production in countries where prices are relatively low – grain in France is an important case – thus aggravating the existing pressure on markets. On the other hand, a low level would give an advantage to efficient farmers and gradually force out high-cost production. It has been seen in Chapter 14 that a reduction in prices would necessitate a particularly drastic adjustment in

[1] W. Hallstein, 'The Community enters its second stage', *Bulletin of the EEC*, February 1962, p. 7.

Table 74

PRODUCER PRICES[a] OF AGRICULTURAL PRODUCTS IN THE
EEC IN 1960/61

	Wheat	Barley	Milk[b]	Eggs	Cattle	Pigs
	DM per 100 kg.					
Average price[c]	38	32	31	288	195	209
	Per cent of average price[c]					
Belgium	100	90	99	97	96	86
France	85	82	100	96	87	110[d]
W. Germany	107	132	103	111	102	115
Italy	118	106	103	115	118	95
Netherlands	89	91	95	80	97	94
Luxemburg	118	..	120	..	102	126

[a] Average prices received for all qualities.
[b] In terms of 3·7 per cent fat content.
[c] Luxemburg excluded from calculation of average.
[d] First quality only.

.. Not available.

Source: EEC, *Bilans et études*, Série B, No. 2, March 1962.

German agriculture: consequently Germany has tried to persuade her partners to raise their prices to the German level.

The EEC Commission has made proposals for the initial stages which if adopted would tend to reduce the gap between the highest and the lowest prices currently prevailing. It has not committed itself as to the levels at which prices should eventually settle, though in November 1962 it submitted to the Council proposals for the criteria which should be observed in fixing prices. The main factors to be taken into consideration were the importance of prices for farm incomes, their role in guiding production and their effects on overall economic trends. The document in question, however, made little attempt to resolve the conflict between these factors, and there remained ample scope for different interpretations.

The question of the price level is indeed one of the points on which, owing to the conflict of interest between France and

Germany in particular, agreement has proved most difficult to reach. It is nevertheless crucial not only to producers within the Community but also to agricultural exporters in other countries, who are liable to lose markets if high prices stimulate production in the Community; this problem is further discussed in Chapter 18.

The clash between France and the five other members on the question of Britain's admittance into the EEC has already led to the postponement of decisions on the harmonization of grain prices and on the market regulations for certain products. The financial regulations, concerning the use of proceeds from import levies and the means of subsidizing exports to destinations outside the Community, also remain a serious problem: the provisions laid down in January 1962 and outlined above provide abundant material for disagreements and misunderstandings.

It seems important, nevertheless, that the opportunities offered by the common market in agriculture should not be missed. Besides the benefit which should accrue to consumers from cheaper and more varied supplies, and the advantage which low-cost producers should obtain from a wider market, the growth of competition should stimulate the necessary adaptations and in the long run create better conditions of agricultural production throughout the Community.

Chapter 17. Britain and Europe

Britain's problem

Previous chapters have shown that the development of agriculture in Britain took place in a manner fundamentally different from that of the other major European countries. Already by the nineteenth century, Britain's early start in industrialization had caused her agricultural population to decline to a comparatively small proportion of the whole. Subsequently, this trend was pursued, aided by the policy of laissez-faire during the depression at the end of the century, and Britain became heavily dependent on imports of foodstuffs from overseas. The intervention which took place during the 1930s and the assistance given to agriculture during and after the Second World War have restored prosperity to agriculture but have not arrested the fall in the agricultural population, and Britain remains the world's largest importer of foodstuffs. Trade with the countries of the Commonwealth has been especially favoured, in particular by the institution of Commonwealth Preference during the 1930s. In France and Germany, on the other hand, the relative decline in agriculture as compared with other activities began later and was subsequently restrained by protectionist policies; France has become self-sufficient in almost all the foodstuffs that can be produced on French soil; Western Germany, severed from the agricultural regions of Prussia, is a large food importer but has subjected its imports to drastic controls in order to maintain a high price level for its producers.

The restrictions applied by Britain to imports of foodstuffs are few and generally unimportant. It has been seen in Chapter 12 that, apart from certain limitations on imports from the dollar area, only a few products (apples, pears and main-crop potatoes being the most important) are subject to quota. Imports from the Commonwealth are free from duty, except for revenue duties on sugar and some other items. Even in the case of foreign countries, duties are generally low – 10 per cent on barley and bacon, specific duties equivalent to about 5 per cent on beef and butter; some products – wheat in particular – are admitted free of duty from all sources (Table 75).

The policy of free or nearly-free entry for foodstuffs into the British market meant that support for British farmers had to be given by the special system of deficiency payments (see Chapter

Table 75

U.K. IMPORTS OF MAJOR FOODSTUFFS IN 1958, AND IMPORT DUTIES

	Sources of imports			Tariffs	
	Common-wealth	OEEC area	Other coun-tries	Preferen-tial	Full
	£ million			per cent	
TOTAL FOOD, BEVERAGES, TOBACCO	795	293	416		
of which:					
Wheat (unmilled)	71	13	30	–	–
Barley „	21	1	6	–	10
Beef and veal[a]	26	1	43	–	5[c]
Mutton and lamb	59	1	4	–	–
Bacon	9	65	12	–	10
Butter	55	34	9	–	5[c]
Sugar (unrefined)	64	–	30	13[bc]	24[c]

[a] Fresh, frozen or chilled.
[b] A lower rate is granted to the Colonies under certain conditions.
[c] Estimate based on conversion of specific duty.

Source: M. A. Tracy, 'Agriculture and a European Economic Union', *Westminster Bank Review*, February 1961.

12) – a system which operates in a manner totally different from the protection at the frontier practised by most other countries, and under which the returns to British farmers depend above all on the level of the guaranteed prices. It is only for horticulture that import restrictions are the main instrument of support: here there are no guaranteed prices, but import duties are frequently high.

The replacement of this system by one of protection at the frontier, in the context of a European common market, might not greatly affect British farmers so long as the overall level of prices they receive is approximately the same. The difference would be mainly one of the *method* of support, and though the details of the change-over could give rise to numerous difficulties, these should not be insoluble. The change in the method of support would however involve increased market prices, hence higher food prices to consumers; this would be offset by a reduced burden on the Exchequer which might permit a reduction in taxation, but it does not necessarily follow that each consumer would thereby be fully compensated for his increased expenditure on food.

On the other hand, a change from the present system to one of support through market prices would have far-reaching consequences for Britain's imports of agricultural products. As Table 75 shows, by far the greater part of Britain's food imports come from overseas, and over half from the Commonwealth; supplies from other Western European countries are relatively small (bacon and butter from Denmark and the Netherlands being the major items). Participation in an agricultural common market in Western Europe therefore means removing restrictions on a small part of British food imports and imposing or intensifying restrictions on a much larger part. Commonwealth countries, in the first place, would lose the preference from which they benefit on the British market. This is perhaps not so important: the degree of preference has been eroded since before the war by the rise in price levels which has reduced the incidence of specific duties. Calculations made by the author (Table 76) show that the average margin of preference on foodstuffs in 1957 was only about 6 per cent: for the four largest suppliers enjoying Commonwealth preference (New Zealand, Australia, Canada and the Irish Republic), the margin varied between 3 and 8 per cent according

Table 76

VALUE OF U.K. IMPORTS FROM THE COMMONWEALTH IN 1957 (£MILLION) AND AVERAGE MARGINS OF PREFERENCE (PER CENT)

	Total Commonwealth		New Zealand		Australia		Canada		Irish Republic	
	Imports	Margin	Imports	Margin	Imports	Margin	Imports	Margin	Imports	Margin
Live animals for food	45	–	–	–	–	–	–	–	45	–
Meat	123	6	69	2	39	10	–	–	12	11
Dairy products, etc.	87	8	59	8	20	7	1	15	5	6
Fish	5	8	–	–	–	–	3	5	1	10
Cereals	114	3	–	–	23	2	81	3	1	11
Fruit and vegetables	104	11	3	9	20	9	2	5	1	11
Sugar, etc.[a]	7	16	–	–	2	11	–	–	–	–
Coffee, tea, cocoa, etc.	166	5	–	–	–	–	–	–	5	–
Feeding-stuffs	24	12	–	–	–	–	8	14	1	9
Total food and feed[a]	676	6	132	5	104	8	96	4	71	3

[a] Excluding sugar under the Commonwealth Sugar Agreement and molasses exempted from duty.

Source: Commonwealth Preference in the United Kingdom (P.E.P., 1960).

to the composition of their exports.[1] What is much more serious is that Commonwealth countries would face a barrier from which Britain's European partners would be exempt. Other overseas agricultural exporters – the United States and the Argentine in particular – would be confronted with the same barrier in place of the relatively mild restrictions to which their exports to Britain have so far been subjected.

The degree of restriction on imports from overseas involved in

[1] Average margins of preference were calculated by weighting the margin on each item (i.e. the difference between the duty on foreign supplies and that on supplies from the Commonwealth, the latter being generally nil) by the value of imports from the Commonwealth country or countries concerned. The Irish Republic, though not a member of the Commonwealth, enjoys Commonwealth Preference.

this barrier would depend on the price level aimed at in the common market. Given the existing situation in Western European countries, there is little immediate prospect of a low price level. It is indeed doubtful whether Britain herself, under such a system, could press very energetically for lower prices, since by doing so she might benefit the Commonwealth but not her own farmers. The combination of a high price level and freedom of trade within a common market, with severe restrictions on imports from outside sources, could cause overseas countries to lose a large part of their sales to what at present is their largest market.

It is therefore not surprising that the history of post-war negotiations on European agriculture has been marked by a conflict between the British and French views. Britain was originally unwilling to modify her system of support and has continually sought arrangements that would preserve her imports of foodstuffs from the Commonwealth and other overseas sources. France, anxious to obtain outlets for her expanding agricultural production, has insisted on a unified system that would give a preference to European supplies over imports from overseas. This conflict was already responsible for the failure, in 1954, of the Green Pool negotiations (already discussed in Chapter 16); it played a part in the lack of success which attended Britain's effort to set up a Free Trade Area; and it was the main economic problem in the negotiations on Britain's entry into the EEC.

The Free Trade Area negotiations

The prospect of an economic union between the major Continental countries was a cause of serious concern to Britain, who found herself in danger of being isolated economically and even politically. Yet the British Government did not originally consider joining EEC: besides the agricultural problem, the idea of a common external tariff seemed unacceptable, and there was in Britain a general suspicion of supranational tendencies.

In July 1956, shortly after the Six had embarked on serious negotiations, the British Government made its proposal for a Free Trade Area incorporating the common market which the Six intended to create. Such an arrangement would have given Britain the best of both worlds: there would have been no

barriers to trade in manufactured goods between member countries, and tariffs on imports from other countries need not have
been made uniform; the institutional framework envisaged would
have enabled each member to keep the control of its own affairs.

The negotiations which followed the British proposal soon ran
into difficulties. France in particular stressed the problems which
would arise from different external tariffs and objected to the
idea of each member country keeping its autonomy in matters of
trade. The discussions dragged on till in November 1958 the
French Government declared that it would be impossible to
create a Free Trade Area without a single external tariff and
without harmonization of economic and social policies.

The main cause of the failure, underlying the technical issues,
was no doubt the basic difference in principle between full
economic integration as envisaged by the Six (with political
union as an ultimate objective) and the British intention of
limiting action to the minimum necessary in the economic
sphere. The problem of agriculture added to the difficulties.

Originally, the British Government wanted to exclude agriculture from the scope of the Free Trade Area, arguing that this
was necessary both to preserve Commonwealth Preference and to
maintain protection for British agriculture. Other countries
objected strongly, pointing out that this plan would open their
markets to the competition of British manufactures, while giving
no advantage to their agricultural exports to Britain. In January
1958 Britain modified her position to the extent of submitting a
draft Convention on agriculture. This did not require the removal of tariffs or quantitative restrictions and included only a
vague reference to the possible co-ordination of national marketing
organizations: its main feature was the institution of a procedure
for 'confrontation' and for hearing complaints, but as decisions
by the members would be taken only by unanimous vote this
arrangement was of doubtful value.

In June 1958 the Six in their turn drew up a memorandum
on agriculture. This is of interest in view of the position which
they were to adopt a few years later: their proposal did *not*
envisage the adoption in the Free Trade Area of a common
agricultural policy or a common external tariff on agricultural
products. In a first stage, certain 'very high' duties were to be
lowered, with the eventual aim of abolishing barriers to agri-

cultural trade, but there was no precise commitment. This memorandum was subsequently endorsed by the EEC Commission,[1] which moreover had already included in its first general report in 1958 the following statement:

> It is understandable that Great Britain regards Imperial Preference as so important an element in the Commonwealth that she cannot consider abolishing it entirely; it is necessary however to ensure that this Imperial Preference does not distort the conditions of competition. It will, therefore, be indispensable to draw up special provisions in this connection.[2]

The positions of Britain and the EEC were thus not so far apart that it would have been impossible to reach agreement over agriculture in the Free Trade Area. It has been seen above that import restrictions generally are not an essential feature of support for British farmers, whose returns are primarily dependent on the level of the guaranteed prices; it has also been pointed out that the degree of preference given to the Commonwealth by existing tariffs on foreign agricultural produce is not significant. Britain could therefore have accepted the removal of restrictions on agricultural imports without significant damage either to the Commonwealth or to British farmers, and – at this stage – this was all the Six were asking. Britain's original attempt to exclude agriculture entirely from the scope of the agreement appears as a serious tactical error, which reinforced suspicion of her motives. Later, when Britain approached the Six with a request for full membership of the EEC, she was forced to offer much more substantial concessions.

The European Free Trade Association

After the failure of the Free Trade Area negotiations, the European Free Trade Association (EFTA) was formed by seven countries which for economic or political reasons were unwilling to join the EEC: Britain, Denmark, Norway, Sweden, Austria, Switzerland and Portugal. The arrangements are essentially those

---

[1] In its first memorandum to the Council of Ministers on the European Economic Association, February 26th, 1959.

[2] EEC Commission, *Premier rapport général*, 1958, pp. 127–8.

which Britain had proposed to the Six: restrictions on trade in manufactured goods between the members are to be gradually abolished, but no changes are required in tariffs on imports from outside the Association, and there is no supranational element.

Agriculture was excluded from the overall agreement, but some satisfaction had to be given to Denmark (the only important agricultural exporter among the Seven), especially as Danish farmers were becoming aware of the opportunities offered by the Treaty of Rome. This was done by bilateral agreements between Denmark and other member countries.

Thus Britain agreed to remove the duties on certain Danish exports – bacon, canned pork, canned cream and blue-veined cheese. (These products were carefully selected as being those for which there was little or no competition between Danish and Commonwealth supplies; no concession was made on butter.) The British Government also gave an undertaking that it would not raise the guaranteed prices to British farmers so as to nullify the effects of the tariff reduction, and that generally it would not pursue policies likely to reduce Denmark's share in the British market.

Sweden agreed to give preference to Danish supplies, and to repay to Denmark 60 per cent of the levies imposed on Danish produce. Switzerland arranged for preferences to be given to Danish supplies of several commodities.

Britain's conversion

The EFTA however failed to arouse much enthusiasm in Britain, and meanwhile the EEC was gathering momentum. A movement in Britain in favour of joining EEC gained increasing influence. As regards agriculture, it began to be pointed out that British farming was in a strong competitive position: farms were, on the average, far larger than those of Continental countries and the problem of fragmentation was almost unknown. The prices received by farmers in Britain and in the countries of the EEC were compared, and it was discovered that on the whole the differences were not great: British agriculture might lose on the swings but gain on the roundabouts. A change in the method of support, from deficiency payments to import restriction, would not necessarily be against farmers' interests – perhaps the contrary. This trend of thought was reinforced by the growing feeling that, with the mounting and unpredictable cost of support, the system would soon have to be changed in any case.

The *Economist* lent its weight to these arguments in a number of articles, and in the spring of 1961 the Bow Group published arguments by Graham Hallett to the effect that British agriculture need not suffer from joining the EEC.[1] In May 1961 a pamphlet by Political and Economic Planning sought, not very conclusively, to show that a shift from deficiency payments to controlled markets would not significantly raise food prices and the cost of living; almost simultaneously, Colin Clark issued a statement declaring, with rather scanty statistical backing, that if Britain were to join EEC the retail price of food would rise by only 3·1 per cent.

The National Farmers' Union continued to oppose entry. In a pamphlet in 1961 it emphasized that under the EEC system, with 'target' prices for some commodities and no firm guarantees for others, British farmers would have less assurance of adequate prices than under the British system of guaranteed prices for all major products.[2]

Much less attention was given at this time to the probable effects on the Commonwealth and other overseas suppliers. In September 1960 the Economist Intelligence Unit produced a study of Commonwealth trade: after analysing the trends in food supply and demand, this work concluded that 'there is much to suggest that the European countries will be both unable and unwilling to increase the degree of self-sufficiency in relation to total food supplies'. This enabled the EIU to suggest that there was 'a significant area for negotiations between the overseas Commonwealth and European countries concerning the terms on which food will be imported into Europe'.[3] Further, the EIU declared that Britain could accept a common agricultural policy provided it was sufficiently liberal, with safeguards in case Europe's imports from the Commonwealth fell below agreed levels. However, the analysis of supply and demand on which these conclusions rested was statistically doubtful, and the results

[1] Graham Hallett, 'British Agriculture and Europe', supplement to spring issue of *Crossbow*, 1961.

[2] NFU, 'Agriculture in the Community', *Information Service*, No. 2, 1961.

[3] EIU, *The Commonwealth and Europe* (London, 1960), pp. 94 and 96.

were at odds with the projections carried out by the Commission of the EEC itself.[1]

In July 1961, Political and Economic Planning issued another paper which suggested that imports into an enlarged EEC of basic commodities such as wheat should be regulated by a system of long-term contracts, with a guaranteed annual quota and fixed prices; exporting countries would receive the price level established within the Community and it would then not be necessary to impose levies or tariffs. PEP did not discuss the question of how to prevent rising production within the EEC from displacing imports.[2]

Negotiations with EEC

By the middle of 1961 the British Government was convinced that Britain's interests lay in joining the EEC. On July 31st the Prime Minister, Mr Macmillan, announced the intention of seeking admission, 'if satisfactory arrangements can be made to meet the special needs of the United Kingdom, of the Commonwealth and of the European Free Trade Association'. Denmark and the Irish Republic submitted to the EEC their applications for membership at the same time as Britain. The 'neutrals' – Austria, Sweden and Switzerland – had political problems, but in December 1961 they asked for negotiations with EEC on possible terms of association, followed in the course of 1962 by Spain and Portugal. In May 1962 Norway requested full membership.

The course of the subsequent negotiations between Britain and the Six is well known and need not be described in detail. They began in November 1961; by the summer of 1962 a considerable number of problems had been solved or nearly so. With few reservations, Britain accepted the general economic implications of the Treaty of Rome: the removal of internal trade barriers, the common external tariff, the free movement of labour and other aspects of the economic union. Arrangements were agreed upon for imports of manufactured products from the Common-

[1] In particular, EIU used an improbably high income elasticity of demand. and its projections of production were unduly influenced by the short harvest of 1956.

[2] PEP, *Agriculture, the Commonwealth and EEC* (Occasional Paper No. 14), July 10th, 1961.

wealth, and relationships between the EEC and the less-developed Commonwealth countries were virtually settled. Arrangements for safeguarding the trade of India, Pakistan and Ceylon were decided upon. Apart from the level of the common tariff on a few raw materials, agriculture remained the only important unsolved problem. By January 1963 agreement had still not been reached, though it was generally held that solutions were in sight. On January 14th, President de Gaulle declared in his famous press conference:

> It is possible that one day England will transform herself sufficiently to participate in the European Community, without restriction or reservation and preferring it to every other connection, and in that case the Six would open the door and France would raise no objection ... It is also possible that England is not yet willing to do so, and this indeed is what seems to result from the long, much too long, conversations at Brussels.

The French representatives at Brussels, against the will of all the other members of the Community, accordingly refused to allow the negotiations with Britain to continue.

The British Government had recognized from the start of the negotiations that its only chance of success lay in full acceptance of the agricultural provisions of the Rome Treaty. Its policy was thus forced to come full circle, from excluding agriculture from even the relatively modest arrangements of the Free Trade Area, to endorsing a policy bound to bring about a fundamental change in the British system of agricultural support and in the treatment of food imports. Discussions with the Six therefore turned not on the question of whether Britain could accept the common agricultural policy, but on the form which this policy should take. The Six, having with difficulty agreed among themselves on at least the framework of future policy, were unwilling to consider different arrangements; Britain's room for manœuvre was thus limited. The system of import levies could not be called in question, but Britain attempted to ensure that it would be applied in a manner such as to minimize adverse effects on British farmers and consumers as well as on Commonwealth exporters.

So far as British agriculture was concerned, it was agreed

without much difficulty that there should be an annual review of the agricultural situation, similar to that practised in Britain, on the basis of which the Commission would make whatever proposals might seem necessary in order to maintain a fair standard of living to farmers. The main difficulty concerned the manner in which the change-over from deficiency payments to the import levy system should take place. Britain asked for a transitional period corresponding to that which the Six themselves had at their disposal – i.e. twelve years. But as this meant that the common agricultural policy would not be achieved throughout the enlarged EEC by 1970, the Six rejected this demand. Finally, Britain agreed to accept 1970 as the end of the transitional period.

Britain also insisted that the system of deficiency payments should not be replaced overnight by import levies, but should be allowed to phase out through a gradual raising of market prices. The Six, having agreed among themselves to replace national measures of support by the new system without delay, wanted Britain to follow suit. When the British negotiators pointed out that this would cause a sudden rise in the retail prices of foodstuffs in Britain, the Six suggested that consumer subsidies could be used during the transitional period – a suggestion which the British regarded as impracticable. After a detailed study of this problem by the Ministers of Agriculture, possible arrangements for different products were under consideration when the negotiations were interrupted in January 1963.

For horticulture, Britain wanted arrangements to ease the impact of increased competition. This question had scarcely been discussed by the time the negotiations broke down.

It has been pointed out above that the issues involved in the treatment of Britain's food imports are much more significant than those concerning her domestic agriculture. From the outset of the negotiations, the British Government was under strong pressure from Commonwealth Governments and from certain groups in Britain to preserve Commonwealth interests, and Ministers gave repeated assurances that Britain would not enter the EEC unless satisfactory terms were obtained for the Commonwealth. Early in the discussions, the British representatives laid stress on the need for 'comparable outlets' for Commonwealth produce – i.e. markets in the enlarged EEC comparable to those currently enjoyed in Britain. The Six were prepared to admit some degree of preference for Commonwealth supplies during the transitional period, by granting them a part of the *montant forfaitaire* applicable to intra-EEC trade: this preference however must decrease over time and disappear entirely by the end of the transitional period. Commonwealth produce would then be admitted on the same terms as that from other outside suppliers. The French representatives declared that the EEC could not be expected to commit itself to maintaining specific quantities or prices after the transitional period, nor to giving more favourable treatment to the Commonwealth than to other outside suppliers. They introduced into the discussion their plan for reorganizing world agricultural markets (see the discussion of the 'Pisani Plan' in the following chapter): they suggested that long-term contracts between the enlarged EEC and overseas food exporters would cure the instability of world markets and give a guarantee of outlets at satisfactory prices. The British were prepared to accept this in principle, but tried to get more specific commitments: they wanted assurances as to what would happen if such agreements could not be concluded, and safeguards against an increase in food production within the EEC which would reduce its import requirements. On the first point, the Six agreed that if world-wide agreements could not be concluded, the enlarged EEC would enter into separate negotiations with any food exporting country that so desired. On the second point, they agreed on an explicit statement that the common agricultural policy should be such as to offer reasonable opportunities on EEC markets for outside supplies of temperate foodstuffs, but they refused to give any more specific guarantees. Agreement was apparently reached that the problems of New Zealand should be given special attention, but the French afterwards seemed to contest this. This was the state of play following meetings in July and August 1962, and the question of Commonwealth trade was not brought up again before the negotiations collapsed.

The financial question – the use to be made of receipts from import levies – which was a bone of contention between the Six, was not directly an issue in the negotiations on British entry, since Britain declared herself ready to accept whatever agreement the Six reached between themselves. However, at one stage (in the session of August 4th–5th, 1962) the French asked the British to endorse a document on this question which they had prepared and which included an interpretation upon which the Six were not yet agreed. The British negotiators refused, and this question too was left in suspense.

What next?

It is hardly surprising that a system of agricultural support which has evolved to suit the needs of a highly industrialized country, heavily dependent on food imports and maintaining special trading links with a number of overseas countries, cannot easily be adapted in conformity with another system, devised by countries with a long history of agricultural protectionism, in which the agricultural population continues to form a relatively large part of the whole and in which imports are generally regarded only as marginal to domestic supplies.

It is now to be expected that the British system of support will in any case be modified. The need for a change, following the rise in expenditure in deficiency payments, has been widely recognized: this point has already been discussed in Chapter 12. Future policy is likely to involve some degree of control over imports: this will no doubt be sought in the first instance through agreements with exporting countries, but it may also prove necessary for Britain to regulate supplies in some way. This might facilitate an eventual reconciliation with the system of agricultural support in force in the EEC, particularly if some of the mechanisms used by the common agricultural policy are adopted in Britain. Nevertheless, for the time being Britain will presumably continue to admit imports with the minimum of restriction; the degree of preference enjoyed by Commonwealth countries may diminish still further, but is unlikely to be reversed in favour of European suppliers. The difference between this and the system of the EEC, based on protection at the frontier and involving a significant degree of preference between the member states, would remain considerable. Britain may still agree to adopt the EEC system in its essentials: this may be necessary and desirable in the light of overall economic and political considerations. But it should be realized that drastic surgery would be involved, and that the effects on overseas food suppliers might be serious.

A full reconciliation of the British and EEC systems is unlikely to become easy unless there is a reduction in the degree of dependence on price support on both sides of the Channel. If the level of guaranteed prices and hence of deficiency payments could be gradually reduced in Britain, and if in the EEC the level of the target prices could likewise be brought down, the difference in the method of support would become steadily less significant. It has been seen in Part III that a shift of emphasis from price support to measures designed to raise agricultural efficiency is already taking place in almost all Western European countries, and is indeed being forced on them by the twin problems of rising production and low farm incomes; this trend is bound to be reinforced in coming years. A solution to the problem of agriculture in both the national and the international context depends ultimately on a transformation of the agricultural scene such that producers can obtain a reasonable standard of living without the need for more market regulation than is required to even out the fluctuations inherent in agricultural supply.

Chapter 18. Europe and the World Market

Trends in agricultural trade

Western Europe accounts for the greater part of world trade in agricultural products. Some of its imports from other regions consist of tropical and semi-tropical products which – with the important exception of sugar – do not compete directly with the produce of European agriculture. However, Western Europe is also a large, often the major market for the foodstuffs produced in other temperate zones: in particular North America, Oceania, and the southern tip of South America. Developments in Western European agriculture are thus of vital concern to the exporting countries in these regions.

The growth of production, the relatively slow growth of demand and the increased degree of self-sufficiency in Western Europe have reduced the scope for imports of temperate foodstuffs. Figure 10 shows that by the early 1950s, the volume of production of foodstuffs in Western Europe was well above the pre-war level, while the volume of imports had fallen. In the course of the 1950s, both production and imports have risen, but imports have not made good the ground lost during and after the war. Trade between the Western European countries rose faster than the net imports of Western Europe from other regions: the latter, by 1960, had barely recovered to the pre-war level. This contrast is largely a consequence of the composition of trade in the two cases: meat and livestock, as well as fruit and vegetables, play

344

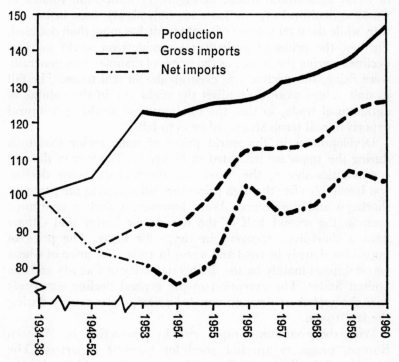

VOLUME OF PRODUCTION AND IMPORTS OF FOOD AND
FEEDING-STUFFS IN WESTERN EUROPE (1934–38 = 100)

Source: FAO, *State of Food and Agriculture,* 1962 (and earlier issues).

FIG. 10

an important part in intra-European trade, and demand for these commodities has been rising relatively fast. In the case of imports from overseas, the favourable development for these products has been offset by the much less satisfactory trends for grains, sugar and dairy products.

The slow growth of imports by Western Europe has been the factor mainly responsible for the generally unfavourable trend of world agricultural trade: as Figure 11 shows, the volume of world agricultural exports has risen only slowly since before the war, while the total volume of world trade has more than doubled. Further, the prices of agricultural products on world markets declined during the 1950s; as the prices of manufactures generally were rising, this decline was even greater in real terms. The fall in unit values more than offset the slight rise in the volume of agricultural trade, so that the total value of world agricultural exports in real terms stagnated or even fell.

Developments in the world prices of some major foodstuffs during the 1950s are indicated in Figure 12. For four of the five commodities shown, the trend was downwards. Some decline was inevitable after the high prices prevailing during the post-war shortages and the Korean War: however, a decline continued even in the second half of the decade for barley and – apart from a short-lived recovery in 1957 – for sugar. The price of butter fell sharply in 1958 and again in 1960. The price of wheat was stabilized mainly by the deliberate policy of Canada and the United States. The exception to the general decline was beef: here the growth of demand enabled prices to rise steeply during the late 1950s.

With the continuing rapid rise in production in Western Europe, prospects are not good for overseas exporters. The creation of the European Economic Community adds to the uncertainty. While trade in agricultural products within the EEC is due to be freed from restrictions, the common market thus established will be largely insulated from the outside world through the import levy system. It is true that this merely involves carrying over to the common agricultural policy the drastic import restrictions already in force in France and Germany in particular. It would no doubt have been impossible to agree on the creation of a common market in agriculture within the EEC if at the same time this was to involve increased competition

TRENDS IN WORLD TRADE (1934-38=100)

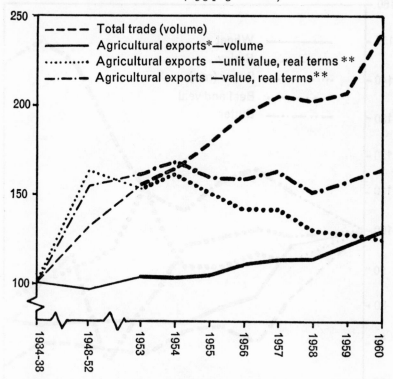

*Excluding U.S. shipments under special terms.
**Current prices deflated by UN index of unit value of exports of manufactured goods.

Source: FAO, *State of Food and Agriculture,* 1962 (and earlier issues).

FIG. II

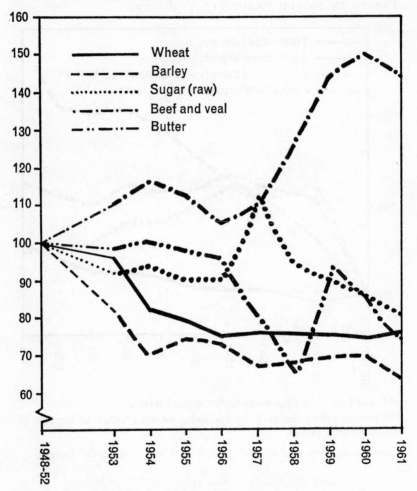

Source : FAO, *State of Food and Agriculture,* 1962 (and earlier issues).

FIG. 12

from outside suppliers. Already in its initial proposals the Commission declared:

> In order to bring about, in the interests of producers and consumers in the Community, the necessary stability of agricultural markets, it is necessary to eliminate the effects of the excessive fluctuations in world market prices on the markets of the Community. Account must also be taken of the fact that the conditions of production and the nature of farming enterprises in the Community are not the same as those of the non-European countries which are large agricultural exporters. Moreover, the prices of agricultural products on world markets are often distorted by artificial measures. Consequently, agricultural prices within the Community generally cannot be at the same level as world prices, but must be stabilized at a higher level.[1]

The question of the price level eventually established in the EEC is therefore crucial not only for producers within the Community but also for agricultural exporters in other countries. These agricultural exporters have in any case to face a situation where the import levy system gives a degree of preference to intra-EEC trade over supplies from outside, and where the advantages of cheaper production are practically eliminated. A high price level in the EEC is liable to stimulate increased production in the low-cost areas within the Community, without discouraging output in high-cost areas: the result could be to make the Community increasingly self-sufficient in agricultural produce.

The production and demand trends for agricultural products in the six members of the EEC, as well as in three prospective members – Britain, Denmark and Norway – have been analysed by the secretariat of the EEC, and the following conclusions were reached as to the situation which may exist in 1970:

1. For wheat, the 'Six' may no longer have any net import requirement, while that of the 'Nine' may be reduced. Net imports of feed grains, on the other hand, may rise in both cases. These results, however, depend on certain important assumptions: rapid growth in incomes and hence in demand, no significant improvement in the amount of feed grains required per unit of

---

[1] EEC Commission, *Propositions concernant l'elaboration et la mise en oeuvre de la politique agricole commune*, Brussels, June 30th, 1960, p. II. 21.

livestock output, and above all no change in acreage. This last assumption is crucial, yet it is unlikely to be fulfilled: the expected rise in the price of grain in France towards a common price level in the EEC is likely to stimulate an expansion in grain cultivation in France which could substantially raise the overall degree of self-sufficiency. If actual developments should contradict all three assumptions, net imports of all grains by the Six could become insignificant, while those of all the Nine together could fall from 20 million to 11 million tons.

2. In the case of butter, the EEC secretariat calculates that imports (almost all by Britain) could be maintained at about the 1958 level, provided that the numbers of dairy cows do not increase. The difficulty is to prevent such an increase, especially in view of the expected rise in demand for meat: if the increase in the number of beef cattle is accompanied by a corresponding increase in the number of cows, the result could be to create an export surplus of dairy products exceeding the amount which the British market can absorb.

3. Demand for meat, assuming a fairly rapid growth in incomes, is expected to rise much faster than that for most other foodstuffs. This could lead to some increase in the net import requirements of the Nine.

4. For sugar, assuming that production from sugar-beet can be restrained, the net imports of the Nine could rise slightly. This would be mainly due to increased consumption in Italy.[1]

Intervention in overseas countries

Faced with these difficulties on the world market, most overseas agricultural exporters have resorted, as in the 1930s, to various measures of intervention. These countries are generally too

[1] The results of the EEC study were apparently so controversial that publication was delayed. The present account is based on certain 'leaks': an article by H.-B. Krohn (the head of the responsible section in the EEC secretariat) in *Agrarwirtschaft*, November 1962, and an article in *Le Monde*, December 18th, 1962. When this study was prepared, the accession to EEC of the three other countries was still expected in the near future. However, the analysis apparently did not take account of the effects of their membership (via changes in prices and policy measures) on supply and demand trends. The results therefore remain valid for all nine countries, the Six and the Three being considered independently.

dependent on their agricultural trade to afford large-scale subsidies to their farmers, but they have tried to get the best possible
terms for their exports, often by centralizing trade in marketing
boards, and at the very least they have attempted to shield their
farmers from the worst of the price fluctuations.

Thus in CANADA the Wheat Board is responsible for marketing
most grain; no price support is given (with minor exceptions),
but the Government contributes to the cost of storage. The
prices of various other agricultural products are supported, but –
with the exception of dairy products – the level of support is
normally below average market prices and the aim is stabilization rather than permanent support.

AUSTRALIA has given its wheat producers a guaranteed price
for a certain quantity of exports, based on costs of production.
As costs rose while export prices remained low, this involved
subsidies on exports beginning in the 1959/60 season; as a result
the Wheat Stabilization Fund, in which the proceeds of all sales
are pooled, was nearly exhausted. A subsidy is also given for
dairy produce; exports are centralized in the Dairy Produce
Board. Exports of various other products are regulated by
marketing boards.

NEW ZEALAND is even more dependent than Australia on
agricultural exports, and cannot give subsidies as a long-term
policy. Exports of dairy products pass through a Marketing
Commission, and an attempt has been made, through a special
fund, to equalize receipts from one year to another and as between different dairy products; this fund has been supported by
a Government loan. Exports of meat are regulated by a Meat
Producers' Board, and here too a stabilization fund is operated.

Both Australia and New Zealand have derived some benefit
from their relationship with Britain. During and after the war,
their trade with Britain was regulated by bulk purchase agreements. When these were terminated in the early 1950s, a fifteen-
year agreement was drawn up under which Australia agreed to
encourage increased exports of meat in return for an assured
market in Britain; Britain undertook to make deficiency payments to Australia if the price received for these exports fell
below certain minima. New Zealand in 1952 obtained only an
understanding that Britain would continue to admit all her exportable surplus of meat without restriction of quantity; in 1958

Britain agreed to maintain New Zealand's existing rights of free entry to the British market and the preferences on major exports; consultations would be held before any major change in these arrangements.

In ARGENTINA, the Peron regime operated extensive controls over foreign trade; these were progressively removed by subsequent Governments, and free trading was established for most agricultural products. The system of multiple exchange rates, which in effect subsidized agricultural exports, has been abandoned. For grains, minimum prices are guaranteed to producers, but at fairly low levels. There are regulations affecting the number of cattle that can be kept and slaughtered, and exports of meat are promoted by a Meat Board.

The UNITED STATES presents the paradox of a highly-developed and industrialized country, with less than 10 per cent of its population engaged in agriculture, which nevertheless is a major agricultural exporter. It has experienced problems concerning farm prices and incomes similar to those of the developed countries of Western Europe; it has also suffered from the restricted market for its agricultural exports. The policy introduced in the 1930s of supporting prices for the major products through purchase at Government expense was pursued after the war; support prices were maintained at a high level through the application of the rigid 'parity' formula. This stimulus to production, combined with rapid technical progress, led from the mid-1950s to mounting surpluses of wheat, maize, cotton, dairy products and other items. In exporting to commercial markets, the United States has been compelled to resort to a large element of export subsidy to bring prices down from domestic levels to those of world markets. In 1954, under Public Law 480, the United States embarked on a vast programme for disposing of surpluses overseas, later turned to constructive use as an important element in its aid to underdeveloped countries (the 'Food for Peace' programme).

In spite of this action, the pressure of supplies on prices, together with mounting production costs, caused farm incomes in the United States to stagnate while industrial incomes were rising fast. Many and conflicting proposals were put forward for dealing with the problem, but it proved extremely difficult to put any of them into practice. The Republican Administration in the late 1950s attempted to reduce price supports and make them more flexible, but this programme could not be applied effectively because of the adverse consequences for farm incomes. From 1961 the Democratic Administration embarked on the opposite course of high prices with strict production controls; this too has encountered stiff opposition, but some successes have been achieved for wheat and feed grains. Like Western European countries, the United States seeks also to deal with the farm income problem by measures of structural improvement, in particular through a programme for assisting the development of depressed rural areas.

The Agricultural Adjustment Act of 1933 empowered the President to restrict imports of agricultural products when this appeared necessary to safeguard any programme of domestic price support; extensive use has been made of this power. The Democratic policy of 'supply management' will presumably necessitate the maintenance of import controls.

This has not prevented the United States from making a determined effort to break down the barriers to its own agricultural exports. It feels particularly concerned at the risk of losing sales in the European Economic Community, and the Secretary of Agriculture, Mr Freeman, has launched a series of vigorous attacks on the common agricultural policy of the Six. The following passage from one of his many speeches on the subject is worth quoting:

> Protective devices adopted or proposed by the Common Market centre around the use of a variable levy fee. To some people these levies appear as a gate on a dam which can be raised or lowered depending on the amount of water needed on the other side. To others, these levies appear to be more like a moving high-jump bar which rises to disqualify even the most proficient competitor.[1]

It is hoped by agricultural circles that the Trade Expansion Act of 1962, which greatly increases the power of the President to reduce U.S. tariffs in exchange for concessions by other countries, will provide a weapon through which import barriers in the EEC can be forced down. Section 252 of the Act directs the President to take appropriate steps to eliminate restrictions on

[1] Address to the National Council of Farmer Co-operatives, Miami Beach, Florida, on June 8th, 1962.

12

U.S. agricultural exports, including if necessary withholding concessions from the countries concerned. Consequently, unless the EEC is prepared to admit U.S. agricultural exports on easier terms, the negotiations due to take place in the GATT on the basis of the Trade Expansion Act seem unlikely to make much progress.

International organizations

In September 1961 the Organisation for European Economic Co-operation was replaced by the Organisation for Economic Co-operation and Development. The OECD includes Canada and the United States as full members, and it has as a new task the promotion of aid to underdeveloped countries. In agriculture, the OECD retains the interest of its predecessor in problems of policy, and is particularly concerned with the implications for agriculture of general economic growth. It has also published a report on the extent to which food aid programmes can contribute to economic growth in the underdeveloped countries. A meeting of the Ministers of Agriculture of member countries in November 1962 provided the opportunity for a lively exchange between the U.S. Secretary of Agriculture, Mr Freeman, and the French Minister, M. Pisani, on the agricultural policy of the EEC.

The effectiveness of the General Agreement on Tariffs and Trade, so far as agriculture is concerned, has been limited by the extent to which trade is affected by measures of domestic policy as well as by direct restrictions on imports. The GATT has therefore concerned itself increasingly with the effects of agricultural policies. In 1958 it published a report written by a panel of eminent economists headed by Gottfried Haberler. The foreword to this report by the Executive Secretary, Mr Wyndham White, pointed to the disturbing elements in world trade: the prevalence of agricultural protectionism, the accumulation of surplus stocks, the sharp variations in the export earnings of primary products and the failure of the export trade of underdeveloped countries to expand at a rate commensurate with their needs. The report itself analysed trends in world trade, stressing the relatively slow growth in the volume and value of trade in agricultural products. The authors of the report considered that the main factor responsible for the unsatisfactory development of trade in temperate foodstuffs was protectionism in the industrialized countries; this protectionism appeared in the form of subsidies on domestic production and on exports, as well as of import restrictions of various kinds. Nevertheless, a moderate change in agricultural policies in the industrialized countries would suffice to bring about a substantial change in the volume of net imports of foodstuffs. The report pointed out that measures to assist the primary producing countries would also be in the long-term interest of the developed countries:

> The highly industrialized countries require a steady and expanding market for their products in the other countries of the world, and measures which will expand and stabilize the markets for primary products in the industrialized countries will encourage the primary producing countries to expand their exports of primary products to, and their imports of manufactures from, the highly industrialized countries, to the general benefit of both groups of countries.[1]

Following the publication of the Haberler Report, the GATT instituted a committee (Committee II) to examine trade in agricultural products, with particular reference to the effects of non-tariff measures of protection. This committee examined the policies of a large number of countries. In 1961 it reported that non-tariff measures were widespread and that they had seriously affected international trade; the restrictions on trade imposed a heavy burden of adjustment on exporting countries, causing them in their turn to apply measures of intervention. In a statement to the Council of GATT in September 1961, the Executive Secretary pointed out that this report showed only too clearly that GATT rules were not applied in agriculture. He was sceptical as to the usefulness of further attempts to persuade the countries concerned to take remedial measures: it would be better to examine the prospects for negotiating terms of access to agricultural markets. He referred to the problem of surpluses, and to the possibility of some link between increased trade in agricultural products and the disposal of surpluses through non-commercial channels.[2]

[1] GATT, *Trends in International Trade* (Geneva, 1958), p. 123.
[2] Press Release GATT/623, November 23rd, 1961.

Later the same month a ministerial meeting in GATT paid special attention to agricultural problems. The French Minister of Finance, M. Baumgartner, declared that the existing situation on world markets was absurd:

[This situation] is characterized essentially by the accumulation of surpluses at a time when there are enormous unsatisfied needs. Moreover, to sell their produce, producing countries engage in a ruinous price war which leads them to subsidize the consumption of foodstuffs in countries which are their main industrial rivals. It is obvious that we must adopt a new policy, and try to reconcile the aspirations of each country by looking for solutions based not on free trade – which is impracticable – but on the principle of market organization.[1]

The meeting recommended the negotiation of 'practical measures for the creation of acceptable conditions of access to world markets for agricultural commodities'. Discussions concerning grains were accordingly begun in February 1962, but initially little progress was made.

The GATT has also paid attention to the implications for agricultural trade of the formation of the EEC. Its Committee II, in November 1962, examined the regulations adopted by the EEC for six groups of products, and exporting countries showed themselves much concerned at the risk of losing trade as a result of the Community's protective and preferential system.

The Food and Agriculture Organization, in its annual reports on the *State of Food and Agriculture*, has laid increasing stress on the contrast between overproduction in the industrialized countries of the world and hunger in the underdeveloped regions. In the former, technical progress and an adequate supply of capital are promoting a rapid increase in food production, while demand for food, at the prevailing high levels of income and with a fairly slow growth in population, is rising comparatively slowly. But in the underdeveloped countries, efforts to raise production are meeting serious obstacles, and demand is expanding very fast as a result of rapid population growth. Consequently:

In the more-developed countries agricultural policies were

[1] Press Release GATT/633, November 27th, 1961.

increasingly concerned with problems of surplus production of certain commodities, while most of the countries in the other group continued to grapple with the problem of shortages of basic foodstuffs.[1]

The statisticians of the FAO calculate that about 10 to 15 per cent of the world's population are undernourished, and that over half the population of the less-developed countries suffer from malnutrition (inadequacy in the quality of the diet): hence between one-third and one-half of the world's people suffer from under-nutrition or malnutrition, or both.[2]

With the publication in 1962 of projections of agricultural supply and demand throughout the world up to 1970, FAO have made it clear that the disparity in the food situation between the developed and the underdeveloped parts of the world is likely to continue into the foreseeable future. Surpluses of grain and dairy produce will persist and even increase in North America and Western Europe, while the potential demand for food in other regions can be met only by a large acceleration in the growth of production.[3]

The FAO has therefore taken an increasing interest in the possibilities of food aid programmes, which hitherto have been almost exclusively an American affair. Already in 1955, an FAO team headed by Dr Mordecai Ezekiel carried out a pilot study in India which showed how extra food supplies could be used to promote economic development. In October 1960 the General Assembly of the United Nations expressed an interest in the possibilities of giving surplus food to food-deficient peoples, and in 1961 FAO produced a further report on the subject. On the initiative of the United States, it was agreed to set up an experimental, three-year World Food Programme, which would provide food for relief and for social and economic development. The fund amounts to approximately $90 million, mostly in the form of agricultural commodities but including some cash; the United States is by far the biggest contributor. This is small in relation to the enormous U.S. programme under P.L. 480,

[1] FAO, *State of Food and Agriculture*, 1959, p. 51.

[2] P. V. Sukhatme, 'The world's hunger and future needs in food supplies', *Journal of the Royal Statistical Society*, series A, vol. 124, part 4, 1961.

[3] 'Agricultural Commodities – Projections for 1970', *FAO Commodity Review*, 1962, special supplement.

currently running at around $1·5 billion annually, but the World
Food Programme is nevertheless an interesting experiment. It
entered into force on January 1st, 1963.

International commodity agreements

Through the operation of international agreements for a few
commodities, attempts have been made to restore stability to
international markets. The first post-war International Wheat
Agreement entered into force in August 1949, when supplies
were still short and prices high. Each exporting country agreed
to supply a stated amount at a maximum price, and each importer undertook to buy a stated amount at a minimum price.
During the Korean War, market prices rose above the maximum,
and exporters were called upon to fulfil their obligations. The
second Agreement ran from 1953 to 1956. Britain, having benefited from the first Agreement, now withdrew in the expectation
of falling prices. This expectation was fulfilled: surpluses grew
and prices fell, but they were kept within the limits by the action
of Canada and the United States. Britain also stayed out of the
third Agreement, for 1956–9, on the grounds that it did not
contain provisions for the orderly disposal of surpluses. The
fourth Agreement, 1959–62, introduced slightly different arrangements: exporting countries agreed that, at prices within the
stated range, they would make wheat available to importing
countries in quantities sufficient to meet their needs, while importing countries committed themselves to purchasing a certain
proportion of their imports from the exporting countries which
were parties to the Agreement; if prices rose above the maximum,
importing countries could purchase from any source. This Agreement also included provisions for an annual review of the world
wheat situation and for discussion of national policies: this
apparently satisfied Britain, who rejoined. The fifth Agreement,
1962–5, is similar to its predecessor, except that the price range
is slightly higher.

The International Wheat Agreements have had no power
to curb the rising trend of production in exporting and importing
countries, and the recent arrangements for discussion of policies
seem unlikely to be effective unless backed by more specific
commitments. Wheat prices on the world market have been kept

reasonably stable not so much through the operation of the Agreement as by the policy of the major wheat exporters.

An International Sugar Agreement came into force in 1953. It provided for export quotas, which could be modified in order to keep prices within a given price range. As sugar production – especially in importing countries – continued to rise, there was a downward trend in market prices, together with wide price fluctuations, in face of which the export quota system proved inadequate. The Agreement was nevertheless renewed in 1959, but in 1961 it was impossible to draft a new Agreement because of the demand by Cuba (following its breach with the United States) for greatly increased quotas, and the Agreement lapsed.

Coffee too has been in excess supply and prices have fallen. After some agreements confined to Latin American exporters, the International Coffee Agreement was signed in 1959 by the majority of exporting countries; it provided for export quotas. A further Agreement negotiated in 1962 also provided for export quotas, but in addition various importing countries undertook to restrict their imports of coffee from countries that were not parties to the Agreement. This Agreement is due to enter into force when a sufficient number of countries have ratified it.

In 1953 the International Tin Agreement came into force; it was renewed in 1962. Though this is outside the field of agriculture, it is of interest as the only scheme so far to include a 'buffer stock', financed by producing countries. The Agreement also provides for controls on exports when necessary. It ran into serious trouble arising mainly from exports by the U.S.S.R., which is not a member: the buffer stock was forced to buy large quantities of tin in order to support the market, till in September 1958 its funds were exhausted.

The agreements introduced so far thus contain a number of different elements. The most common feature is export control, with the object of restricting supplies and raising prices. In principle, this may be criticized as a monopolistic device to exploit consumers: in practice the various schemes have been concerned rather with preventing an excessive fall in prices. A more immediate problem is that of allocating quotas, as the experience of the Sugar Agreement with Cuba has shown. Further, such schemes are liable to be disrupted by the action of non-member exporting countries: here the case of Russian tin exports is relevant. Export control schemes are therefore more effective if they can be combined with undertakings by importing countries not to allow excessive imports from non-members, as in the latest Coffee Agreement. This leads into the agreement based on a multilateral contract, of which the Wheat Agreement is the only example to date: here both exporting and importing countries give undertakings, each accepting a risk of loss in return for compensating safeguards. Such an arrangement is only possible where a balance of advantage can be drawn, as was demonstrated by the refusal of Britain to co-operate at a time when prices seemed certain to fall.

A buffer stock may in principle give added stability. However, it has some serious limitations. The most obvious is that it can be used only for commodities that are not too difficult to store: apart from grains and sugar, most foodstuffs can be stored, if at all, only by expensive refrigeration techniques. In principle a buffer fund or compensatory financing mechanism would avoid this difficulty: contributions might be paid into a fund in times of high prices, and subsidies paid out of it in periods of depression. Such schemes are common enough in a national context, but it is not easy to devise international arrangements of this kind. The problem of finding an equitable basis for financing is already serious enough in the case of a buffer stock, and governments may hesitate to contribute large sums unless they expect corresponding advantages in return. For this reason the Haberler Report suggested the creation of a number of national buffer stocks which would work together to stabilize the market. Various schemes have been studied by the United Nations Commission on International Commodity Trade, the International Monetary Fund and the Organization of American States, but so far without result.

A buffer stock can only be used to even out short-term fluctuations, buying at times of surplus and selling when supplies are short: it cannot cure a long-term imbalance. It is indeed difficult to forecast how long a situation of surplus is likely to last: if the authorities in charge of the fund purchase large quantities, only to find that the depression continues, they are liable to exhaust their funds and find themselves compelled to sell off their stocks, further upsetting the market.

Since any agreement presupposes a balance of interests, there can be no question of using it to force a country to change its policies. In some cases a country may be willing to place long-term political or economic interests before immediate commercial advantages; nevertheless, international commodity agreements cannot correct a basic disequilibrium, where this involves important sacrifices by some or all of the countries concerned. One possibility would be that of negotiating agreements covering several commodities together: countries may then be more willing to make concessions on one commodity in return for advantages for another. There would undoubtedly be serious difficulties in reaching such agreements, but if the formation of the European Economic Community is followed by joint action on the part of agricultural exporting countries, the bargaining process might be simplified.

Reorganization of world markets?

Experience with international commodity agreements is not encouraging. Nor is it particularly relevant to the current situation of world agricultural markets, where the problem is not just one of instability but rather that of basic disequilibrium in face of which stabilization agreements are ineffective. It has been seen above that the agricultural scene in the developed countries of the world is characterized by rapidly expanding production and falling prices, by increased self-sufficiency and import restrictions in importing countries, by growing surpluses and – in some cases – extensive export subsidies in exporting countries. The interests of exporting countries in maintaining their markets are directly opposed to the desire of importing countries to protect their producers.

In the context of the negotiations between Britain and the Six, the need to reorganize world markets was frequently stressed. To Britain it appeared as the means whereby the agricultural producers of the Commonwealth could be compensated for the disadvantages they were likely to be caused by Britain's accession to the EEC. To the Six, and to France in particular, it offered an opportunity of expanding agricultural exports without the need for costly subsidies.

Mention has been made above of the plan put forward in

GATT, in November 1961, by the French Minister of Finance, M. Baumgartner. The same proposal has been developed by the French Minister of Agriculture, M. Pisani, on a number of occasions.[1]

The Baumgartner-Pisani Plan is based on the assertion that world prices for agricultural products are artificially depressed, being well below the prices actually received by producers; export subsidies are held to be widespread. The remedy for this is to eliminate export subsidies and to raise world market prices, by international agreement, to a 'fair' level. The possibility of excess production is recognized, but it is thought that this can be solved through expanded programmes of food aid to under-developed countries.

Similar features are contained in the 'Farm and Food Plan' which the National Farmers' Union of England and Wales has put forward and for which it is seeking support through the International Federation of Agricultural Producers (IFAP). To relieve the pressure on the British market, the NFU advocates co-operation between the major food trading countries. This would take the form, firstly, of international commodity agreements, which would iron out short-term price fluctuations and would enable exporting countries to have reasonable access to markets within agreed price ranges. Secondly, national policy objectives would be harmonized in order to facilitate 'the maximum volume of trade consistent with maintaining a fair standard of living for farmers in all countries'. Thirdly, there would be a world food policy designed to utilize surplus production for the benefit of the underdeveloped countries: this was already advocated by the member organizations of the IFAP in the 'International Food and Farm Policy' which they adopted at their conference in New Delhi in 1959.

These schemes have the merit of concentrating attention on the elements which must enter into any attempt to reorganize world agricultural markets, and which no doubt will be the object of much discussion in the years to come. One of the major problems is that of the level of prices which would be justified. There is room for argument as to the extent to which world prices are in fact artificially depressed: many important exporting

[1] A fairly full statement appeared in the *Revue de Défense Nationale*, August–September 1962.

countries – Canada for wheat, Argentina for beef, New Zealand and Denmark for butter – can sell profitably at prices which appear very low indeed to most European producers. Indeed, the prices received by the latter are often still more artificial, since they are supported by a variety of measures and determined in the light of political and social considerations.

Agreements limited to the conditions of trade would be inadequate, and domestic agricultural policies must also come under closer scrutiny. With present trends towards oversupply of several commodities, some degree of control over production can hardly be avoided, and may even be made all the more necessary if world market prices are raised. However, the experience of the United States has shown the difficulty in devising and applying effective production controls; in countries where small-scale peasant agriculture predominates, the difficulties would be even greater.

The idea of using the productive capacity of agriculture in the developed countries to contribute to the needs of hungry people in other parts of the world has an obvious appeal. But food aid needs to be given on a regular planned basis. The amount of food which can be absorbed in an underdeveloped country, without adverse effects on the market, is limited, and the types of food which the developed countries can easily produce are not necessarily those which the underdeveloped countries can use. Food aid programmes therefore cannot simply provide a safety-valve for the surpluses of Western Europe and North America. Further, such programmes would not be acceptable to the receiving countries if the cost were to be deducted from overall financial aid, which is more useful to them.[1]

The fact remains that the problem of overproduction in the developed parts of the world cannot be considered in isolation from the much graver problem of hunger in much of Asia, Africa and Latin America. If surpluses are built up while people starve, this is because the hungry nations lack the purchasing power with which to satisfy their needs. Programmes of food aid are a crude and inadequate instrument with which to solve this problem, though they are perhaps the only immediate possibility. If the countries now underdeveloped can reach a significantly higher standard of living, through their own efforts, and

[1] Cf. OECD, *Food Aid – Its Role in Economic Development* (Paris, 1963).

with the assistance of the more advanced countries, then it is possible that they could meet their requirements of foodstuffs partly through increased domestic production but also partly through commercial imports, and thereby eliminate the problem of abundance as well as that of want.

Conclusions

Lessons of past experience

This account of developments in Western European agriculture over approximately the past hundred years demonstrates that the present problems of agriculture – low farm incomes, pressure on markets, burden of price support – are largely attributable to past failures to adapt in response to changed circumstances.

The significance of events in the late nineteenth century is now clear, though at the time it was not generally recognized. The opening-up of virgin lands in overseas countries, together with the spectacular improvement and cheapening in the means of transport, meant that the comparative advantage in products suited to extensive farming – grains above all – had shifted to the New World. The correct response for European countries was to concentrate on products for which nearness to the market was an important advantage: in particular, dairy products, meat, fruit and vegetables (these, moreover, were products for which, as a result of rising incomes, the trend of demand was favourable). If agriculture, even when adapted in this way, could no longer provide adequate incomes for the farming population, then the necessary course was to facilitate a shift of manpower from farming to the growing industrial sector.

In fact Denmark and the Netherlands were almost the only countries to take positive action in order to adapt their agriculture. They reaped an immediate benefit: their exports of livestock products conquered the markets of Britain and Germany, their farmers prospered, and agricultural progress made an important contribution to national economic growth. Great Britain did nothing, and the result was a forced adaptation: arable farming went into decline and the agricultural population, already small, fell still further. Though the extra labour thus made available probably contributed to industrial expansion, the process took place only with severe hardship for a large part of the farming community. The extent even of the long-term benefits for agriculture is open to doubt, for the need to economize compelled farmers to run down their capital equipment and lower their standards of cultivation.

France, Germany and Italy reacted defensively to the challenge of overseas competition, raising their tariffs on grains in particular and thereby maintaining or even expanding grain production. This protection was retained even after overseas competition had spent its force; in Germany the rates of duty were actually raised still higher by the Bülow tariff of 1902. It probably retarded the shift of manpower from agriculture to other sectors, and in the case of Germany set up an obstacle to industrial expansion by impeding the conclusion of commercial treaties. In all three countries, this action was taken mainly at the behest of the larger farmers and in their interests: support for grain prices gave little benefit to the livestock-producing peasantry, and may even have harmed them. Though tariffs were also imposed on livestock products, the effects were much less significant than in the case of grains. The maintenance of grain prices through tariffs prevented consumers in these countries from enjoying the benefits of the cheaper produce made available by overseas countries. Pre-occupation with tariff policy diverted attention from more constructive lines of action, and little was done to make agricultural production and marketing more efficient.

The crisis of the 1930s forced all Western European countries into protection, employing in addition to tariffs a variety of new and more effective devices. In most cases, their domestic markets were thereby insulated from outside pressures. But restrictive measures in one country harmed another, thereby prolonging the depression on the international market and perpetuating the need for protection. Behind these protective barriers, domestic agriculture was enabled to expand. This led in France to overproduction of wheat and wine, necessitating measures of intervention on the domestic market. In Nazi Germany, food production was deliberately encouraged regardless of cost; in Italy under Mussolini the same was true for wheat. In Britain, where markets were generally left open to imports from the Empire, subsidies granted at a high level encouraged a recovery in wheat cultivation and a great expansion of sugar-beet. In almost every case (Nazi Germany excepted) these measures were taken piecemeal; no consistent agricultural policy was developed and the structural problems of agriculture continued to be neglected.

Since the Second World War, the emphasis laid on price support, initially in order to raise output and more permanently as a means of maintaining farm incomes, has further stimulated uneconomic production. But farm incomes have failed to rise sufficiently, despite the high degree of support, and output of many commodities has reached the limit of what the market can absorb. Increasing attention is being given to various measures designed to raise farming efficiency, but the leeway which remains to be caught up is enormous. A large proportion – perhaps even the greater part – of the farms in France, Germany and other countries of the Continent are too small or too fragmented, or both, to be viable. Even in Britain, where the farm population is comparatively small and farms are relatively large, there are many holdings whose scale of enterprise is insufficient to give a decent living.

The acuteness of the problem today demonstrates the failure of both laissez-faire and protectionism in the past. Laissez-faire failed because of its mistaken belief that, if economic pressures were left to work themselves out, a new equilibrium would be created: but in agriculture a forced adaptation does not necessarily have good results – on the contrary, a long period of depressed prices is liable to cause the better farmers to leave while the others remain, and while the fixed equipment of the farms and the quality of the soil is allowed to deteriorate. Protectionism failed because it insulated agriculture from the economic forces which should have stimulated changes, and diverted attention from the need for more constructive measures.

An adaptation in agriculture of the scale required over the past hundred years could not take place automatically: it required positive action by governments and by the farmers themselves, and the example of Denmark showed what could be done. As a result of land reforms in the late eighteenth and early nineteenth century, and as a result of the measures taken during the Great Depression to promote livestock farming and to create an efficient co-operative system, the conditions for a prosperous agriculture, independent of support, were laid down. If in the 1930s, and again in recent years, even Denmark has been forced to assist her farmers in various ways, the cause lies not so much in any deficiencies of Danish agriculture as in the protectionist policies of other countries.

If we ask why in the majority of countries little or no constructive action was taken, a number of reasons can be given. Perhaps the first is that the need for adaptation was not always recognized. In the late nineteenth century, the increase in overseas competition was often not seen for what it was: a basic and irreversible transformation in the agricultural scene. Consequently, France and Germany resorted to protection partly in the hope that the crisis would pass; in Britain, inaction during at least the early stages of the depression was largely due to the belief that bad weather and other natural causes were the factors responsible. One reason why Denmark's reaction was so much more positive was that a sufficiently large body of opinion foresaw the increase in overseas competition in grains before it even began.

In times of crisis, moreover, the most obvious means of helping agriculture was to restrain the fall in agricultural prices – this was particularly so when other sectors were benefiting from tariff protection. Price supports of various kinds have also been used in periods when increased food production was required, whether to meet a shortage, to safeguard food supplies in the event of war or to relieve the balance of payments. These price supports have afterwards proved difficult to remove, even when they have served their immediate purpose. By maintaining or stimulating uneconomic production, they have perpetuated the need for their own existence. In cases where increased production has been a deliberate aim of policy, it has afterwards proved difficult to keep the expansion within suitable limits. The aim of raising output is by no means incompatible with measures to raise agricultural efficiency, but in practice the emphasis laid on price policy as the means of stimulating output has diverted attention from other types of action and has even concealed the need for reform.

In general, governments have found it easier to satisfy their farmers with short-term benefits than to embark on long-term programmes of structural reform. This feature is by no means peculiar to agriculture: policies which may give a long-term benefit and are in the interests of the nation as a whole have much less political appeal than those which offer an immediate advantage to the sector most concerned.[1]

Farmers themselves, through their organizations, have tended to concentrate their demands on immediate advantages, neglecting long-term action. The return to protection in France, Germany and Italy in the late nineteenth century was largely the work of organized pressure-groups, composed mainly of large farmers and landowners with a vested interest in grain prices. The influence of farm organizations has been built up in all countries during and since the 1930s: at the present time, the NFU in Britain, the FNSEA and the Chambres d'Agriculture in France, the Deutsches Bauernverband, the Union des Paysans Suisses and similar organizations in other countries are powerful bodies generally committed to maintaining and improving the standard of living of their members in what appears to them the most direct way – higher prices and increased outlets for their produce. The farm organizations are generally unwilling to envisage far-reaching changes in the structure of agriculture: a notable exception is the Centre National des Jeunes Agriculteurs in France.

There has often been resistance – not only from the farmers themselves – to a reduction in the number of farms and in the size of the farm population. Belief in the advantages of rural life is widespread: it may be expressed in sentimental terms – Jules Méline in France remains the outstanding example – or in a carefully elaborated theory, as with Adolf Wagner in Germany; it appeared in an extreme form in Nazi racial philosophy. The desire to preserve a large rural population has had an important influence on policy in France, Switzerland and Austria; it is present to some extent in almost every country. Yet it cannot be

---

[1] This point is well made by K. L. Robinson, 'Political obstacles tending to retard the increased economic welfare offered by technical change in agriculture', *Proceedings of the Ninth International Conference of Agricultural Economists* (London: O.U.P., 1956).

said to have been a decisive factor and it has had little effect on policy when more material interests were at stake It has been seen above that in France and Germany, when practically all other agricultural products were protected, wool was left open to the full blast of overseas competition, in deference to the interests of manufacturers; the result was a decimation of the sheep population in Western Europe. Yet the shepherd and his flock play an even more important role in our mythology than other members of the farming community.

Economists have often tended to neglect these political and social aspects. But in fact it is difficult to discuss problems of agricultural policy without giving non-economic considerations their due weight. Indeed, one of the lessons of past experience is the almost complete ineffectiveness of economic opinion where agriculture is concerned. Free trade arguments were not lacking in either France or Germany during the Great Depression, nor in Britain early in the 1930s: yet these arguments were quite powerless to stop the resort to protection. Possibly the economists in question would have exerted greater influence on policy if their proposals had been more realistic in political terms, had taken more account of the human problem in agriculture and had been directed primarily to constructive action.

The present crisis and the adaptation required

Past experience shows that the first requirement in dealing with a crisis is correct diagnosis. This is particularly important today, for the present crisis of agriculture in Western Europe is more complex than those of the past. It is essentially the problem of adaptation to an age of rapid technological and economic progress – a problem which concerns both incomes and production, for the growth of incomes in other sectors tends to leave agriculture behind, while technological improvements in agriculture itself tend to raise production faster than demand.

The income problem of agriculture is of course not new. Thus J. R. Bellerby observes: 'For many years before 1939 agriculturists in many countries received little more than half the incentive income obtained per man-equivalent in non-farm enterprises.' Similar results are obtained by Marc Latil.[1] What

[1] J. R. Bellerby, *Agriculture and Industry – Relative Income* (London: Macmillan,

is new is above all the extent of preoccupation with standards of living, both in the community as a whole and in the farm sector. Progress in other sectors provides farmers with a basis of comparison: they are no longer isolated from the urban world and are not willing to be left behind.

Bellerby stresses those elements which keep the 'supply price' of agricultural labour low. Farmers are prepared to put up with lower incomes because of 'occupational immobility', personal inertia, the attractions of farm life, the lower cost of living in rural areas and so on. This list of factors does not make clear an essential point: whether the 'supply price' is low because farmers like farming or because they cannot do anything else. Thus Anne Martin points out:

> Correct choice between the possible meanings is important, because it will affect our views both as to whether, and on what grounds, the situation should be changed, and as to the likely efficiency of the remedies proposed. If farmers freely choose less money and more fresh air and independence, it is not clear why we should feel obliged to change the situation on grounds of social justice: if, however, they find themselves in a position which they feel to be disadvantageous and are unable to change by their own efforts, they may well have a case for help.[1]

In fact it seems impossible to quantify these psychological factors, but it is clear that elements of choice and of inability to choose are both present. It follows that farm incomes may be somewhat below incomes in other sectors without this being a cause for concern, but that farmers need help to enable them to move into other occupations if they wish to do so.

Factors on the demand side are no less important in keeping agricultural incomes low. The basic cause is stated by Engel's Law, to the effect that expenditure on food forms a declining proportion of total expenditure as incomes rise.[2] What is true for

1956), pp. 223–4; and Marc Latil, *L'évolution du revenu agricole* (Paris: Colin, 1956).

    [1] Anne Martin, 'A comment on J. R. Bellerby's explanation of the low level of income in agriculture', *Farm Economist*, vol. IX, no. 6 (1959), p. 272.

    [2] Ernst Engel first stated his law in 1857, after studying family budgets in Saxony. See C. C. Zimmerman, 'Ernst Engel's law of expenditure for food', *Quarterly Journal of Economics*, November 1932.

an individual household is true for a nation as a whole: economic growth involves a relative decline of agriculture in the national income. This historical process has been abundantly documented by Colin Clark and E. M. Ojala.[1] It seems likely that the past trend is reinforced at the present time, since it is primarily when a high level of food consumption has been reached that further increases in income bring only small increases in expenditure on food – and even lead to decreased expenditure on some items.[2]

Various factors may counteract this tendency to some extent. If agricultural prices are raised in relation to other prices, for example by restrictive marketing schemes, the farmer may benefit at the expense of the consumer; however, such price increases tend to discourage consumption and beyond a certain point will lead to a fall in total consumer expenditure. The farmer may also gain a larger share of the consumer's expenditure if distribution margins can be reduced: there is certainly scope for improved marketing in many cases. Costs of production in agriculture per unit of output may be reduced; this too is an important line of action. Also, agricultural income within a given country may be raised by an increase in the proportion of food requirements met by domestic production as opposed to imports, or by increased net agricultural exports; but it is obvious that all countries cannot simultaneously pursue this policy.

In the long run these factors are not sufficient to offset the declining share of agriculture in the national income. Consequently, if incomes per head in agriculture are to rise at least as fast as incomes in general, the part of the population living from agriculture must also decline. In the more developed countries today, with a fairly rapid growth of income per head in the economy as a whole and a comparatively slow increase in demand

[1] C. Clark, *The Conditions of Economic Progress* (London: Macmillan, 3rd ed., 1957); and E. M. Ojala, *Agriculture and Economic Progress* (London: O.U.P., 1952).

[2] Expenditure elasticities for food (measuring the percentage change in food expenditure resulting from a 1 per cent rise in total income) are currently estimated for countries of North-Western Europe at around 0·2–0·4, in terms of value at the farm gate. The highest elasticities are found for meat, eggs, fruit and vegetables, while negative elasticities are usual for bread grains and potatoes. The elasticities, moreover, are declining as incomes rise. See 'Agricultural Commodities – Projections for 1970', *FAO Commodity Review*, 1962, special supplement.

for food, it is likely that the farm population will have to fall in absolute as well as in relative terms.[1]

In practice, the move out of agriculture is unlikely to take place fast enough. Latil observes that a persistent disequilibrium results from the fact that the constant relative decline of agriculture requires an equally constant adaptation:

> If a new adaptation is required before the first has even exhausted its effects, the tendency is for the temporary disparity, which should have caused the initial disequilibrium to be corrected, to be perpetuated. Thus in a sector which has constantly to give up its manpower, rates of remuneration substantially below those of other sectors will prevail as a matter of course.[2]

The declining share of agriculture in the national income and the insufficient mobility of labour out of agriculture thus not only explain why, in a dynamic economy, agricultural incomes tend to be relatively low: they also indicate that some gap between farm and non-farm incomes is to be expected and that the aim of

[1] An illustration may help to make the relationships clear. The following example, though highly simplified, is not too unrepresentative of most North-Western European countries today. Suppose national income is 400 million currency units and the total income of agriculture 50 million units; total population 40 million persons and agricultural population 10 million. Income per head in the whole economy is then 10 units, income per head in agriculture is half this, 5 units. Suppose then that over a period of some ten years there is a 50 per cent increase in national income, which (owing to a comparatively slow rise in demand for agricultural produce) is associated with only a 20 per cent rise in agricultural income; suppose too that total population rises 10 per cent. Income per head in the whole economy is now $\frac{600}{44} = 13 \cdot 6$ units. For incomes per head in agriculture to rise to half of this, i.e. $6 \cdot 8$ units, then – other things being equal – the agricultural population must fall to $\frac{60}{6 \cdot 8} = 8 \cdot 8$ million – a decline of 12 per cent. An absolute decline in the agricultural population could be avoided, while maintaining the same income differential, only if the general rate of income growth per head were lower or the associated rise in total agricultural income higher than in fact is likely to be the case. To close the income gap, the agricultural population would of course have to fall still faster; to reach 'parity', in the present example, it would have to be reduced to $4 \cdot 4$ millions, i.e. by more than half.

[2] Op. cit., p. 181. A similar point is made by Gavin McCrone, *The Economics of Subsidising Agriculture* (London: Allen & Unwin, 1962), p. 16.

'parity', unless carefully defined, is a will-o'-the-wisp. This however does not justify a gap of the order which generally exists today, and which would be still bigger in the absence of the extensive measures of support granted to farmers. It is clear that the mobility of the farm population is inadequate, and that the appropriate policy today is to facilitate the move out of agriculture, besides taking any other steps which may raise the productivity of agricultural manpower.

We have to face the question of whether an adaptation involving as a major feature an accelerated move out of agriculture is socially desirable. Reference has already been made to the continuing belief in the virtues of rural life, and the force of this feeling must be recognized. Even an economist may well regret the trend towards an increasingly industrialized economy and feel that the contemporary emphasis on material progress is misplaced. But the fact today is that farmers themselves, rightly or wrongly, are caught up in the race for higher standards of living, and that they cannot all achieve this aim by remaining in agriculture. Keeping a large agricultural population by means of an expensive and permanent subsidy from the rest of the community is hardly the way to preserve the sense of independence which is regarded as one of the assets of the farmer. The answer to this problem, therefore, is to be found not in further retarding the inevitable shift from agriculture to other sectors, but in a forward-looking policy which would ensure that the new industrial society is more desirable than the old: the association with grimy factories and congested cities must be finally broken.

The question also arises whether an accelerated fall in the agricultural population will help to solve the other aspect of the present crisis – the problem of overproduction. Indeed, a small number of large, efficient, highly-mechanized farms may well be able to produce more than a large number of small, inefficient ones: the solution to the income problem may therefore aggravate the production problem. This difficulty has to be recognized, but it should not be exaggerated. The commodities in excess supply in Western Europe are to a large extent the typical products of the small farm – milk, pigs and eggs – and the difficulty in dealing with this problem lies precisely in the consequences which price reductions or output limitations would have on the incomes, already low, of these small producers. On the other hand, farms with a larger scale of operations have greater flexibility in both the volume and the pattern of production: they can operate in a manner more like that of industrial enterprises, raising their net income by reducing costs as well as by raising output, and can more easily switch from one line of production to another. The trend to larger farms would in particular facilitate the desirable shift from dairy cows to beef cattle.

It should also be remembered that an important aspect of the adaptation currently required may be a shift from full-time to part-time farming: holdings now giving an inadequate income on a full-time basis could in many cases be run profitably if the farmer had another occupation. Such a development would normally be associated with a fall in output.

Another objection (which is the reverse of the one just stated) is that there is no justification for taking measures likely to reduce production at a time when there are great unsatisfied needs for food in much of the world. This too is a point which should not be overlooked. However, it has been observed in Chapter 18 that there are practical difficulties in transferring foodstuffs produced in Western Europe to underdeveloped regions – difficulties connected both with the nature of the produce and the arrangements necessary to enable the receiving countries to absorb the extra food supplies without adverse effects. At present, the scope for a massive increase in food aid programmes hardly exists; but if the opportunity should arise, there is no doubt that food production in Western Europe could be increased even if the farm population was much smaller than it is now. This too is the reply to those who fear that, with rising demand by the countries now underdeveloped, the cost of importing food from overseas will rise, making it more economic to expand production in Western Europe.

If the need for an adaptation involving an accelerated transfer of manpower to other sectors is admitted, the question is how this can be brought about. The first requirement is that the need for adjustment should no longer be masked by high price supports: as Honor Croome aptly points out, if prices are to stimulate desirable changes, they cannot at the same time be a means of creating economic security for those who do not want to change.[1] Similarly Bellerby observes:

---

[1] Honor Croome, 'Progress without tears', *Lloyds Bank Review*, July 1959.

The fixing of prices affording farmers a return greater than their supply price is liable to be self-defeating if applied independently. It strengthens the tendency to overcrowding and overproduction in agriculture and perpetuates the fundamental causes of agricultural poverty, unless these are countered by other means.[1]

This consideration applies not only to price measures within each country, but also to measures currently envisaged for substantially raising prices on world markets by international agreement: the fact that world prices now frequently lie below economic levels should not be an excuse for going to the opposite extreme. International agreements for this purpose do not yet seem imminent: nevertheless, if protection and price support in the national context have in the past been the opium discouraging adaptation, there is some risk that reliance on action to raise world prices, and on the utilization of surpluses in underdeveloped countries, may be the opium of the period to come.

At the same time, it is obvious that adaptation cannot simply be forced on farmers by removing price supports. Developments which were tolerated in Britain in the nineteenth century are quite inconsistent with present-day concepts of social justice. Moreover, experience in Britain shows that a forced adaptation does not necessarily give good results even in the long run.

The need is therefore for a constructive policy which takes account of the human problems facing those who, by no fault of their own, find themselves in a sector undergoing a relative decline. It will be necessary to continue providing financial assistance for several years to come, for the necessary changes cannot take place quickly. But assistance should be shifted away from price support and towards measures designed to facilitate the adaptation. The possibilities are numerous, and already several countries have devised schemes of various kinds, which have been referred to in Chapter 11. Within agriculture itself, action may be taken to promote what the Swedes call 'internal rationalization': improvements to existing farms in order to raise their efficiency. Such programmes need to concentrate on farms at present suffering from particularly low incomes; this is the object of the British Small Farmer Scheme. They need also to put more emphasis on

[1] Op. cit., p. 308.

ways to raise incomes by reducing costs rather than by increasing output, and where possible to promote a shift to part-time farming. Also within the agricultural sector, 'external rationalization' is essential in countries where agriculture suffers from an excess of small, fragmented holdings: holdings must be amalgamated and regrouped, and further fragmentation must be prevented, by a combination of legislative action and field programmes supported by institutional arrangements such as the Dutch Foundation for Land Administration, the Swedish County Agricultural Boards and the French SAFER. In several countries, in particular France and Italy, certain regions call for and are already receiving special attention.

The shift from agriculture into other occupations needs to be promoted by efforts to raise the general educational level in the rural population: such efforts are already under way in all countries. Those who wish to move also need to be helped by financial and other assistance to learn a new trade and to install themselves: Sweden, France and the Netherlands have programmes of this kind. Elderly farmers may be encouraged to give up all or part of their farm by additional pension schemes or special payments, such as exist in Germany, France and the Netherlands.

An adjustment of the size required cannot be tackled only from the agricultural end. The problem of agriculture needs to be taken into account in general economic planning: industrial and urban development should make provision for the absorption of labour from agriculture. Above all, the decentralization of industry, which is made possible by modern communications, transport facilities and sources of energy, and which would make life more agreeable to all concerned, would make a vital contribution to the problem of agriculture by providing increased opportunities for part-time work and by easing the movement from the farm to the factory.

Bibliography

Works of particular importance in the present context are marked with an asterisk. Names of publishers are indicated only for the more recent works.

General

A. THEORETICAL: AGRICULTURAL INCOMES AND MANPOWER

*Bellerby, J. R. *Agriculture and Industry: Relative Income*. London: Macmillan, 1956.

Clark, C. *The Conditions of Economic Progress*. London: Macmillan, 3rd ed., 1957.

Croome, Honor. 'Progress without tears', *Lloyds Bank Review* (July, 1959).

International Labour Office. *Why Labour leaves the Land*. Geneva, 1960.

*Latil, M. *L'évolution du revenu agricole*. Paris: Colin, 1956.

Martin, Anne. 'A comment on J. R. Bellerby's explanation of the level of income in agriculture', *Farm Economist*, Vol. IX, No. 6 (1959).

Ojala, E. M. *Agriculture and Economic Progress*. London: O.U.P., 1952.

Robinson, K. L. *Political obstacles tending to retard the increased economic welfare offered by technical change in agriculture* ('Proceedings of the Ninth International Conference of Agricultural Economists'). London: O.U.P., 1956.

Zimmerman, C. C. 'Ernst Engel's law of expenditure for food', *Quarterly Journal of Economics* (November, 1932).

B. DESCRIPTIVE
Overall
Ashworth, W. *A Short History of the International Economy, 1850–1950*. London, New York, Toronto: Longmans, 1952.
Birnie, A. *An Economic History of Europe, 1760–1939*. London: Methuen, 1961.
Clough, S. B., and Cole, C. W. *Economic History of Europe*. Boston: Heath, 1952.
Malenbaum, W. 'The World Wheat Economy', *Harvard Economic Studies*, vol. XCII, Cambridge, Mass., 1953.
Warriner, Doreen. *Economics of Peasant Farming*. London: O.U.P., 1939.
Yates, P. Lamartine. *Forty Years of Foreign Trade*. London: Allen & Unwin, 1959.

To 1914: The Great Depression
Ashley, P. *Modern Tariff History*. 3rd ed., London, 1920.
Board of Trade (U.K.). British and Foreign Trade and Industry (Cd. 1761, 1903, and Cd. 4954, 1909).
―――― Cost of Living in Foreign Towns (Cd. 4032, 1908; Cd. 4512, 1909; and Cd. 5065, 1910).
Coppock, D. 'The causes of the Great Depression, 1873–96', *Manchester School of Economic and Social Studies* (September, 1961).
Crawford, R. F. 'An inquiry into wheat prices and wheat supply', *Journal of the Royal Statistical Society* (March, 1895).
Farnsworth, Helen. *The decline and recovery of wheat prices in the 'nineties* ('Wheat Studies of the Food Research Institute'). Stanford University, June–July, 1934.
Földes, B. 'Die Getreidepreise im 19. Jahrhundert', *Jahrbücher für Nationalökonomie und Statistik* (Juni, 1905).
Grunzel, J. *Economic Protectionism*. Oxford, 1916.
Kindleberger, C. P. 'Group behavior and international trade', *Journal of Political Economy* (February, 1951).
Poinsard, L. *Libre échange et protection*. Paris, 1893.

1914–1939: The crisis of the 1930s
Bacon, L. B. and Schloemer, F. C. *World Trade in Agricultural Products*. Rome: International Institute of Agriculture, 1940.
Berkelbach, Ann, and Hutton, D. G. *The Pinch of Plenty*. London, 1932.

Delle Donne, O. *European Tariff Policies since the World War*. New York, 1928.

Dietze, C. von. *Preispolitik in der Weltagrarkrise*. Berlin: Weidmannsche Buchhandlung, 1936.

Food Research Institute, Stanford University. 'Economic nationalism in Europe as applied to wheat', *Wheat Studies* (February, 1932).

Gordon, Margaret S. *Barriers to World Trade*. New York: Macmillan, 1941.

Heuser, H. *Control of International Trade*. London: Routledge, 1939.

Liepmann, H. *Tariff Levels and the Economic Unity of Europe, 1913–1931*. London: Allen & Unwin, 1938.

Panaitesco, P. N. *Les contingentements dans les relations commerciales avec les pays agricoles*. Paris, 1935.

Royal Institute of International Affairs. *World Agriculture*. London, 1932.

U.S. Senate. World trade barriers in relation to American agriculture (73rd Congress, 1st Session, Senate Document No. 70, 1933).

Yates, P. Lamartine. *Food Production in Western Europe*. London: Longmans, 1940.

International action, 1918–1939

Guillain, R. *Les problèmes douaniers internationaux et la Société des Nations*. Paris: Sirey, 1930.

Houillier, F. *L'organisation internationale de l'agriculture*. Paris: Librairie technique et économique, 1935.

International Institute of Agriculture. *Agricultural problems in their international aspect* (Documentation for the International Economic Conference, Geneva, May 1927).

League of Nations. International Economic Conference: report and resolutions (Geneva, 1927).

—— (Economic Committee). *The Agricultural Crisis*. Geneva, 1931.

—— —— Considerations on the present evolution of agricultural protectionism. Geneva, 1935.

—— *Commercial Policy in the Interwar Period*. Geneva, 1942.

Vitta, C. *La coopération internationale en matière d'agriculture*. Académie de Droit International, Recueil des Cours, Tome 56. Paris: Sirey, 1936.

Since 1945
Economic Commission for Europe. *European Agriculture, a Statement of Problems*. Geneva, 1954.
——— *Economic Survey of Europe in 1960* (chapter on problems of agricultural development). Geneva, 1961.
Food and Agriculture Organization. 'The State of Food and Agriculture.' Rome, annual.
——— *Agricultural commodities and the European Common Market* ('Commodity Series Bulletin,' No. 29, 1957).
——— 'Plans for the European Common Market and their possible repercussions on exporters of agricultural commodities', *Monthly Bulletin* (April, 1958).
Forschungsgesellschaft für Agrarpolitik und Agrarsoziologie. 'Agrarstrukturpolitik im Rahmen regionaler Wirtschaftspolitik in westeuropäischen Ländern', *Berichte über Landwirtschaft*, 175. Sonderheft, 1962.
General Agreement on Tariffs and Trade. *The possible impact of the European Economic Community, in particular the Common Market, upon world trade* ('Trade Intelligence Paper', No. 8, Geneva, December 1957).
*——— *Trends in International Trade* (the 'Haberler Report'). Geneva, 1958.
——— Reports of Committee II (various dates).
International Federation of Agricultural Producers. Conference reports (various dates).
Kirk, J. H. *Agricultural support measures* ('Proceedings of the Tenth International Conference of Agricultural Economists'). London: O.U.P., 1960.
*Organisation for European Economic Cooperation. *Agricultural Policies in Europe and North America* (five reports, from 1956 to 1961). Paris.
Wheeler, L. A. 'The new agricultural protectionism and its effect on trade policy', *Journal of Farm Economics* (November, 1960).
*Yates, P. Lamartine. *Food, Land and Manpower in Western Europe*. London: Macmillan, 1960.

European Integration
General
Baade, F. *Brot für ganz Europa*. Hamburg und Berlin: Parey, 1952.

Forschungsinstitut der Deutschen Gesellschaft für Auswärtige Politik. *Die Europäische Zusammenarbeit auf dem Gebiet der Landwirtschaft.* Frankfurt, 1957.

*Robinson, A. D. *Dutch Organised Agriculture in International Politics, 1945–1960.* The Hague: Nijhoff, 1961.

BLEU and Benelux

Arnim, V. von. *Die Agrarprobleme Belgiens unter besonderer Berücksichtigung der Probleme, die sich aus der Benelux-Union ergeben* ('Gegenwartsprobleme der Agrarökonomie'). Hamburg: Hoffmann & Campe, 1958.

Conix, A. 'L'agriculture belge et le protocole de Luxembourg', *Études économiques,* Mons (décembre, 1950).

Institut National de la Statistique et des Études Économiques. *Le Benelux.* Paris, 1953.

Meade, J. E. *The Belgium-Luxembourg Economic Union, 1921–1939* ('Essays in International Finance', No. 25). Princeton, 1956.

——— 'Benelux: the formation of the common customs', *Economica* (August, 1956).

——— *Negotiations for Benelux, 1943–1956* ('Princeton Studies in International Finance', No. 6). Princeton, 1957.

Secrétariat Général de l'Union Douanière. *Benelux* (Bulletin trimestriel). (In particular Annex to No. 4 of March 1958, providing text of the Treaty of Economic Union.)

Vermeren, R. 'Dix ans d'application des protocoles agricoles Benelux, 1947–1957', *Revue de l'Agriculture,* Bruxelles (juin 1959, octobre-novembre 1959 et février 1960).

Green Pool

Auswärtiges Amt (Germany). Gutachten zu Fragen einer europäischen Agrargemeinschaft (1953).

Chambres d'Agriculture. 'L'organisation européenne des marchés agricoles' (Bulletin du 15 mars 1953). Paris.

Council of Europe. Reports of the Consultative Assembly, Second Session (August 1950), Third Session (November-December 1951) and Fourth Session (May 1952).

——— Documents of the Special Committee on Agriculture (1951).

European Conference on the Organisation of Agricultural Markets. Documents (1952–1954).

Fédération Nationale des Syndicats d'Exploitants Agricoles. *La réalisation d'une Communauté Européenne de l'Agriculture.* Paris, 1953.

Fromont, P. 'Les équivoques du pool vert et les projets d'expansion agricole européenne', *Revue économique* (septembre, 1953).

Krumhoff, J. *Gemeinsame Wege der Europäischen Agrarwirtschaft.* Institut für Weltwirtschaft an der Universität Kiel, 1957.

Seraphim, H.-J. and others. *Probleme einer europäischen Agrarintegration.* München: Oldenbourg, probably 1952.

European Economic Community[1]

Comité Intergouvernemental créé par la Conférence de Messine. Rapport des Chefs de Délégation aux Ministres des Affaires Etrangères (the 'Spaak Report') (21 avril, 1956). Brussels.

European Economic Community. Various documents, including:

Bulletin (monthly) (for general account of current activities);

Journal officiel (for texts of Council decisions, etc.);

General reports by the Commission (annual);

Documents of the Commission on Agriculture of the Parliamentary Assembly;

Documents of the Stresa Conference;

**Propositions concernant l'élaboration et la mise en oeuvre de politique agricole commune* (Commission, 30 juin 1960).

Houdet, R. E. 'Stresa, ou l'évolution de l'agriculture dans le Marché Commun', *Revue du Marché Commun* (juillet–août, 1958).

United Kingdom

General

*Ernle, Lord (formerly R. E. Prothero). *English Farming, Past and Present.* 6th edition, with introduction to Part II by O. R. McGregor. London: Heinemann, 1962.

Orwin, C. S. *A History of English Farming.* London: Nelson, 1949.

Corn Laws

Clark, G. K. 'The repeal of the Corn Laws and the politics of the forties', *Economic History Review* (1951, No. 1).

Fay, C. R. *The Corn Laws and Social England.* Cambridge, 1932.

---

[1] Works concerning EEC are also listed on p. 381 and under individual countries.

Mongredien, A. *History of the Free-Trade Movement in England.* London, 1880.

Nicholson, J. S. *The History of the English Corn Laws.* London, 1904.

Woodward, E. L. *The Age of Reform, 1815–1870* ('Oxford History of England'). Oxford, 1938.

1846–1914: The Great Depression

Armitage-Smith, G. *The Free-Trade Movement and its Results.* London, 2nd ed., 1903.

Ashworth, W. *An Economic History of England, 1870–1939.* London: Methuen, 1960.

Caird, Sir James. *The Landed Interest and the Supply of Food.* London, 4th ed., 1880.

Clapham, J. H. *An Economic History of Modern Britain*, vols. II and III. C.U.P., 1932.

Ensor, R. C. K. *England, 1870–1914* ('Oxford History of England'). Oxford, 1936.

*Fletcher, T. W. 'The Great Depression of English Agriculture, 1873–1896', *Economic History Review* (April, 1961).

*Fuchs, C. J. *The Trade Policy of Great Britain and her Colonies since 1860.* London, 1905. (First published in German, Leipzig, 1893.)

Green, J. L. *Agriculture and Tariff Reform.* London, 2nd ed., 1911.

Leadam, J. S. *What Protection does for the Farmer and Labourer.* London: Cobden Club, 3rd ed., 1887.

Matthews, A. H. H. *Fifty Years of Agricultural Politics, being the History of the Central Chamber of Agriculture, 1865–1915.* London, 1915.

Rea, R. Paper submitted to International Free Trade Congress, August 1908 ('Report of the Proceedings'). London, 1908.

Robertson, J. M. *The Political Economy of Free Trade.* London, 1928.

*Royal Commission on Agriculture (appointed 1879). Reports of 1881 (C. 2778), and 1882 (C. 3309).

*Royal Commission on Agriculture (appointed 1893). Reports of 1896 (C. 7981) and 1897 (C. 8540).

Sheldon, J. P. *The Future of British Agriculture.* London, 1893.

Stearns, R. P. 'Agricultural Adaptation in England, 1875–1900', *Agricultural History* (April and June, 1932).

Tariff Commission. Reports of the Agricultural Committee. London, 1906 and 1914.

Tremayne, H. *Protection and the Farmer.* London, 1903.

1914–1939 : The crisis of the 1930s

Addison, Lord. *A Policy for British Agriculture*. London: Left Book Club, 1939.

Astor, Viscount, and Murray, K. A. H. *The Planning of Agriculture*. London: Milford, 1933.

—— and Rowntree, B. S. *The Agricultural Dilemma*. London: King, 1935.

*—— —— *British Agriculture – The Principles of Future Policy*. London: Longmans, 1938.

Beaverbrook, Lord. *The Farmers' Crusade: How Empire Free Trade will help British Agriculture*. London, undated but probably about 1930.

Benham, F. *Great Britain under Protection*. New York: Macmillan, 1941.

Beveridge, Sir William. *British Food Control*. London, 1928.

—— and others. *Tariffs: The Case Examined*. London, 2nd ed., 1932.

Edminster, L. R. 'Agriculture's Stake in the British Agreement and Trade Agreements Program', *International Conciliation* (February, 1939).

Fordham, M. *Britain's Trade and Agriculture*. London, 1932.

Hall, A. D. *Agriculture after the War*. London, 1917.

Harkness, D. A. E. *War and British Agriculture*. London: King & Staples, 1941.

Hobson, J. A. *The New Protectionism*. London, 1916.

Jeffcock, W. P. *Agricultural Politics 1915–1935, being a History of the Central Chamber of Agriculture during that Period*. Ipswich, 1937.

McGuire, E. B. *The British Tariff System*. London: Methuen, 1939.

Middleton, T. H. *Food Production in War*. Oxford 1923.

Murray, K. A. H. and Cohen, Ruth. *The Planning of Britain's Food Imports*. Oxford: Agricultural Economics Research Institute, 1934 and supplements.

National Institute of Economic and Social Research. *Trade Regulations and Commercial Policy of the United Kingdom*. C.U.P., 1943.

Plummer, A. 'The British Wheat Act, 1932', *Quarterly Journal of Economics* (November, 1932).

Richardson, J. H. *British Economic Foreign Policy*. London, 1936.

Robbins, L. C. 'L'agriculture dirigée' (dans *L'Economie dirigée: publication à part de la Revue d'Economie Politique*). Paris, 1935.

13

Royal Commission on Agriculture. Interim Report (Cmd. 473, 1919).

Venn, J. A. *The Foundations of Agricultural Economics, together with an Economic History of British Agriculture during and after the Great War*. Cambridge, 1933.

The Second World War and after

Allen, G. 'The National Farmers' Union as a pressure group', *Contemporary Review* (May and June, 1959).

Blagburn, C. H. 'Import-replacement by British agriculture', *Economic Journal* (March, 1950).

Brembridge, P. and Briggs, E. *Agriculture and Politics – Party Records and Policies*. London: Conservative Central Office, 3rd ed., 1955.

Hallett, G. 'The economic position of British agriculture', *Economic Journal* (September, 1959).

Hammond, R. J. *Food and Agriculture in Britain, 1939–45: Aspects of Wartime Control*. Stanford, California, 1954.

Imperial Chemical Industries Ltd. *Agriculture in the British Economy* (Proceedings of Conference held in November 1956, published by I.C.I. in March 1957): papers by E. A. G. Robinson, E. F. Nash, J. R. Raeburn, R. C. Tress and others.

Kirk, J. H. 'Some objectives of agricultural support policies', *Journal of Agricultural Economics* (December, 1958).

McCrone, G. 'The relevance of the theory of tariffs to agricultural protection', *Journal of Agricultural Economics* (June, 1958).

———— The Economics of Subsidising Agriculture. London: Allen & Unwin, 1962.

Menzies-Kitchin. *The Future of British Farming*. London: Pilot Press, 1945.

Murray, K. A. H. *Agriculture* ('History of the Second World War, U.K., Civil Series') London: H.M.S.O., 1955.

Nash, E. F. 'The competitive position of British agriculture', *Journal of Agricultural Economics* (June, 1955).

———— and Attwood, E. A. *The Agricultural Policies of Britain and Denmark: A Study in Reciprocal Trade*. London: Land Books, 1961.

Pollitt, G. P. *Can Britain Feed Herself?* London, 1942.

Raeburn, J. R. 'Agricultural Production and Marketing' (in *The Structure of British Industry*, ed. D. Burn). C.U.P., 1958.

*Robinson, E. A. G. Articles in *Three Banks Review* of March 1953, March 1954, June 1958 and December 1958.
*—— and Marris, R. 'The use of home resources to save imports', *Economic Journal* (March, 1950).
Self, P. and Storing, H. J. *The State and the Farmer*. London: Allen & Unwin, 1962.
Whetham, Edith. *The Economic Background to Agricultural Policy*. C.U.P., 1960.
Williams, H. T. (ed.). *Principles for British Agricultural Policy*. London: O.U.P., 1960.
Winegarten, A. 'Some reflections on the basis of international competition for the British market', *Journal of Agricultural Economics* (December, 1960).

Britain and Europe
Economist Intelligence Unit. *Britain and Europe*. London, 1957.
—— *The Commonwealth and Europe*. London, 1960.
Hallett, G. 'British Agriculture and Europe', supplement to spring issue of *Crossbow*, 1961.
Healey, D. T. *British Agriculture and the Common Market*. London: Britain in Europe, 1962.
National Farmers' Union. 'Agriculture in the Community', *Information Service*, 1961, No. 2.
—— *A Farm and Food Plan*. August, 1962.
Political and Economic Planning. Various 'Occasional Papers' on *Britain and the European Market*, from 1958.
—— (M. A. Tracy). *Commonwealth Preference in the United Kingdom*. London: Allen & Unwin, 1960.
Tracy, M. A. 'Agriculture and a European Economic Union', *Westminster Bank Review* (February, 1961).

France
General
*Augé-Laribé, M. *La politique agricole de la France de 1880 à 1940*. Paris: P.U.F., 1950.
Haight, F. A. *A History of French Commercial Policies*. New York: Macmillan, 1941.
Nogaro, B. et Moye, M. *Le régime douanier de la France*. Paris, 1931.

To 1914: The Great Depression

Amé, G. *Le libre-échange en Angleterre et en France* (Conférence faite à la Gare Saint-Jean, à Bordeaux). Paris, 1868.

Amé, L. *Étude sur les tarifs de douanes et sur les traités de commerce.* Paris, 1876.

Arnauné, A. *Le commerce extérieur et les tarifs de douane.* Paris, 1911.

Augier, C. et Marvaud, A. *La politique douanière de la France dans ses rapports avec celle des autres États.* Paris, 1911.

Beaurieux, N. *Les prix du blé en France au XIXe siècle.* Paris, 1909.

Châle, J. *Transformation du problème douanier, relativement au blé.* Paris, 1901.

*Clapham, J. H. *The Economic Development of France and Germany, 1815–1914.* C.U.P., 4th ed., 1945.

Dijol, M. *Situation économique de la France sous le régime protectionniste de 1892.* Paris, 1911.

Dunham, A. L. *The Anglo-French Treaty of Commerce of 1860.* Michigan, 1930.

*Golob, E. O. *The Méline Tariff: French Agriculture and Nationalist Economic Policy.* New York: Columbia U.P., 1944.

Guyot, Y. 'La cherté et le protectionnisme', *Journal des Économistes* (octobre, 1911).

Imbart de la Tour, J. *La crise agricole en France et à l'étranger.* Nevers, 1901.

LaChapelle, G. *Le ministère Méline.* Paris, 1928.

*Méline, J. *Le retour à la terre et la surproduction industrielle.* Paris, 6e éd., 1912.

*Meredith, H. O. *Protection in France.* London, 1904.

Paturel, G. 'Le protectionnisme et le coût de la vie', *Journal des Économistes* (juin, 1911).

Risler, E. 'La crise agricole en France et en Angleterre', *Revue des Deux Mondes* (1er février, 1885).

Ronce, P. *La crise agricole.* Paris, 1900.

Rosier, C. *La France Agricole.* Paris: Alsatia, 1943.

Théry, E. *Les progrès économiques de la France: Bilan du régime douanier de 1892.* Paris, 1908.

1914–1939: The crisis of the 1930s

Augé-Laribé, M. 'Nouveaux fondements du protectionnisme agricole', *Revue d'économie politique* (mars-avril, 1933).

Augé-Laribé and Pinot, P. *Agriculture and Food Supply in France during the War.* Yale, 1927.

Braibant, M. *L'agriculture française – son tragique déclin, son avenir.* Paris, 1936.

Confédération Nationale des Associations Agricoles. *La nouvelle loi douanière va-t-elle consacrer la déchéance de notre agriculture?* Paris, 1927.

Conseil National Economique. *Les échanges internationaux et la politique douanière française au cours de la crise économique.* Paris, 1932.

―――― *La politique agricole de la France.* Paris, 1935.

―――― *La protection et les encouragements à donner par les pouvoirs publics aux diverses branches de l'économie nationale.* Paris, 1936.

―――― *La politique agricole destinée à réduire le déficit de la balance commerciale et à coordonner les productions métropolitaines et coloniales.* Melun, 1939.

Fouchet, J. *La politique commerciale de la France depuis 1930.* Paris, 1938.

Hallé, P. and others. *Conférences sur la crise agricole.* Paris: Institut National Agronomique, 1930–1.

Hauser, H. 'La concurrence internationale et le problème de l'économie dirigée', *Revue économique internationale* (avril, 1937).

Hunter, N. *Peasantry and Crisis in France.* London, 1938.

*Lautman, J. *Les aspects nouveaux du protectionnisme.* Paris, 1933.

Long, O. *Le contingentement en France.* Paris, 1938.

Maspétiol, R. 'L'Office français du blé', *Revue économique internationale* (juin, 1937).

*Moroni, P. *L'agriculture française et le contingentement des importations.* Paris, 1934.

Nogaro, B. 'La crise de l'agriculture et la politique agricole en France', *Revue économique internationale* (janvier, 1936).

Perthuis de la Salle, J. *La politique française de contingentement.* Macon, 1935.

Prault, L. *Protectionnisme douanier et commerce extérieur français: Agriculture – Industrie.* Amiens, 1935.

Proix, J. *La politique douanière de la France.* Paris, 1931.

Queuille, H. *Le drame agricole.* Paris, 1932.

Tugwell, R. G. 'The agricultural policy of France', *Political Science Quarterly* (June, September and December, 1930).

Vignaud, M. du. *La réforme de la Loi de Cadenas en France.* Paris, 1931.

The Second World War and after

Association Française de Science Politique. *Les paysans et la politique dans la France contemporaine.* Paris: Colin, 1958.

Bergmann, D. 'Les principes directeurs d'une politique agricole française', *Economie rurale* (octobre, 1957).

Braibant, M. *La France, Nation agricole.* Paris, 1943.

―――― *Vocation agricole de la France.* Paris, 1959.

Cépède, M. *Agriculture et alimentation en France durant la IIe guerre mondiale.* Paris: Génin, 1961.

Commissions de la Production Agricole et de l'Equipement Rural. Rapport général au Commissariat Général au Plan (Deuxième Plan de Modernisation et d'Equipement) (octobre, 1953).

Fauchon, J. *Economie de l'agriculture française.* Paris: Génin, 1954.

Fromont, P. 'Le plan agricole français d'hier et d'aujourd'hui', *Revue des sciences économiques* (mars, 1950).

―――― 'Les problèmes actuels de l'agriculture française', *Problèmes économiques* (7 août, 1956).

Klatzmann, M. J. *Revenus agricoles et non-agricoles* (Études statistiques', I.N.S.E.E., octobre-décembre, 1959).

Maspétiol, R. 'Les options de la politique agricole', *Revue politique et parlementaire* (décembre, 1953).

Services Français d'Information. *L'agriculture française.* Paris, 1947.

Société Française d'Economie Rurale. 'L'économie agricole française, 1938–58', *Bulletin* 39–40 (janvier-juin, 1959).

Germany

General

Abel, W. *Agrarpolitik.* Göttingen: Vandenhoeck & Ruprecht, 2. Auflage, 1958.

Decken, H. v.d. 'Paritätssystem und Agrarstruktur', *Wirtschaftsdienst* (Juli, 1954).

Doebel, W. 'Zwei Jahrzehnte staatlicher Agrarpreisbildung', *Berichte über Landwirtschaft,* 1953, Heft 4.

Frauendorfer, S.v. and Haushofer, H. *Ideengeschichte der Agrarwirtschaft und Agrarpolitik im deutschen Sprachgebiet.* 2 vols. München: Bayerischer Landwirtschaftsverlag, 1957 and 1958.

*Gerschenkron, A. *Bread and Democracy in Germany.* University of California, 1943.

Macbride, Hope. 'Note on the Economic Basis of the Junker Class' (in *The United States in a Multi-National Economy* by

J. Viner and others), Council on Foreign Relations, New York, 1945.

To 1914: The Great Depression

Beckmann, F. *Einfuhrscheinsysteme.* Karlsruhe, 1911.
―――― *Die Futtermittelzölle.* München, 1913.
Brentano, L. *Das Freihandelsargument.* Berlin-Schöneberg, 1901.
―――― *Die deutschen Getreidezölle.* Berlin, 1910.
Buchenberger, A. *Grundzüge der deutschen Agrarpolitik.* Berlin, 2. Auflage, 1899.
Burger, C. *Die Agrardemagogie in Deutschland.* Lichterfelde, 1911.
Clapham, J. H. *The Economic Development of France and Germany, 1815–1914.* C.U.P., 4th ed., 1945.
Cobden Club. *The Influence of Protection on Agriculture in Germany.* London, 1910.
Conrad, J. *Die Stellung der landwirtschaftlichen Zölle in den 1903 zu schliessenden Handelsverträgen Deutschlands* ('Schriften des Vereins für Sozialpolitik', 90, 1900).
Dade, H. *Die Agrarzölle* ('Schriften des Vereins für Sozialpolitik', 91, 1901).
*Dawson, W. H., *Protection in Germany.* London, 1904.
Dietzel, H. 'Kornzoll und Sozialreform', *Volkswirtschaftliche Zeitfragen,* 177–178, Berlin, 1901.
*―――― 'The German tariff controversy', *Quarterly Journal of Economics* (May, 1903).
Gläsel, E. J. *Die Entwicklung der Preise landwirtschaftlicher Produkte und Produktionsmittel.* Berlin, 1917.
Guichen, Vicomte de. *Le problème agricole allemand* (Conférence faite le 5 octobre 1917 à la Société d'Économie Politique).
Lotz, W. *Die Ideen der deutschen Handelspolitik, 1860 bis 1891* ('Schriften des Vereins für Sozialpolitik', 50, 1892).
―――― 'Der Schutz der deutschen Landwirtschaft', *Volkswirtschaftliche Zeitfragen,* 170–171, Berlin, 1900.
―――― *Die Handelspolitik des deutschen Reiches unter Graf Caprivi und Fürst Hohenlohe, 1890–1900* ('Schriften des Vereins für Sozialpolitik', 92, 1901).
Louis-Dop. *La politique agraire en Allemagne.* Rome: Institut International de l'Agriculture, 1911.
Ritter, K. *Die deutschen Agrarzölle* ('Schriften des Vereins für Sozialpolitik', 171, 1925).

Schäffle, A. *Die agrarische Gefahr*. Berlin, 1902.

Schmoller, G. *Grundriss der allgemeinen Volkswirtschaftslehre* (zweiter Teil). Leipzig, 1904.

Sering, M. *Das Sinken der Getreidepreise und die Konkurrenz des Auslandes*. Berlin, 1894.

*Tirrel, Sarah. *German Agrarian Politics after Bismarck's Fall*. Columbia U.P., 1951.

Treue, W. *Die Deutsche Landwirtschaft zur Zeit Caprivis und ihr Kampf gegen die Handelsverträge*. Berlin, 1933.

*Wagner, A. *Agrar- und Industriestaat*. Jena, 2. Auflage, 1902.

Weihe, E. M. *Der Einfluss der deutschen Schutzzollpolitik auf die Entwicklung der Industrie und Landwirtschaft*. Heidelberg, 1902.

1914–1933

Aereboe, F. *Der Einfluss des Krieges auf die landwirtschaftliche Produktion in Deutschland*. Stuttgart, 1927.

Beckmann, F. *Die weltwirtschaftlichen Beziehungen der deutschen Landwirtschaft und ihre wirtschaftliche Lage, 1919–1926*. Berlin, 1926.

Brentano, L. *Agrarpolitik*. Berlin, 1925.

Dietze, C. von. *Die deutsche Landwirtschaft und die neue Handelspolitik* ('Schriften des Vereins für Sozialpolitik', 171, 1925).

Friedrich List-Gesellschaft. *Deutsche Agrarpolitik im Rahmen der inneren und äusseren Wirtschaftspolitik*. Berlin, 1932.

Fuchs, C. J. *Deutsche Agrarpolitik vor und nach dem Kriege*. Stuttgart, 3. Auflage, 1927.

Häfner, K. 'Die Politik der mengenmässigen Einfuhrregulierung', *Weltwirtschaftliches Archiv* (Juli, 1934).

Holt, J. B. *German Agricultural Policy, 1918–1934*. University of North Carolina, 1936.

Ritter, K. *Die deutschen Agrarzölle* ('Schriften des Vereins für Sozialpolitik', 171, 1925).

Röpke, W. *German Commercial Policy*. London, 1934.

Salin, E. *Wirtschaft und Staat – Drei Schriften zur deutschen Weltlage*. Berlin, 1932.

Sering, M. *Agrarkrisen und Agrarzölle*. Berlin, 1925.

———— *Schutzzoll oder Freihandel* ('Schriften des Vereins für Sozialpolitik', 170, 1925).

———— *Deutsche Agrarpolitik auf geschichtlicher und landeskundlicher Grundlage*. Leipzig, 1934.

―――― and others. *Die deutsche Landwirtschaft unter volks- und weltwirtschaftlichen Gesichtspunkten*. Berlin, 1932.

1933–1945 : The agricultural policy of National Socialism
Backe, H. *Um die Nahrungsfreiheit Europas : Weltwirtschaft oder Grossraum*. Leipzig, 1942.
Bertrand, R. *Le corporatisme agricole et l'organisation des marchés en Allemagne*. Paris, 1937.
Brandt, K. 'Farm relief in Germany', *Social Research* (May, 1934).
―――― 'German agricultural policy', *Journal of Farm Economics* (February, 1937).
Darré, R. Walther. *Das Bauerntum als Lebensquell der Nordischen Rasse*. München, 6. Auflage, 1937.
―――― Um Blut und Boden (Reden und Aufsätze). München, 1940.
Dietze, C. von. 'La lutte contre la crise agraire' (dans *L'Économie dirigée*: publication à part de la *Revue d'Économie Politique*). Paris, 1935.
Gatheron, J.-M. *Hitler et la Paysannerie*. Paris, undated.
Luxenberg, B. *Der Niedergang der deutschen Landwirtschaft : ein Rückblick auf den Landwirtschaftlichen Markt der Jahre 1930 und 1931*. München, 1932.
Mehrens, B. *Die Marktordnung des Reichsnährstandes*. Berlin, 1938.
Meyer, K. (ed.) *Gefüge und Ordnung der deutschen Landwirtschaft*. Berlin, 1939.
*Schürmann, A. *Deutsche Agrarpolitik*. Neudamm, 1940.

Since 1945
Baade, F. *Die deutsche Landwirtschaft im Gemeinsamen Markt*. Baden-Baden/Bonn: Lutzeyer, 1958.
Boerckel, W. *Einfuhr- und Vorratsstellen als Mittel der Agrarpolitik*, Mainz-am-Rhein: Diemler, 1959.
European Economic Commission. *Wirkungen einer Senkung der Agrarpreise im Rahmen einer gemeinsamen Agrarpolitik der EWG auf die Einkommensverhältnisse der Landwirtschaft in der Bundesrepublik Deutschland* ('Studien, Reihe Landwirtschaft', No. 11, 1962). Brussels. (Also in French.)
Martinstetter, H. 'Agrarzollpolitik', *Berichte über Landwirtschaft*, 1956, Heft 3.
Niklas, W. *Ernährungswirtschaft und Agrarpolitik*. Bonn, 1949.

Plate, R. 'Wirtschaftspolitische Interventionen und Landwirtschaft', *Agrarwirtschaft* (März, 1956).

*———, Woerman, E., and Grupe, D. 'Landwirtschaft im Strukturwandel der Volkswirtschaft', *Agrarwirtschaft*, Sonderheft 14, 1962.

*Bundesministerium für Ernährung, Landwirtschaft und Forsten. *Grüner Bericht und Grüner Plan* (annual, from 1956).

Denmark

*Arnim, W. von. *Die Landwirtschaft Dänemarks als Beispiel intensiver Betriebsgestaltung bei starker weltwirtschaftlicher Verflechtung* ('Kieler Studien,' 17, 1951).

Danish Council of Agriculture. *Danemark: L'Agriculture*. Copenhagen, 1935.

Desbons, G. *La crise agricole et le remède coopératif – l'exemple du Danemark*. Paris, 1917.

Faber, H. *Co-operation in Danish Agriculture*. London, 1931.

Gøtrik, H. P. *Danish Economic Policy, 1931–1938* (report to 12th International Studies Conference at Bergen in 1939). Copenhagen, Institute of Economics and History.

Jensen, E. *Danish Agriculture – Its Economic Development*. Copenhagen, 1937.

Nash, E. F., and Attwood, E. A. *The Agricultural Policies of Britain and Denmark: A study in Reciprocal Trade*. London: Land Books, 1961.

Schürmann-Mack, F. 'Die Marktregulierungen in der dänischen Vie hund Fleischwirtschaft', *Weltwirtschaftliches Archiv* (September, 1937).

*Skrubbeltrang, F. *Agricultural Development and Rural Reform in Denmark* (FAO 'Agricultural Studies', No. 22, April 1953). Rome.

Austria

Dorfwirth, L. A. *Die österreichische Agrarpolitik seit dem Ende des Weltkrieges*. Wien: Schöler, 1937/8.

Meihsl, P. 'Die Landwirtschaft im Wandel der politischen und ökonomischen Faktoren' (in *Österreichs Wirtschaftsstruktur*, ed. W. Weber, Zweiter Band). Berlin: Duncker & Humblot, 1961.

Belgium

Baudhuin, F. *Histoire économique de la Belgique, 1914–1939.* Bruxelles: Bruylant, 2e ed., 1946.

Leener, G. de. *La politique commerciale de la Belgique* (publication de l'Institut Universitaire de Hautes Études Internationales, Genève). Paris: Sirey, 1934.

Italy

Bandini, M. *Agricoltura e Crisi.* Firenze: Barbera, 1937.

Porri, V. *La politique commerciale de l'Italie* (publication de l'Institut Universitaire de Hautes Études Internationales, Genève). Paris: Sirey, 1934.

Schmidt, C. T. *The Plough and the Sword: Labour and Property in Fascist Italy.* New York: Columbia U.P., 1938.

Schüttauf, A. W. 'Strukturpolitik und Marktregulierung in der italienischen Weizenwirtschaft', *Weltwirtschaftliches Archiv* (November, 1936).

Smith, D. M. *Italy – A Modern History.* University of Michigan, 1959.

Ucker, P. *Die italienische Agrarpolitik seit 1925, unter besonderer Berücksichtigung des 'Kampfes um das Getreide'* ('Schweizerische Beiträge zur Wirtschafts- und Sozialwissenschaft'). Aarau, 1935.

Netherlands

Buning, E. de Cock. *Die Aussenhandelspolitik der Niederlande seit dem Weltkriege* ('Berner wirtschaftswissenschaftliche Abhandlungen', 17, 1936).

Frost, J. 'Landwirtschaft und Agrarpolitik in den Niederlanden' (in Friedrich List-Gesellschaft, *Deutsche Agrarpolitik: Ergänzungsteil*). Berlin, 1932.

Mary, G. *La politique agricole de l'Etat néerlandais pendant la crise de 1929.* Paris, 1943.

Schiller, K. 'Das niederländische Marktregulierungssystem für Weizen und Weizenprodukte', *Weltwirtschaftliches Archiv* (September, 1936).

——— 'Die Regulierung der niederländischen Schweinewirtschaft', *Weltwirtschaftliches Archiv* (September, 1937).

Norway, Sweden

International Labour Office. 'Agricultural policy in Scandinavian countries', *International Labour Review* (January, 1960).

Svenska Handelsbanken. 'Government measures for the relief of agriculture in Sweden', supplement to *Svenska Handelsbanken Index* (March, 1939).

Switzerland

Bickel, W. *Landwirtschaft und Landwirtschaftspolitik der Schweiz.* Bern: Unionsdruckerei, 1961.

Conseil Fédéral. Second rapport à l'Assemblée fédérale sur la situation de l'agriculture suisse et la politique agricole de la Confédération (29 décembre, 1959).

*Landmann, J. *Die Agrarpolitik des schweizerischen Industriestaates* ('Kieler Vorträge', 26, Jena, 1928).

Laur, E. *Swiss Farming.* Bern: Verbandsdruckerei, 1949.

Neuhaus, J. *Die Entwicklung der bundesstaatlichen Agrarpolitik seit 1948.* Turbenthal: Furrers Erben, 1948.

Miscellaneous

Allen, G. C. *A Short Economic History of Modern Japan.* London: Allen & Unwin, 1946.

Farnsworth, Helen. *Wheat growers and the tariff.* Carnegie Endowment, California, 1946.

Johnson, D. G. *Agricultural price policy and international trade* ('Essays in International Finance', No. 19, Princeton, June, 1954).

Low, A. M. *Protection in the United States.* London, 1904.

Nasu, S. 'Ziele und Ausrichtung der japanischen Agrarpolitik in der Gegenwart', *Weltwirtschaftliches Archiv* (Juli, 1937).

Morgan, O. S. (ed.) *Agricultural Systems of Middle Europe.* New York, 1933.

Rau, A. *Agricultural Policy and Trade Liberalisation in the United States, 1934-56.* Geneva, 1957.

Tibal, A. 'La crise des États agricoles européens et l'action internationale', *Conciliation Internationale*, bulletins nos. 2-5, Paris, 1931.

Index

Index

(t) table; (f) figure; (n) note